MEDICAL
INTELLIGENCE
UNIT

POLYAMINES IN CANCER:
BASIC MECHANISMS
AND CLINICAL APPROACHES

Kenji Nishioka, Ph.D., D.M.Sc.

The University of Texas M. D. Anderson Cancer Center
and Nishioka Consulting
Houston, Texas, U.S.A.

CHAPMAN & HALL
ITP An International Thomson Publishing Company

New York • Albany • Bonn • Boston • Cincinnati • Detroit • London • Madrid • Melbourne •
Mexico City • Pacific Grove • Paris • San Francisco • Singapore • Tokyo • Toronto • Washington

R.G. LANDES COMPANY
AUSTIN

MEDICAL INTELLIGENCE UNIT
POLYAMINES IN CANCER: BASIC MECHANISMS AND CLINICAL APPROACHES

R.G. LANDES COMPANY
Austin, Texas, U.S.A.

Please address all inquiries to the Publishers:
R.G. Landes Company, 909 Pine Street, Georgetown, Texas, U.S.A. 78626
Phone: 512/ 863 7762; FAX: 512/ 863 0081

North American distributor:
Chapman & Hall, 115 Fifth Avenue, New York, New York, U.S.A. 10003

CHAPMAN & HALL

U.S. and Canada ISBN: 1-412-11051-2

Library of Congress Cataloging-in-Publication Data

Polyamines in cancer : basic mechanisms and clinical approaches / [edited by] Kenji Nishioka.
  p. cm. — (Medical intelligence unit)
 Includes bibliographical references and index.
 ISBN 1-57059-346-9 (RGL - alk. paper) — ISBN 1-412-11051-2 (CH - alk. paper)
 1. Polyamines--Pathophysiology. 2. Carcinogenesis. 3. Polyamines in the body.
 I. Nishioka, Kenji, 1942- . II. Series.
  [DNLM: 1. Polyamines--metabolism. 2. Neoplasms--metabolism. QU 61 P779 1996]
RC254.6.P65 1996
616.99'4—dc20
DNLM/DLC
for Library of Congress
                96-15935
                CIP

PUBLISHER'S NOTE

R.G. Landes Company publishes six book series: *Medical Intelligence Unit, Molecular Biology Intelligence Unit, Neuroscience Intelligence Unit, Tissue Engineering Intelligence Unit, Environmental Intelligence Unit* and *Biotechnology Intelligence Unit.* The authors of our books are acknowledged leaders in their fields and the topics are unique. Almost without exception, no other similar books exist on these topics.

Our goal is to publish books in important and rapidly changing areas of bioscience for sophisticated researchers and clinicians. To achieve this goal, we have accelerated our publishing program to conform to the fast pace in which information grows in bioscience. Most of our books are published within 90 to 120 days of receipt of the manuscript. We would like to thank our readers for their continuing interest and welcome any comments or suggestions they may have for future books.

Deborah Muir Molsberry
Publications Director
R.G. Landes Company

DEDICATION

This book is dedicated to three persons who have shaped my life, my mother Masanoi, my sister Nobuko and my spouse Jeanne.

CONTENTS

ABBREVIATIONS

AdoMet   S-adenosylmethionine

AdoMetDC   S-adenosylmethionine decarboxylase

DFMO   DL-α-difluoromethylornithine

MGBG   methylglyoxal bis(guanylhydrazone)

NMDA   (N-methyl-D-aspartate) receptors

ODC   L-ornithine decarboxylase

PAO   polyamine oxidase

SSAT   spermidine/spermine N^1-acetyltransferase

TPA   12-O-tetradecanoylphorbol-13-acetate

EDITOR

Kenji Nishioka, Ph.D., D.M.Sc.
Department of Surgical Oncology
The University of Texas M. D. Anderson Cancer Center
and Nishioka Consulting
Houston, Texas, U.S.A.
chapters 1, 9 and 11

CONTRIBUTORS

Jaffer A. Ajani, M.D.
Department of Gastrointestinal
  Oncology and Digestive Diseases
The University of Texas M. D.
  Anderson Cancer Center
Houston, Texas, U.S.A.
chapter 11

Leena Alhonen
A.I. Virtanen Institute and
  Department of Biochemistry &
  Biotechnology
University of Kuopio
Kuopio, Finland
chapter 5

Uriel Bachrach
Department of Molecular Biology
Hebrew University-Hadassah
  Medical School
Jerusalem, Israel
chapter 4

John M. Buatti
Department of Radiation Oncology
University of Florida
Gainesville, Florida, U.S.A.
chapter 8

Bernard Cipolla, M.D.
Groupe de Recherche en
  Thérapeutique Anticancéreuse
Institut de Recherche Contre le
  Cancer
Rennes Cedex, France
chapter 10

Seymour S. Cohen
American Cancer Society Research
  Professor, Emeritus
Marine Biological Laboratories
Woods Hole, Massachusetts, U.S.A.
chapter 2

Jean-Guy Delcros, Pharm.D., Ph.D.
Groupe de Recherche en
  Thérapeutique Anticancéreuse
Institut de Recherche Contre le
  Cancer
Rennes Cedex, France
chapter 10

Eugene W. Gerner
Department of Radiation Oncology
University of Arizona
Tucson, Arizona, U.S.A.
chapter 8

CONTRIBUTORS

V. Bruce Grossie, Jr., Ph.D.
Department of Surgical Oncology
The University of Texas M. D.
    Anderson Cancer Center
Houston, Texas, U.S.A.
chapter 9

Maria Halmekytö
A.I. Virtanen Institute and
    Department of Biochemistry &
    Biotechnology
University of Kuopio
Kuopio, Finland
chapter 5

Paul M. Harari
Department of Human Oncology
University of Wisconsin
    Comprehensive Cancer Center
Madison, Wisconsin, U.S.A.
chapter 8

Juhani Jänne, M.D., Ph.D.
A.I. Virtanen Institute and
    Department of Biochemistry &
    Biotechnology
University of Kuopio
Kuopio, Finland
chapter 5

Leila Kauppinen
A.I. Virtanen Institute and
    Department of Biochemistry &
    Biotechnology
University of Kuopio
Kuopio, Finland
chapter 5

Debora L. Kramer
Grace Cancer Drug Center
Roswell Park Cancer Institute
Buffalo, New York, U.S.A.
chapter 7

Michele Follen Mitchell, M.D.,
    M.S.
Department of Gynecologic
    Oncology
The University of Texas M. D.
    Anderson Cancer Center
Houston, Texas, U.S.A.
chapter 11

Jacques-Philippe Moulinoux, M.D.,
    Ph.D.
Groupe de Recherche en
    Thérapeutique Anticancéreuse
Institut de Recherche Contre le
    Cancer
Rennes Cedex, France
chapter 10

Ralph E. Parchment
Division of Pharmacology &
    Toxicology
Center for Drug Evaluation and
    Research
U.S. Food & Drug Administration
Laurel, Maryland, U.S.A.
chapter 6

Lo Persson, Ph.D.
Department of Physiology
University of Lund
Lund, Sweden
chapter 3

CONTRIBUTORS

Michael A. Pickart
Department of Cell & Molecular
  Biology
University of Wisconsin
  Comprehensive Cancer Center
Madison, Wisconsin, U.S.A.
chapter 8

Véronique Quemener, Pharm.D.,
  Ph.D.
Groupe de Recherche en
  Thérapeutique Anticancéreuse
Institut de Recherche Contre le
  Cancer
Rennes Cedex, France
chapter 10

Riitta Sinervirta
A.I. Virtanen Institute and
  Department of Biochemistry &
  Biotechnology
University of Kuopio
Kuopio, Finland
chapter 5

Fredrik Svensson
Department of Physiology
University of Lund
Lund, Sweden
chapter 3

Eva Lövkvist Wallström
Department of Physiology
University of Lund
Lund, Sweden
chapter 3

PREFACE

I came to the University of Texas M. D. Anderson Cancer Center in 1972 as a junior faculty member. In the following year, as I recall, I had a chance to listen to the late Dr. Diane H. Russell's presentation regarding the potential of polyamines as biochemical markers for cancer, at the annual meeting of the American Association for Cancer Research, which was held in Houston. I was very much fascinated with this group of compounds and their possible biological functions in cancer. In 1974, I published my first paper on polyamines. Reading this publication, Dr. Russell called me and asked me to attend the first Gordon Research Conference on Polyamines that she was organizing for 1975. This was how I started my association with investigators in polyamine research. Since then, I have attended numerous national and international polyamine conferences including all biannual Gordon Research Conferences on Polyamines. One of my concerns regarding these meetings was that not enough time was allocated to deal with specific issues related to polyamines in cancer. Returning from the International Symposium on Polyamines in Biochemical and Clinical Research, held in Sorrento, Italy in 1988, I discussed this concern with my colleagues, Drs. Jaffer A. Ajani, V. Bruce Grossie Jr. and David M. Ota, and convinced them that we need to work toward holding the first International Symposium on Polyamines in Cancer, in Houston. At that time we viewed the world of polyamine research as follows. It was obvious that polyamines play critical roles in proliferation, differentiation and neoplastic transformation of mammalian cells. The enzymes involved in metabolism of polyamines were being studied extensively by molecular biological approaches. The knowledge obtained from basic studies of polyamines was actively translated into clinical studies. This we viewed as one of most unique characteristics of this field of research. Specific inhibitors of polyamine biosynthesis became available for almost every enzyme in polyamine metabolism. In addition, a new series of polyamine analogs was pointing toward an interesting future in cancer treatment. These situations provided clinical investigators with new promising therapeutic agents for cancer treatment. In view of the active developments in this field, we decided to devote an entire symposium to a critical examination of the roles of polyamines in cancer and to evaluate the future directions of polyamine research in cancer. Although the critical importance of polyamines in cancer had long been well recognized, there had been no symposium dealing solely with the subject of polyamines in cancer. Thus one of the aims of this symposium was to provide an international forum for exchange between basic scientists and clinical oncologists, allowing them to evaluate polyamine research, particularly in cancer, from the perspective of clinical approaches based upon basic scientific studies. Therefore, we organized the content of this symposium into three stages: basic studies in mammalian cells, in vitro and in vivo studies and clinical studies. This international symposium was successfully held at the Del Lago Resort and Conference Center located outside of Houston on November 6-10, 1992, under the title of Critical Roles of Polyamines in Cancer: Basic Mechanisms and Clinical Approaches. A meeting report was published (Cancer Res 1993; 53: 2689-92).

Rather than publishing the proceedings of the symposium, I wanted to publish a book on this subject for those who are interested in polyamines in cancer regardless of their background in polyamines. In organizing this book, I selected contributors who are international experts on each subject whether they were able to attend the symposium or not. Those who participated in the symposium were asked to update the content for this book. The contents are organized to progress from basic studies to clinical studies.

Today polyamines are known to be involved in many biological phenomena such as proliferation, differentiation, transformation, metastasis, angiogenesis and apoptosis. Investigators come from different disciplines such as molecular biology, biochemistry, cell biology, immunology, microbiology, parasitology, neurochemistry, pharmacology including medicinal chemistry, oncology and clinical research including clinical chemistry and translational research. Thus our hope is to entice as many researchers as possible to join us to share our excitement through communication made possible by this book.

Kenji Nishioka, Ph.D., D.M.Sc.
The University of Texas
M. D. Anderson Cancer Center
and Nishioka Consulting

ACKNOWLEDGMENTS

I wish to thank all contributors to this book as well as acknowledge the help of Ms. Leslie L. Wildrick of the Department of Scientific Publications at the University of Texas M. D. Anderson Cancer Center for identifying the publisher and initial editorial assistance; Ms. Lynn O'Neill, Manuscript Coordinator; Ms. Deborah Molsberry, Publications Director; and Dr. Renate Wise, Editorial Director of the Landes Bioscience Publisher. Special gratitude is given to other people who gave me encouragement and support during this endeavor, Drs. Marvin M. Romsdahl, John A. Benvenuto and Chiyeko Tsuchitani, and last but not least, my spouse Jeanne.

===== CHAPTER 1 =====

INTRODUCTION TO POLYAMINES

Kenji Nishioka

The purpose of this chapter is to introduce polyamines to those who usually do not work with them.

I. INTRODUCTION

Table 1.1 depicts the structures of the polyamines putrescine, spermidine and spermine and two of their acetyl compounds. Since spermidine is an asymmetrical molecule, there exist two forms of monoacetylspermidines, N^1- and N^8-acetylspermidine. Cadaverine, though not listed here, is another diamine with the hydrocarbon chain longer by a CH_2 and normally produced from lysine by the action of lysine decarboxylase.[1] Under normal conditions, mammalian cells do not produce this diamine. Thus, the presence of cadaverine in physiological fluids may indicate the presence of infection in the host. Polyamines are determined in various samples using a variety of procedures; high-performance liquid chromatography is used in many research laboratories.[2]

At biochemical levels, polyamines are known to interact directly with nucleic acids, proteins and phospholipids. Thus, they are capable of interacting with membrane and various organelles.[3,4] While many investigators are interested in specific interactions of polyamines with DNA,[5,6] Igarashi proposed that polyamines primarily bind to RNA in the cell.[7]

II. POLYAMINE METABOLISM

The major pathways of polyamine metabolism are depicted with chemical structures in Figure 1.1. Polyamine metabolism in mammalian cells starts at arginine through the action of arginase. The

Polyamines in Cancer: Basic Mechanisms and Clinical Approaches, edited by Kenji Nishioka. © 1996 R.G. Landes Company.

resultant ornithine is converted to putrescine by one of the key enzymes in polyamine metabolism, ornithine decarboxylase (ODC). This enzyme in known to have one of the shortest half-lives among all known enzymes, and its enzymatic activity is uniquely regulated by multiple mechanisms.[8] ODC can be specifically and irreversibly inhibited by α-difluoromethylornithine (DFMO), a suicide inhibitor. Putrescine is then converted to spermidine and spermine by spermidine synthase and spermine synthase, respectively. These two enzymes are aminopropyl-transferases and thus require supply of aminopropyl moiety, which derives originally from an amino acid methionine. S-adenosylmethionine synthase produces S-adenosylmethionine (AdoMet) from methionine and ATP. AdoMet is a specific substrate for another key enzyme in polyamine biosynthesis, S-adenosylmethionine decarboxylase (AdoMetDC), which has a short half-life and can be inhibited by methylglyoxal bis(guanylhydrazone) (MGBG). The resultant decarboxylated AdoMet serves as a donor of aminopropyl moiety, although normally AdoMet is used as a methyl donor. Through a back conversion pathway spermidine and spermine can be converted back to putrescine and spermidine, respectively. Spermidine/spermine N^1-acetyltransferase (SSAT) is capable of acetylating spermidine and spermine using acetyl CoA. This enzyme also has a short half-life. The resultant N^1-acetylspermine and N^1-acetylspermidine can be converted by the action of polyamine oxidase (PAO) to spermidine and putrescine, respectively. Acetylated polyamines can also be excreted from cells. Regulation of polyamine metabolism is the subject of chapter 3 in this book.

Table 1.1. Structures of polyamines

Polyamine	Chemical Structure
Putrescine	$H_2N(CH_2)_4NH_2$
Spermidine	$H_2N(CH_2)_3NH(CH_2)_4NH_2$
N^1-acetylspermidine	$CH_3CONH(CH_2)_3NH(CH_2)_4NH_2$
Spermine	$H_2N(CH_2)_3NH(CH_2)_4NH(CH_2)_3NH_2$
N^1-acetylspermine	$CH_3CONH(CH_2)_3NH(CH_2)_4NH(CH_2)_3NH_2$

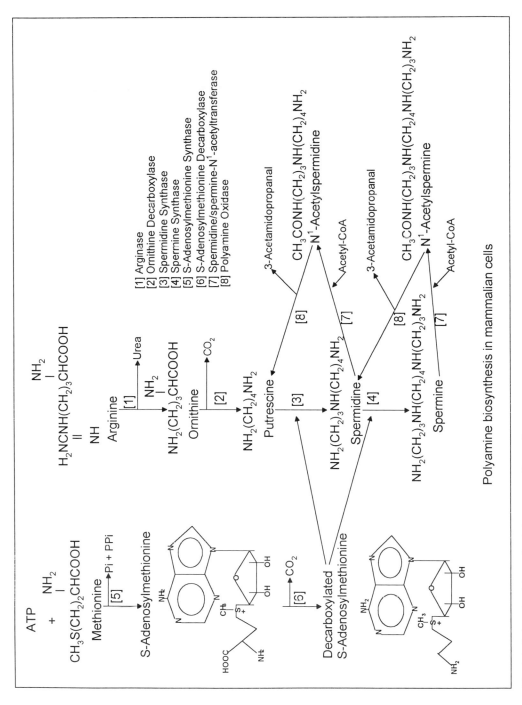

Fig. 1.1. *Polyamine biosynthesis in mammalian cells.*

III. RELEVANCE TO CANCER

At biological levels, polyamines are known to play critical roles in the proliferation, differentiation, maintenance and neoplastic transformation of mammalian cells. In addition, polyamines have been shown to be involved in both apoptosis and angiogenesis;[9-11] angiogenesis is essential for tumor growth and metastasis.[12] ODC is now considered a putative protooncogene critical to the regulation of cell growth and transformation. This particular subject will be reviewed in chapters 4 and 5 in this book. Chapter 6 discusses issues related to apoptosis. Based on their biological implications, polyamines appear to be very relevant in the following areas of cancer research:

1) Polyamines as biological markers for cancer
2) Polyamine-based chemotherapeutic agents
3) Polyamine-based chemoprevention approaches
4) Polyamine-directed nutritional modulation in cancer patients
5) Polyamine-based modulation of radiotherapy and hyperthermia

Issues related to polyamines as markers of malignancy have been recently reviewed by Bachrach.[13] In particular chapter 10 deals with circulating polyamines as biological markers for cancer. Chapters 7 and 11 discuss polyamine inhibitors and analogs as possible chemotherapeutic agents. Chapter 11 also reviews attempts to use DFMO as a chemoprevention agent. Chapter 9 deals with possible enhancement of tumor growth by external nutritional supports and its polyamine-based control. Chapter 8 reviews polyamine modulation of responses to radiation and hyperthermia.

REFERENCES

1. Tabor CW, Tabor H. Polyamines in microorganisms. Microbiol Rev 1985;49:81-91.
2. Muskiet FA, Dorhout B, van den Berg G-A et al. Investigation of polyamine metabolism by high-performance liquid chromatographic and gas chromatographic profiling methods. J Chromatography B: Biomed Application 1995; 667:189-98.
3. Pegg AE. Recent advances in the biochemistry of polyamines in eukaryotes. Biochem J 1986;234:249-62.
4. Jänne J, Alhonen L, Leinonen P. Polyamines: From molecular biology to clinical application. Ann Med 1991;23:241-259.

5. Feuerstein BG, Williams LD, Basu HS et al. Implications and concepts of polyamine-nucleic acid interaction. J Cell Biochem 1991; 46:37-47.

6. Basu HS, Marton LJ. Biological and therapeutic implications of the effects of polyamines on chromatin condensation. In: Casero RA, ed. Polyamines: Regulation and Molecular Interaction. Austin: RG Landes, 1995:101-28.

7. Igarashi K. Role of polyamines in cell proliferation and differentiation. Seikagaku 1993; 65:86-104.

8. Hayashi S, Murakami Y. Rapid and regulated degradation of ornithine decarboxylase. Biochem J 1995; 306:1-10.

9. Takigawa M, Enomoto M, Nishida Y et al. Tumor angiogenesis and polyamines: 2-Difluoromethylornithine, an irreversible inhibitor of ornithine decarboxylase, inhibits B16 melanoma-induced angiogenesis in ovo and the proliferation of vascular endothelial cells in vitro. Cancer Res 1990; 50:4131-38.

10. Monte M, Klein S, Jasnis MA et al. Inhibition of lymphocyte and tumor-induced angiogenesis by the administration of difluoromethylornithine. Cancer J 1993; 6:147-50.

11. Jasnis MA, Klein S, Monte M et al. Polyamines prevent DFMO-mediated inhibition of angiogenesis. Cancer Lett 1994;79:39-43.

12. Sunkara PS, Prakash NJ, Rosenberger AL. An essential role for polyamines in tumor metastasis. FEBS Lett 1982; 150:397-99.

13. Bachrach U. Polyamines as markers of malignancy. Progr Drug Res 1992; 39:9-33.

======= CHAPTER 2 =======

THE PACE AND DIRECTIONS OF POLYAMINE RESEARCH

Seymour S. Cohen

I have supposed that my role in this book on critical roles of polyamines in cancer is to introduce the process of growth and sophistication of our knowledge in this field. We can start with the realization that as late as 1945, it was not known if the diamine, 1,4-diaminobutane, or putrescine, which is found in human tissues or fluids such as urine, was not merely a bacterial product. This diamine and its homolog cadaverine had been detected toward the end of the 19th century by German chemists and clinicians as products of bacterial fermentation. Between the 1920s and the 1940s, it was found that some bacteria including *E. coli*, were capable of metabolizing various amino acids, and their extracts could decarboxylate L-ornithine and L-lysine to putrescine and cadaverine, respectively.

Although the tetramine, spermine, had been seen some three hundred years ago by Leeuwenhoek as a crystalline phosphate in human seminal fluid, the undisputed presence of this polyamine in eucaryotic cells (generally e.g., yeast and mammalian tissue) awaited the work and report of the English chemist Mrs. Mary Tebb Rosenheim in 1917. In the mid 1920s, the proof of the structure, and chemical synthesis of spermine, as well as the discovery and synthesis of the triamine, spermidine, were developed mainly by her husband, Otto Rosenheim, and his colleagues. Little

Polyamines in Cancer: Basic Mechanisms and Clinical Approaches, edited by Kenji Nishioka. © 1996 R.G. Landes Company.

further work was performed on these substances (diamines, triamines and tetramines) until after World War II.

Studies on the nutritional requirements of bacteria had revealed new vitamins, substances that both served as essential cofactors of biochemical reactions and provided leads to chemotherapy for bacterial infection. The efficacy of the sulfa drugs and of antibiotics obviously helped to encourage biochemical studies of microbes. In 1948, Edward Herbst and his colleague, Esmund Snell, discovered that a strain of *Hemophilus parainfluenzae* required a diamine, preferably putrescine, for growth. This promising result led Herbst to pursue micromethods for the separation and estimation of the polyamines in various bacteria and was the beginning of more than 40 years of productive study of the cellular metabolism and functions of the polyamines. For his part, Snell turned to the bacterial metabolism of histidine and discovered a new type of decarboxylase, whose apparently unique active site has proved essential for the enzyme's providing the immediate reactant for the conversion of putrescine to spermidine. Snell's work is an outstanding example of the unanticipated convergence of diverse experimental results in the evolution of scientific knowledge.

By the 1950s, the exploitation of microbiology by geneticists, enzymologists and virologists had become a major path of biochemical study. In 1952-3 Giulio Cantoni discovered the unexpected intermediate of methyl transfer, S-adenosylmethionine (AdoMet). At about the same time, the pharmacologist, Sanford Rosenthal, who was interested in the toxicity of animal sera, found that oxidized spermine is lethal to microbes and animal cells, and supported a broad program of polyamine research involving younger colleagues Celia and Herbert Tabor, and several other younger scientists. Israeli investigators were also interested in the toxicity of oxidized spermine, and one of them, Uriel Bachrach, who has written another chapter of this book, joined the Tabors for one year to clarify important parts of the puzzle.

The subsequent dissection and clarification of the action and specificity of the amine oxidases proved to be an important introduction for many workers to oxidative transformation of the polyamines by all organisms. The products were found to have diverse functions in various organisms, from urinary excretion products in humans to neurochemical transmitters such as γ-amino-butyrate (GABA), to secondary plant metabolites such as nicotine. The diversity of the products of oxidation required sharpened analytical skills that have been exploited by all polyamine workers.

Some years after the early work in the 1950s and 1960s, which had revealed that many of the amine oxidases were copper-containing enzymes, a new type of mammalian amine oxidase was discovered by Erki Höltta in the 1970s. This enzyme functioned with a flavin coenzyme. The new amine oxidase operated on acetyl polyamines to produce a polyamine reduced by one aminopropyl moiety; thus an acetylspermine was converted to spermidine, and an acetylspermidine formed putrescine. In a very few years, by 1980, Nikolaus Seiler and his colleagues deduced the complete cycle of the synthesis and degradation of the polyamines with its numerous side branches to eliminable metabolic products. This cycle has proved to be of great interest in the study of human patients.

The dissection of the mode of action of the copper-containing amine oxidases proved to be most difficult. In the last few years, some 30 years after the initial study, it was found that the active site of these enzymes contains a new amino acid, trihydroxy-phenylalanine (TOPA), which is not coded for by the mRNA for the enzyme.

It is characteristic of science in general that the uncovering of phenomena raises many more problems to be resolved. The 40 year saga of work on the amine oxidases has achieved a significant measure of clarification, but is only now beginning to be revealed widely as a major problem in biochemical structure and function relevant to many problems of human biology. For example, we can note the burst of new work on human epidermal lysyl oxidase, in which the presumed copper-containing TOPA active site may prove to be a key to the control of aging of skin and metastasis of skin cancer.

In the 1950s relatively newly available radioactive methionine was used to demonstrate the role of this amino acid as a precursor of the aminopropyl moiety of spermidine in fungi and bacteria. In a very few years thereafter the Tabors took the major steps of showing that AdoMet is decarboxylated in a bacterial extract and that the product transfers the residual aminopropyl moiety of methionine to putrescine to form spermidine. Furthermore, the Tabors devised ion-exchange procedures to separate the numerous reactants and products. Decarboxylated AdoMet was not easily synthesized at that time, and for a decade the difficulty in obtaining this substance as a standard product and reactant slowed work on the enzymology of the synthesis of spermidine and spermine. Decarboxylated AdoMet has become widely available, primarily as a result of synthetic work in Japan and Italy.

I became interested in the polyamines at the end of the 1950s when Alfred Hershey discovered that the T-even DNA bacteriophages have arginine-derived bases. These bases were shown later to be putrescine and spermidine, and to account for almost 40% of the cation necessary to neutralize the virus DNA.

The notion that the basic polyamines might normally neutralize the nucleic acids led us and others to examine and to find polyamines associated with ribosomes. Many workers have found that numerous steps in protein synthesis and ribosome function in bacteria are activated by spermidine and spermine. In a surprising discovery, it was also found that the aminobutyl moiety of spermidine is transferred to a lysine in a single eucaryotic protein and oxidized further to generate the amino acid, hypusine. The formation of hypusine is essential to the survival of yeast and animal cells. Thus the polyamines are clearly involved in several essential functions.

The possible relationship of spermidine to cellular RNA led a Finnish colleague, Aarnk Raina, and myself to explore the bacterial contents of these substances. We found a close parallelism of the contents of these substances in many different physiological conditions. A similar result was obtained by N. Seiler in his important study of the livers of starved, normal and hypertrophied animals.

These quantitative studies of cells or cell components with ever smaller samples demanded improvements in the sensitivity and accuracy the polyamine separations and measurements. The relatively gross colorimetric analyses with dinitrofluorobenzene were supplanted by the use of ninhydrin, and eventually in the early 1970s by fluorimetric measurement with dansyl chloride and ophthalaldehyde (OPA) reagents. As sample size could be decreased from the μmol to nmol to pmol ranges, the improved automated high-performance liquid chromatography (HPLC) or gas liquid chromatography (GLC) methods were eventually adopted for separation of these substances. Enzymatic assays were also made more specific and adapted to the new supersensitive gadgetry.

I was interested in the possible role of the polyamines in virus multiplication and pursued this problem for some years. We know now that virus multiplication is slowed, perhaps considerably, in cells depleted of polyamine, but the roles of the polyamines are so numerous in bacterial metabolism, in the synthesis and structuring of proteins and nucleic acids, that it has been difficult to pinpoint the specific molecular functions of the individual polyamines in the multiplication of the T-even phages and of viruses generally. We note that the T7 RNA polymerase which is so widely used for in vitro transcription in many types of studies is routinely activated by mM levels of spermidine, and the RNA product, unless carefully purified, tends to be rich in this polyamine. The role of this spermidine in subsequent investigations of RNA products has been widely and unfortunately neglected.

In the 1960s studies of the heat stability of polynucleotides revealed that spermidine and spermine have a stabilizing effect on the melting of the nucleates. Did the polyamine fulfill this type of role in the biological nucleates generally? The small tRNAs were among the first to be isolated and sequenced, and in 1969 the development of the new very sensitive analytical methods made it possible for us to seek and find spermidine in the newly chemically defined bacterial tRNAs. The two molecules of spermidine in a bacterial tRNA does in fact stabilize the structure, and spermidine does increase the activity of tRNA in several enzymatic reactions. With a few exceptions the formation of crystals of nucleic acids for crystallographic investigation has required the presence of polyamine in the crystallization mix.

The spermidine contents of some RNA viruses, i.e., phages (r17), plant viruses (turnip yellow mosaic virus) and some animal viruses, are quite high, i.e., several hundred molecules of polyamine per RNA, and in the case of R17 there is evidence that the polyamine has a role in folding and condensing the viral RNA. Actually the role of the polyamines in the folding and tightening of double-stranded regions of nucleic acids raises the possibility that the natural amines might be thought of as the chaperones of the nucleic acids.

At the end of the 1950s the Tabors' important work established the enzymatic sequence of spermidine synthesis. They and their colleagues then began to characterize additional metabolic phenomena in *E. coli,* i.e., the acetylation of the polyamines, the accumulation of the amines after transport and extrusion of modified polyamines. The enzymology of these events was explored initially in bacteria and eventually in animal organs and cells. The complexities of the bacterial decarboxylases of ornithine and arginine were examined by David Morris and Arthur Pardee. In 1967 and 1968 normal extrapolative studies on the eucaryotic enzymes involved in making putrescine, spermidine and spermine produced new, unexpected results, that determined the need for much later work.

Several quite separate groups began to examine the initial enzyme in putrescine biosynthesis, ornithine decarboxylase (ODC), in regenerating or hormonally stimulated liver. These groups included the Finnish group of A. Raina, J. Jänne and their colleagues who had demonstrated patterns of synthesis of polyamine and RNA similar to that in bacteria. Both the Finnish group and an American group (Diane Russell and Sol Snyder) found a rapid appearance of ODC activity during regeneration. The enzyme activity could also be induced to fall rapidly, suggesting an unusually rapid turnover. These results demanded purification of the enzyme, production of antibody to assess that enzyme activity and enzyme protein content were equivalent, systematic analysis of the transcription of the ODC gene and translation of the mRNA. It took the next two decades to develop answers to the problem of the regulation of the ODC gene and of the ODC protein itself in eucaryotic cells.

The unusual pattern of increase and decrease, i.e., the regulation of ODC, proved to be general to all growing tissues, and this unusual pattern implied that putrescine and the other polyamines had a significant role in the life of the cell. This result suggested the synthesis of ODC inhibitors, which by depleting polyamines might reveal the essential roles of these substances or even arrest of certain pathologies dependent on active cell growth and multiplication. The reaction product of ODC actron was not a potent feedback inhibitor. Other potentially competitive compounds of this class, i.e., analogs such as 1,3-diaminopropane and substrate analogs, proved only partially effective in the inhibition of ODC and even evoked some previously unknown regulatory responses in eucaryotic cells. A new protein was found that combined with and inactivated ODC, and it has only recently become widely accepted that this protein, dubbed antizyme, is not an artifact but an apparently important genetically determined component in the inactivation and proteolytic degradation of ODC. High spermidine levels in cells somehow evoke an increase in antizyme and a rapid decrease in ODC.

Investigation by Guy Williams-Ashman and his colleagues of androgen-stimulated prostate in castrated animals revealed a separable array of biosynthetic enzymes in addition to ODC, i.e., a decarboxylase of AdoMet and two propylamine transferases, namely spermidine synthase and spermine synthase. The AdoMet decarboxylases (AdoMetDCs) of animal cells and of some fungi were found to be stimulated by the diamine putrescine. A compound reported in 1963 to kill cancer cells, which may be protected by spermidine, was identified by this group as a potent inhibitor of eucaryotic AdoMetDC. This compound, methylglyoxal bis(guanylhydrazone), familiarly known as MGBG, proved to be too toxic to humans when used in many experiments to explore its mode of action. MGBG combined with the decarboxylase stabilized the enzyme in cells and evoked a great increase in the intracellular level of the enzyme. This fact has been used to produce large amounts of AdoMetDC.

The availability of tissues rich in ODC and AdoMet decarboxylase permitted the isolation of these enzymes in sufficient purity to prepare inactivating precipitating antibodies. With these materials it was possible to demonstrate an equivalence between enzyme activity and the amount of enzyme protein under many growth conditions. This established the validity of research programs in which these conditions of growth were correlated with the extent of transcription from the respective genes and the extent of translation from the newly synthesized mRNA. Thus despite the introduction of novelties such as antizyme, by the 1980s the study of the regulation of the polyamine biosynthesis enzymes had merged with research programs in the molecular biology of enzyme regulation generally.

The inadequacies of α-methylornithine and of MGBG as competitive inhibitors led to a more determined effort in the mid-1970s to produce irreversible inhibitors of the polyamine biosynthesis enzymes. Several pharmaceutical companies explored the inhibitory properties of 2-mono- and di-halogenomethyl derivatives of the amino acids. α-Difluoromethylornithine (DFMO), a compound made by the chemists of the Merrell-Dow Company of Strasbourg and Cincinnati, proved to be an extremely active irreversible inhibitor of ODC. It markedly depleted cells of putrescine and spermidine, provoking a late inhibition of cell growth without a lethal effect. These quantitative results confirmed an earlier finding with microbial mutants lacking biosynthetic enzymes, i.e., bacteria, yeasts and eucaryotic cells normally contained a large excess of polyamine that had to be eliminated before decrease in growth could be detected. In addition a block in ODC that produced a serious depletion of putrescine led to a massive accumulation of a somewhat toxic decarboxylated AdoMet. Spermine synthase had not been found in *E. coli*; however, in recent years some other less common bacteria have been found to contain a propylamine transferase capable of converting spermidine to spermine.

The discovery of a powerful irreversible inhibitor of ODC by the Merrell-Dow Company has stimulated the entire pharmaceutical industry to develop irreversible or very tight-binding inhibitors of physiologically significant enzymatic reactions. In the 1980s Merrell-Dow developed an enlightened policy of supplying its newly developed inhibitors of polyamine synthesis to an eager and productive body of research workers. The outstanding result was a major burst of knowledge about the inhibitors and various aspects of polyamine physiology. The inhibitors have been used to manipulate polyamine metabolism and to study the regulation of the polyamine-biosynthesis enzymes. Resistance to the inhibitors was correlated with overproduction of the enzymes and the determining nucleic acids, thereby facilitating the isolation of the proteins, their mRNAs and their genes. It is not my role to summarize for you the enormous progress in these areas of the last decade (after all, there is a whole book on this before you), but I do wish to comment on some potentialities in our growing specialty and our growing disciplines that are addressed in this book.

The 30-year period from the discoveries of Herbst in 1948 to DFMO saw an initially slow development of interest in the polyamines. For the first decade these polyamines were viewed as an open puzzle, and only in the second decade were thus approached as a set of legitimate academic problems of microbial biochemistry. These attracted a slowly increasing number of investigators in both the U.S. and abroad. By 1960, following World War II, small research groups had developed abroad, in Israel, Finland and Italy, to which an initially unpressured research problem such as the polyamines proved attractive. The biological materials necessary were easily available, i.e., embryonated eggs and bacteria, sera and stable spermine, as were eager students, and there was so much to be discovered. By 1968, workers in the field had not only begun to discover new and important details about the polyamines and biology but had also touched hot fields of current research, including protein synthesis, the nucleic acids and virology. The discovery of the bizarre regulatory pattern of ODC in mammalian tissues and a potent inhibitor of AdoMetDC, which was also a promising candidate antitumor agent, introduced numerous workers to the potentialities of the polyamine problems in animal biology as well as the possibility of new investigatory funds.

By 1970 the perception of the scattered polyamine research groups that there was something exciting going on in their field led Ed Herbst and Uriel Bachrach to organize a symposium at the New York Academy of Sciences on this subject. Several years later, the productive and enthusiastic Diane Russell encouraged the National Cancer Institute to sponsor a meeting pointing to a possible relevance of the polyamines to the cancer problem. She also pressed for the development of the biennial Gordon Conferences on polyamines, which entered a 20th year in 1993. I published a book on the subject in 1971, which was followed by another by U. Bachrach in 1973. In the subsequent period national and international meetings sponsored in many countries by national groups became common, and symposia, volumes and reviews of current work have proliferated.

The introduction of interesting inhibitors has extended the work to many groups of biomedically oriented investigators who publish their results in a most diverse collection of journals from many countries. For at least the past five years, the weekly editions of *Current Contents* have listed 10 to 15 papers relevant to polyamine problems. I can attest to the publication of at least 800 to 1000 papers on or related to the polyamines per year. So much for the pace of work in the polyamine field.

The flood of new work in the 1970s eventually stirred the pharmaceutical chemists, who then developed polyamine inhibitors that revealed the increasing complexitites of polyamines and raised major new problems in genetics, protein and nucleic acid structure, metabolism and biosynthesis for the biologists, the biochemists and the chemists respectively. All this occurred against a background of enormous growth and increasing sophistication of these disciplines themselves. Let me illustrate this by describing our changing capabilities in handling proteins in the 1960s and 1970s.

Until the 1970s biochemists purifying an enzyme or other protein were restricted to biological sources that were normally relatively rich in the protein or that overproduced it in response to some form of stimulus. Now we isolate mRNA from such cells, produce a cDNA enzymatically and infect *E. coli*, yeast or whatever with it to overproduce our protein; or we overproduce the respective genes, mRNA and protein in selected inhibitor-resistant strains.

After an initial salt precipitation to concentrate our protein, purifications are accomplished via a large number of newly synthesized chromatographically useful or specific adsorbents. The size of the protein is then determined by its activity or other specific property by a sieving technique, and the size of the subunits of the purified protein is routinely obtained by electrophoresis in a denaturing gel. Protein isolation and characterization have now become a training effort appropriate for graduate students. The elaborate equipment of Svedberg and Tiseliug to estimate size and shape has been displaced by small and inexpensive gadgets.

Given a homogenous protein whose amino acid composition, organization, as well as prosthetic groups and active sites are determined by organic and physical chemists, these characteristics may be compared with the primary sequence obtained by analysis of the cDNA to check for some peculiarities or discordant data. If the protein is not very large, i.e., 100,000 or less in molecular weight, it is appropriate to try to crystallize it, since a great deal more of its organization can be learned from the markedly improved X-ray crystallographic analysis. Close examination of the newly determined tertiary structure, in the absence, and later in the presence of the newly synthesized tight-binding inhibitors, reveals to the chemist the precise organization of the active site and the requirements for a close inactivating fit.

In the last few years, the subunit of the dimeric protease of HIV has been synthesized chemically and shown to cleave specific sites of the HIV polyprotein formed from the viral RNA after infection. The crystalline protease has been demonstrated to have two aspartic acids at the active site, which reacts and cleaves a specific peptide in a sequence of the polyprotein. Replacement of the cleavage site in a small peptide with a transition state analog of the peptide target yields a tight-binding inhibitor active in the nM range against the production of active HIV in tissue cultures. So much for the growing competence of biomedical science.

Some years ago, the growth of and disease caused by the African trypanosome, i.e., sleeping sickness in humans, were shown by C. Bacchi and colleagues to be blocked by DFMO. Anthony Cerami and Alan Fairlamb subsequently found that trypanosomes have an unusual spermidine derivative. This compound is a *bis*-glutathionyl derivative of spermidine, now known as trypanothione. This complex compound was found to be the normal antioxidant of the species of trypanosome, replacing normal glutathione in this function. Furthermore, the trypanosome enzymes do not catalyze glutathione reactions, but are specific for trypanothione. In short, spermidine is an essential and structural component of the protozoan whose function is well-defined. In a more practical vein, the African trypanosome has a specific trypanothione reductase, that, like the protease of HIV, is a valid target for inhibition and chemotherapy. Indeed, some compounds long known as inhibitors of trypanosomiasis are now known to be inhibitors of trypanothione reductase. The steps described above for the HIV protease are being applied to trypanothione reductase. The enzyme has been crystallized and the structure of its active site has been analyzed with and without trypanothione. Inhibitors are being developed to block this important enzyme at this site.

This is one direction of polyamine research that has merged with the general advance of basic biomedical science. If a target for a polyamine inhibitor can be identified in the processes leading to or functional in cancer, modern science and technology might well be adequate to knock out that target.

CHAPTER 3

REGULATION OF POLYAMINE METABOLISM

Lo Persson, Fredrik Svensson and Eva Lövkvist Wallström

I. INTRODUCTION

The results of a multitude of studies have made it clear that several cellular processes are highly dependent on adequate levels of polyamines.[1-5] Too high concentrations of the larger polyamines have been shown to be toxic to the cell, whereas too low concentrations may negatively affect anabolic events such as the synthesis of DNA, RNA and protein in the cell. The introduction of molecular techniques in studies concerning polyamine metabolism has revealed a complex network of regulatory mechanisms involved in the cellular control of polyamine levels (Fig. 3.1).[3] The enzymes catalyzing the regulatory steps in the biosynthesis of polyamines are ornithine decarboxylase (ODC) and S-adenosylmethionine decarboxylase (AdoMetDC). The activities of these enzymes are strongly controlled at several levels, including transcriptional, translational and post-translational.[3,6-8] Cellular regulation of polyamine levels also involves an interconversion pathway in which spermine and spermidine can be converted into spermidine and putrescine, respectively.[9] The rate-limiting step in this metabolic pathway is an acetylation of the primary nitrogen on the aminopropyl group of the polyamine, which is catalyzed by the highly regulated enzyme spermidine/spermine N^1-acetyltransferase (SSAT). The

Polyamines in Cancer: Basic Mechanisms and Clinical Approaches, edited by Kenji Nishioka. © 1996 R.G. Landes Company.

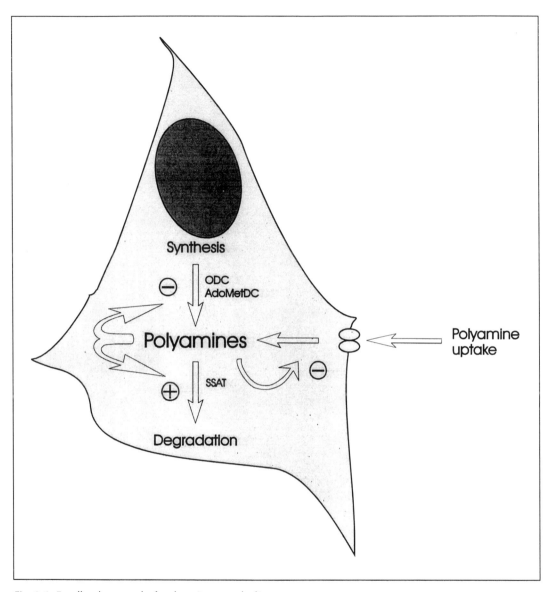

Fig. 3.1. Feedback control of polyamine metabolism.

acetylated derivatives of spermidine and spermine may either be excreted from the cell or further degraded by polyamine oxidase, a flavin adenine dinucleotide (FAD)-dependent oxidase abundantly present in most cells. In addition to these systems for control of polyamine levels, cells are able to actively transport extracellular polyamines into the cell in a regulated manner.[10]

The potential usefulness of polyamine antimetabolites in the therapy of a large variety of diseases, including cancer, is obvious.[2,4,5] However, the biosynthetic and the interconversion pathways together with the polyamine transporter provide the cell with an efficient system for securing an adequate supply of polyamines which may significantly reduce the value of such a treatment.[3] The understanding of the regulatory mechanisms involved in the cellular control of polyamine levels appears to be of utmost importance and may serve as a basis for the rational design of new and more potent pharmaceutical drugs.

II. REGULATION OF POLYAMINE BIOSYNTHESIS

A unique feature of mammalian ODC is its fast turnover with a half-life as short as a few minutes.[8] Thus, the cellular level of ODC is rapidly changed upon a change in the rate of synthesis or degradation (Fig. 3.2). It is not clear from all the studies conducted so far why the cells need such a rapid regulation of the enzyme. The turnover of the polyamines is usually much slower. However, it should be noted that our knowledge of the static and dynamic distribution of the polyamines between cellular compartments is meager, and it is likely that part of the polyamines exists as a free pool which may change more rapidly than bound polyamines. The recent finding that polyamines may act as physiological regulators of inward rectifier potassium channels[11-13] will eventually throw more light onto the need of a rapid turnover of ODC. Another explanation would be that ODC has another function, besides catalyzing the decarboxylation of ornithine, which is dependent on a rapid turnover of the protein. Although this has been suggested in the past no convincing evidence has been presented, and at the moment a dual function of ODC must be considered highly unlikely.

ODC is induced by a variety of stimuli including miscellaneous hormones and growth factors . The induction of ODC is generally connected with an increase in the amount of ODC mRNA, which appears to be caused by a stimulated transcription,[14] although some reports also describe a stabilization of the ODC mRNA.[15,16] The induction of ODC activity usually exceeds that of the increase in ODC mRNA with as much as one order of

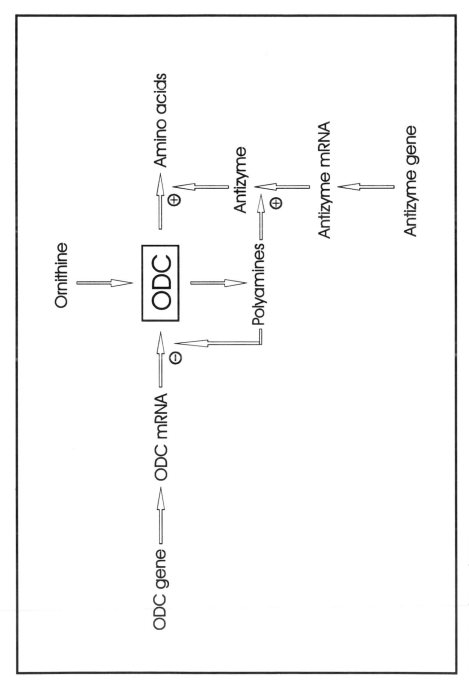

Fig. 3.2. Regulation of ODC.

magnitude.[16-18] This discrepancy has been demonstrated to be caused, at least partly, by a stabilization of ODC against degradation.[16] However, in some experimental systems the increase in ODC activity cannot be fully explained by an increase in ODC mRNA and a stabilization of the enzyme protein, indicating also a change in the translational efficiency.[16]

Polyamines exert a strong feedback control of mammalian ODC, which appears to involve the synthesis as well as the degradation of the enzyme.[3] ODC is rapidly down-regulated when cells are exposed to an excess of polyamines. When, on the other hand, the cellular polyamine content is reduced there is a compensatory increase in ODC activity.[19] Part of this regulation occurs at the level of protein turnover[8] and will be discussed below. However, part of the feedback control of ODC appears to take place at the level of ODC mRNA translation.[19-22] The generation of ODC antibodies[23] as well as molecular probes, i.e., ODC cDNAs,[24,25] provided the tools needed for a closer study of the mechanisms involved in the feedback control of ODC. It was shown that the synthesis of ODC, as measured by determining the incorporation of labeled methionine into the enzyme, was affected by the cellular content of polyamines. When cells are depleted of their polyamines, using specific inhibitors, there is an increase in the synthesis of ODC, and when cells are fed an excess of polyamines the synthesis of ODC is markedly reduced.[20-22] These changes in ODC synthesis rate are not explained by similar changes in the steady-state level of ODC mRNA.[20-22] In fact, the cellular level of ODC mRNA is essentially unchanged in situations when the ODC synthesis rate is altered more than 10-fold due to a change in polyamine content. The obvious interpretation of these results is that in some way the polyamines affect the translation of ODC mRNA. The molecular cloning of mammalian ODC revealed an mRNA with a long GC-rich 5' untranslated region.[26-28] This region could theoretically form strong secondary structures which may hamper the translation of the message. Using various DNA constructs in transient and stable expression systems it was shown that the 5' untranslated region of ODC mRNA in fact markedly inhibits the translation of subsequent sequences.[29-31] That ODC mRNA is indeed poorly translated in cells is demonstrated by its distribution among ribosomal subunits and monosomes in poly-some profiles.[32-34] Interestingly, no effect has been seen on the ribosomal distribution of ODC mRNA by treatments that activate the feedback regulation and affect the synthesis of ODC.[32-34] However, since a large fraction of the ODC mRNA is in the untranslated region of the polysome profile a minor shift in the distribution of the mRNA (which could be difficult to detect) may represent a large change in the translation of the message. Nevertheless, the exact mechanism(s) by which the polyamines affect the translation of ODC mRNA remains to be established.

The idea of a polyamine-mediated translational control of ODC is not without controversy. The conclusion is based on measurements of ODC synthesis using pulse-labeling techniques. Since ODC has a very short half-life it is essential that the labeling time is kept short enough to avoid any influence of labeled ODC being degraded during the experiment. It has been suggested that the observed polyamine-mediated changes in incorporation of labeled methionine into ODC are actually caused by a polyamine-regulated rapid degradation of ODC which occurs at or close to the ribosome.[33] However, so far no conclusive evidence exists of such a regulatory component.

As mentioned earlier the turnover of ODC is extremely fast with a biological half-life of usually less than 1 hour and sometimes as short as a few minutes. This turnover of ODC has also been shown to be influenced by polyamines.[8] Exposure of cells or tissues to high concentrations of polyamines results in a rapid increase in the degradation rate of ODC. The mechanisms behind this degradative induction are presently being unraveled not at least by the pioneering work of Hayashi and colleagues.[35] They demonstrated that the polyamine-mediated stimulation of ODC degradation was dependent on the synthesis of what appeared to be a protein with a rapid turnover. In addition, they connected this observation with the earlier finding of a protein, named antizyme, that was induced by the exposure of an excess of polyamines and that bound to and inhibited ODC with a very strong affinity. The hypothesis was that polyamines induce the production of antizyme which then targets ODC for degradation without being used itself. In a series of experiments they presented results that indirectly confirmed this hypothesis.[36-39] However, it was not until the molecular cloning of antizyme[40,41] that evidence for a function of this protein in targeting ODC for degradation was obtained. Using in vitro as well as in vivo systems it was demonstrated that expression of recombinant antizyme induced an acceleration of ODC turnover which was similar to that obtained by exposure to polyamines.[42-44] The degradation of ODC occurs through what appears to be a unique mechanism. It was shown that ODC is degraded through an ubiquitin independent process catalyzed by the proteolytic complex called the 26S proteasome.[43,45-47] This is the first example of a non-ubiquitinated protein being degraded by the 26S proteasome.

Coffino and colleagues have made an extensive study of what parts of the mammalian ODC molecule are important for the rapid turnover of the enzyme as well as for the binding of antizyme.[44,48-51] It is clear that the carboxyterminal part of ODC is of utmost importance for the short half-life of the enzyme. Truncation of the ODC molecule at the carboxy end transforms the enzyme from a short-lived protein to a protein with a slow turnover.[48] This finding explains the difference in half-lives between the mammalian ODC and ODC from the protozoa *Trypanosoma brucei*. Trypanosomal ODC, which has a long half-life even when expressed in mammalian cells, is shorter than the mammalian enzyme and lacks the part corresponding to the carboxyterminal part of mammalian ODC. Furthermore, recombining trypanosomal ODC with the carboxyl part of mammalian ODC confers a short half-life to the fusion protein.[49,52] Antizyme binds to the N-terminal part of ODC, and this binding appears to induce a conformational change that exposes the C-terminal part for the degradative process.[44,50] However, the C-terminal part of the ODC cannot alone induce degradation. A portion of the N-terminal half of antizyme also has to be present to promote degradation of the ODC molecule.[51]

The molecular cloning of antizyme provided the tools to study the mechanisms regulating the synthesis of this unique protein. Northern blot analysis demonstrated that the antizyme mRNA is an abundant mRNA in all tissues studied and that the level of this mRNA does not change in situations when the amount of antizyme is markedly changed.[40] The sequence of the cDNA revealed an in-frame stop codon close to the initiation codon. Furthermore, the sequence after this stop codon was out of frame suggesting a ribosomal frameshift to occur during translation of the mRNA.[41] The presence of a +1 frameshift was later confirmed and demonstrated to be stimulated by polyamines.[53,54] Thus, it appears that polyamines induce the production of antizyme through a unique mechanism, ribosomal frameshifting. No other examples of mammalian ribosomal frameshifting are hitherto known.

AdoMetDC catalyzes the other regulatory step in the biosynthesis of polyamines (Fig. 3.3). It is a general conception though that ODC catalyzes the rate-limiting step in this biosynthetic pathway. This idea is based on the fact that putrescine stimulates AdoMetDC activity in vitro.[55] However, in some systems it is evident that AdoMetDC and not ODC is the rate-limiting enzyme. Mammalian AdoMetDC, like ODC, has a fast turnover and is induced by a large variety of stimuli.[56] The enzyme uses pyruvate instead of pyridoxal phosphate as a cofactor.[57] AdoMetDC is the only known mammalian enzyme that contains pyruvate as a prosthetic group. Mammalian AdoMetDC is synthesized as a proenzyme which is then processed into two subunits that are both part of the active enzyme.[58] The generation of the covalently bound pyruvoyl group and the subunits occurs through a cleavage of the proenzyme at a serine residue.[58] This process appears to be autocatalytic, but is stimulated by the presence of putrescine.[59] Besides stimulating the conversion of the AdoMetDC proenzyme, putrescine has a direct stimulatory effect on the activity of the enzyme.[55]

Although putrescine stimulates the conversion of the proenzyme as well as the activity of the enzyme, spermidine and spermine exert a negative control of AdoMetDC. When spermidine and spermine are present in an excess AdoMetDC is rapidly downregulated, and conversely, in situations when the cellular levels of spermidine and spermine are reduced AdoMetDC is induced.[60,61] Both polyamines are effective, but spermine appears to be a more potent regulator than spermidine. The underlying mechanisms resemble those of the polyamine-mediated control of ODC, although some clear differences exist. The synthesis of AdoMetDC, like that of ODC, is inversely related to the cellular spermidine and spermine

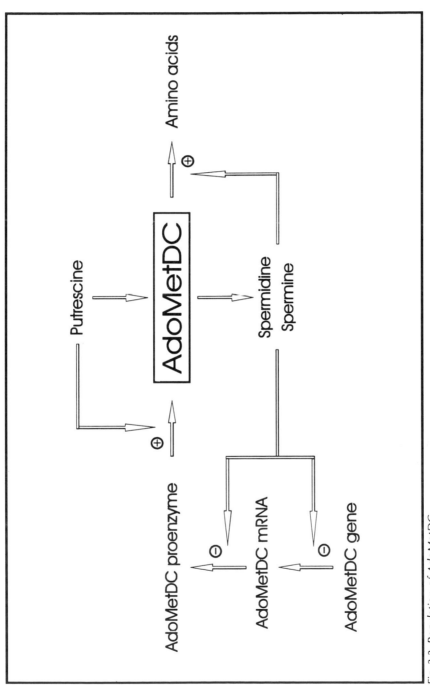

Fig. 3.3. Regulation of AdoMetDC.

levels.[62-65] Treatment with various inhibitors of polyamine synthesis results in an increase in the incorporation of labeled methionine into AdoMetDC. This effect can be reversed by the addition of spermidine or spermine, which down-regulates the synthesis of AdoMetDC. In contrast to the feedback regulation of ODC synthesis, the changes in AdoMetDC synthesis are partly explained by changes in the amount of AdoMetDC mRNA available.[62,66] Whether the change in mRNA content is due to an increased transcription and/or to a stabilization of the mRNA is not yet known. However, the change in AdoMetDC mRNA steady-state level cannot usually fully explain the change in AdoMetDC synthesis rate, indicating also a translational component.[65,66] The polyamine-mediated change in AdoMetDC mRNA content is generally only 2- to 3-fold, whereas the change in synthesis rate could be as large as 10- to 20-fold.

Like ODC mRNA, AdoMetDC mRNA has a long leader sequence (about 320 nucleotides) with potentially strong secondary structures which may be of regulatory importance.[67-69] The sequence contains a small open reading frame close to the cap site, which has been shown to dramatically inhibit the translation of the mRNA in some systems.[70-72] Furthermore, the first part of the leader sequence appears to be of importance for the polyamine-mediated regulation of AdoMetDC mRNA translation.[73,74] Deletion of this part of the message greatly reduces the stimulatory effects on AdoMetDC expression caused by spermine depletion. However, more work is needed to establish the specific function of the AdoMetDC mRNA leader sequence in the feedback regulation of AdoMetDC synthesis.

As mentioned above AdoMetDC is also a protein with rapid turnover. Results from several studies indicate that the turnover of AdoMetDC is affected by polyamines. Treatment of cells with various inhibitors of polyamine synthesis gives rise to a stabilization of AdoMetDC.[75,76] This effect is neutralized by the addition of polyamines. However, so far no protein corresponding to ODC antizyme has been found in connection with AdoMetDC degradation, and thus the regulatory mechanisms behind the effects of polyamines on AdoMetDC turnover are still to be unraveled.

III. REGULATION OF POLYAMINE DEGRADATION

Spermidine and spermine are normally produced in reactions catalyzed by the constitutive enzymes spermidine synthase and spermine synthase, respectively. Although these reactions are essentially irreversible it has been known for a long time that a conversion of spermine into spermidine and of spermidine into putrescine can occur in vivo.[77] The interconversion of polyamines was demonstrated to be stimulated by toxic agents, such as carbon tetrachloride.[77] The injection of this hepatoxin gave rise to an increase in putrescine content and a decrease in spermidine content in the liver. The increase in putrescine content was not affected by ODC inhibitors indicating a different pathway.[78] Later, an enzyme capable of oxidizing spermine into spermidine and spermidine into putrescine was purified and characterized.[79] However, this enzyme appeared to be constitutively expressed and was not induced by treatments that were known to stimulate the interconversion of the polyamines.[79] Moreover, the preferred substrates of the polyamine oxidase were not the natural polyamines but the N^1-acetylated derivatives of spermidine and spermine.[80] These problems were solved by the discovery of a cytosolic enzyme that could catalyze the N^1-acetylation of spermidine and spermine.[81] Treatments that were known to induce the interconversion of polyamines did also induce the activity of this enzyme demonstrating its importance in the polyamine interconversion pathway.[82] Thus the polyamine interconversion pathway consists of two steps: first an acetylation of the aminopropyl group of spermidine or spermine and then an oxidation giving rise to 3-acetamidopropanal together with putrescine or spermidine, respectively. The interconversion of spermine and spermidine may also be considered to be the first part of a polyamine catabolic pathway. Both putrescine and 3-acetamidopropanal, which are products of the interconversion pathway, may be further catabolized. However, the regulatory step of the catabolic pathway still appears to be the acetylation of the polyamines, which are catalyzed by the enzyme SSAT (Fig. 3.4).[9] Furthermore, the acetylated derivatives of spermidine and spermine are much easier excreted from the cell than the corresponding polyamine.

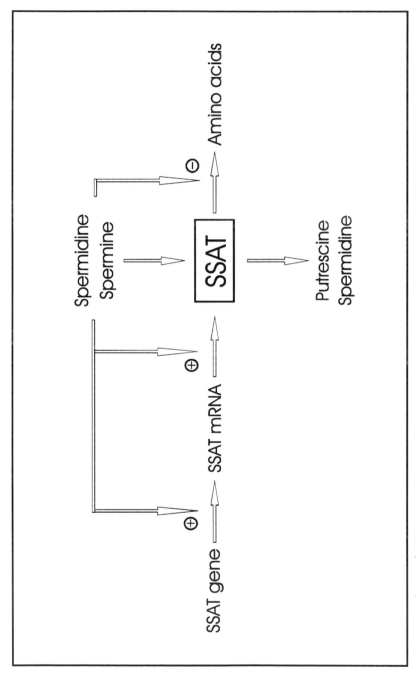

Fig. 3.4. Regulation of SSAT.

Like ODC and AdoMetDC SSAT has a very fast turnover.[83] The enzyme is induced by a large variety of stimuli, including hormones, toxins and miscellaneous polyamines and their analogs.[9] The finding that polyamines may induce SSAT indicates that the enzyme plays a role in the regulation of intracellular levels of polyamines. The enzyme, and thus the degradation and/or excretion of the polyamines, is induced whenever polyamine levels become too high. In addition, the acetylation of the primary nitrogen reduces the tendency of the amino group to be charged at a physiological pH, which may be beneficial for the cellular protection against the harmful effects of too high concentrations of polyamines. Then why is SSAT induced by a variety of toxic agents? Until a few years ago these were the strongest stimuli for SSAT induction. It is conceivable that the toxic effects include a release of intracellularly bound polyamines which then induce SSAT. The strongest inducers of SSAT known today are several polyamine analogs, e.g., bisethyl derivatives of spermine and norspermine.[84,85] Treatments with these analogs may induce the enzyme several 1000-fold to levels corresponding to almost 1% of the soluble protein.[84] This marked induction of SSAT depletes the cell of its content of spermidine and spermine. In addition, some of the analogs also down-regulate ODC and AdoMetDC making them very potent in their polyamine-depleting properties.[86] Being polyamine analogs they also act as competitive inhibitors of the polyamine transport (see below). Thus, these polyamine analogs affect several of the steps involved in polyamine metabolism, and several of them are presently undergoing clinical trials as antineoplastic agents.

The mechanisms by which SSAT is being regulated are presently being unraveled. Using specific antibodies against the enzyme it was demonstrated that the changes in enzyme activity corresponded to similar changes in the amount of enzyme protein.[83] Thus, the enzyme does not appear to be regulated by a post-translational activation/deactivation. The isolation of cDNAs encoding mammalian SSAT enabled more detailed studies of the regulatory mechanisms involved in the polyamine-mediated induction of the enzyme.[87-89] The enormous induction of SSAT caused by the polyamine analogs was shown to be a combined result of increased transcription, translation as well as degradation of the enzyme.[90,91]

However, the exact mechanisms by which the polyamines affect the transcription of the SSAT gene, the translation of the SSAT mRNA and the turnover of the SSAT protein are yet to be disclosed.

As mentioned above the cellular excretion of polyamines is facilitated by an acetylation of the primary nitrogens. However, no evidence has been obtained so far demonstrating that the excretion of acetylated polyamine derivatives is regulated per se. Nevertheless, in some cellular systems it is shown that the diamines putrescine and cadaverine can be what appears to be actively excreted in a regulated manner.[92] Whether this system plays a physiological role in the cellular control of polyamine levels remains to be established. Results obtained indicate that there is also a continuous efflux, or leakage, of polyamines from the cell.[93,94] Most of these polyamines are then salvaged using a specific uptake system that actively transports the polyamines back into the cell.

IV. REGULATION OF POLYAMINE TRANSPORT

Normally, cells are able to synthesize whatever polyamines they need. In spite of this fact, cells are equipped with an efficient transport system for uptake of external polyamines.[10] It is a very efficient energy-requiring transport system capable of accumulating polyamines intracellularly to millimolar concentrations from micromolar concentrations extracellularly. The finding that large amounts of polyamines accumulated in the growth medium of cells deficient in polyamine transport,[93,94] compared to that of other cells, indicates that cells normally excrete polyamines and that the polyamine transport system is important for the salvage of some of these polyamines. However, the polyamine transport system may also fulfill other important functions in relation to supplying the cell with adequate levels of polyamines. The gastrointestinal tract is a potential source for large amounts of polyamines.[95] All the food we eat contains large amounts of polyamines. The intestinal bacteria produce and excrete considerable quantities of polyamines. It is conceivable that a large fraction of these polyamines is absorbed from the intestines and later taken up and used by cells in the body. At the moment we do not know to what extent cells rely upon endogenous compared to exogenous polyamines. However, it is clear that in situations when the polyamine biosynthetic machinery is impaired, due to lack of substrates or to inhibition of ODC or AdoMetDC, cells would be more dependent on extracellularly derived polyamines.

The knowledge of the polyamine transport system is still meager. It is not known whether there are individual transport systems for the various polyamines or only a single transporter, capable of transporting all the polyamines. In some systems there seem to be several polyamine transporters whereas in others only a single transporter appears to exist.[10] The cellular polyamine transport system is stimulated by various factors, e.g., serum, insulin, concanavalin A and epidermal growth factor.[10] It is possible that the stimulatory effect of these factors on polyamine transport is related to their growth promoting activity, since proliferation has been demonstrated to be strongly associated with an increased cellular uptake of polyamines.

The activity of the polyamine transporters is highly regulated by cellular polyamine levels. In situations where the cellular polyamines are depleted, using for instance specific inhibitors of the biosynthesis, there is a marked increase in the cellular uptake of exogenous polyamines.[96] On the other hand, in the presence of an excess of polyamines the polyamine transporter is down-regulated.[97] This feedback regulation was shown to be dependent on protein synthesis and to involve a protein with a very fast turnover.[97] Recently it was demonstrated that antizyme, which is induced by an excess of polyamines, besides regulating the degradation of ODC also appears to regulate the cellular polyamine transporter.[98,99] Cells in which antizyme was expressed to high levels exhibited a marked down-regulation of polyamine uptake.

The polyamine-mediated regulation of cellular polyamine uptake may have a large clinical implication. Various inhibitors of ODC and AdoMetDC have been considered as therapeutic agents against proliferative disorders such as cancer.[2,5-7] However, the therapeutic effects of these inhibitors on tumors in vivo are quite low compared to the marked antiproliferative effects obtained on tumor cells in culture. This may be caused by an increased uptake of exogenous polyamines by the tumor cells, which counteracts the decrease in polyamine content caused by the inhibitors. That

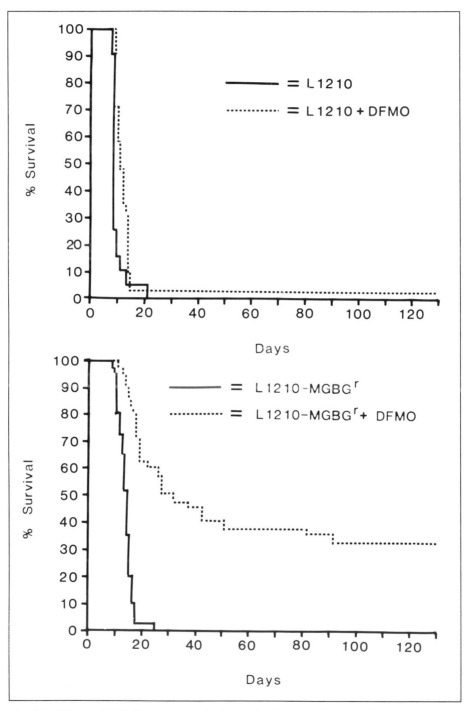

Fig. 3.5. Effects of DFMO on the survival of mice inoculated with polyamine transport deficient cells (L1210-MGBG^r) or parental L1210 cells. DFMO was given in the drinking water (3%) from day 1 on. (Reproduced with permission from Persson L, Holm I, Ask A et al. Cancer Res 1988; 48:4807-11.)

this is really the situation is shown in an experimental system using tumor cells which were unable to take up exogenous polyamines (Fig. 3.5).[100] The therapeutic effect of the ODC inhibitor 2-difluoromethylornithine (DFMO) was much greater on mice inoculated with a mutant L1210 leukemia cell line deficient in polyamine transport than on mice inoculated with the parental cells. Thirty to seventy-five percent of the leukemic mice bearing the mutant tumor cells were cured by DFMO treatment compared to only a slight increase in the survival time of leukemic mice bearing the parental L1210 cells by the same treatment.[100,101] Furthermore, a reduction of the supply of extracellular polyamines, by feeding a polyamine-deficient diet containing antibiotics, also potentiated the therapeutic effects of DFMO on various experimental tumors, demonstrating the importance of the polyamine transport system.[101,102]

V. CONCLUSIONS

Recent results have demonstrated and partly unraveled several unique mechanisms involved in the cellular control of polyamine levels. Future studies will surely provide us with more significant information in this field. The therapeutic usefulness of inhibitors of polyamine synthesis has been shown to be dependent on a repression of the compensatory increase in cellular uptake of exogenous polyamines. Future development of specific inhibitors of polyamine transport should be of great significance. The molecular cloning and characterization of the mammalian polyamine transporter(s) will most likely be an important milestone in this work. In addition, polyamine analogs that affect several steps in the polyamine metabolic pathway have been developed and are presently undergoing clinical trials as antineoplastic agents. Thus, the polyamine metabolic pathway is a potential target for therapeutic agents against a variety of diseases, and the understanding of the mechanisms involved in the cellular control of polyamine homeostasis is of utmost importance.

References

1. Tabor H, Tabor CW. Polyamines. Ann Rev Biochem 1984; 53:749-90.

2. Pegg AE. Polyamine metabolism and its importance in neoplastic growth and as a target for chemotherapy. Cancer Res 1988; 48:759-74.

3. Heby O, Persson L. Molecular genetics of polyamine synthesis in eukaryotic cells. Trends Biochem Sci 1990; 15:153-8.

4. Jänne J, Alhonen L, Leinonen P. Polyamines: From molecular biology to clinical applications. Ann Med 1991; 23:241-59.

5. Marton LJ, Pegg AE. Polyamines as targets for therapeutic intervention. Annu Rev Pharmacol Toxicol 1995; 35:55-91.

6. McCann PP, Pegg AE. Ornithine decarboxylase as an enzyme target for therapy. Pharmacol Ther 1992; 54:195-215.

7. Pegg AE, McCann PP. S-adenosylmethionine decarboxylase as an enzyme target for therapy. Pharmacol Ther 1992; 56:359-77.

8. Hayashi S, Murakami Y. Rapid and regulated degradation of ornithine decarboxylase. Biochem J 1995; 306:1-10.

9. Casero Jr RA, Pegg AE. Spermidine/spermine ^{1}N-acetyltransferase—The turning point in polyamine metabolism. FASEB J 1993; 7:653-61.

10. Seiler N, Dezeure F. Polyamine transport in mammalian cells. Int J Biochem 1990; 22:211-8.

11. Lopatin AN, Makhina EN, Nichols CG. Potassium channel block by cytoplasmic polyamines as the mechanism of intrinsic rectification. Nature 1994; 372:366-9.

12. Ficker E, Taglialatela M, Wible BA et al. Spermine and spermidine as gating molecules for inward rectifier K+ channels. Science 1994; 266:1068-72.

13. Fakler B, Brändle U, Glowatzki E et al. Strong voltage-dependent inward rectification of inward rectifier K+ channels is caused by intracellular spermine. Cell 1995; 80:149-54.

14. Katz A, Kahana C. Transcriptional activation of mammalian ornithine decarboxylase during stimulated growth. Mol Cell Biol 1987; 7:2641-3.

15. Olson EN, Spizz G. Mitogens and protein synthesis inhibitors induce ornithine decarboxylase gene transcription through separate mechanisms in the BC3H1 muscle cell line. Mol Cell Biol 1986; 6:2792-9.

16. Wallon UM, Persson L, Heby O. Regulation of ornithine decarboxylase during cell growth. Changes in the stability and translatability of the mRNA, and in the turnover of the protein. Mol Cell Biochem 1995; 146:39-44.

17. Ruhl KK, Pomidor MM, Rhim JS et al. Post-transcriptional suppression of human ornithine decarboxylase gene expression by phorbol esters in human keratinocytes. J Invest Dermatol 1994; 103:687-92.

18. Fredlund JO, Johansson MC, Dahlberg E et al. Ornithine decarboxylase and S-adenosylmethionine decarboxylase expression during the cell cycle of Chinese hamster ovary cells. Exp Cell Res 1995; 216:86-92.

19. Persson L, Oredsson SM, Anehus S et al. Ornithine decarboxylase inhibitors increase the cellular content of the enzyme: implications for translational regulation. Biochem Biophys Res Commun 1985; 131:239-45.

20. Kahana C, Nathans D. Translational regulation of mammalian ornithine decarboxylase by polyamines. J Biol Chem 1985; 260: 15390-3.

21. Hölttä E, Pohjanpelto P. Control of ornithine decarboxylase in Chinese hamster ovary cells by polyamines. Translational inhibition of synthesis and acceleration of degradation of the enzyme by putrescine, spermidine and spermine. J Biol Chem 1986; 261: 9502-8.

22. Persson L, Holm I, Heby O. Translational regulation of ornithine decarboxylase by polyamines. FEBS Lett 1986; 295:175-8.

23. Persson L. Antibodies to ornithine decarboxylase. Immunochemical cross-reactivity. Acta Chem Scand 1982; B36:685-8.

24. Kontula KK, Torkkeli TK, Bardin CW et al. Androgen induction of ornithine decarboxylase mRNA in mouse kidney as studied by complementary DNA. Proc Natl Acad Sci USA 1984; 81:731-5.

25. McConlogue L, Gupta M, Wu L et al. Molecular cloning and expression of the mouse ornithine decarboxylase gene. Proc Natl Acad Sci USA 1984; 81:540-4.

26. Katz A, Kahana C. Isolation and characterization of the mouse ornithine decarboxylase gene. J Biol Chem 1988; 263:7604-9.

27. Brabant M, McConlogue L, van Daalen Wetters T et al. Mouse ornithine decarboxylase gene: cloning, structure, and expression. Proc Natl Acad Sci USA 1988; 85:2200-4.

28. Wen L, Huang JK, Blackshear PJ. Rat ornithine decarboxylase gene. Nucleotide sequence, potential regulatory elements, and comparison to the mouse gene. J Biol Chem 1989; 264:9016-21.

29. Grens A, Scheffler IE. The 5'- and 3'-untranslated regions of ornithine decarboxylase mRNA affect the translational efficiency. J Biol Chem 1990; 265:11810-6.

30. Manzella JM, Blackshear PJ. Regulation of rat ornithine decarboxylase mRNA translation by its 5'-untranslated region. J Biol Chem 1990; 265:11817-22.

31. Ito K, Kashiwagi K, Watanabe S et al. Influence of the 5'-untranslated region of ornithine decarboxylase mRNA and spermidine on ornithine decarboxylase synthesis. J Biol Chem 1990; 265:13036-41.

32. Holm I, Persson L, Stjernborg L et al. Feedback control of orni-
    thine decarboxylase expression by polyamines. Analysis of ornithine
    decarboxylase mRNA distribution in polysome profiles and of trans-
    lation of this mRNA in vitro. Biochem J 1989; 258:343-50.
33. van Daalen Wetters T, Macrae M, Brabant M et al. Polyamine-
    mediated regulation of mouse ornithine decarboxylase is post-trans-
    lational. Mol Cell Biol 1989; 9:5484-90.
34. Stjernborg L, Heby O, Holm I et al. On the translational control
    of ornithine decarboxylase expression by polyamines. Biochim
    Biophys Acta 1991; 1090:188-94.
35. Hayashi S, Kameji T, Fujita K et al. Molecular mechanism for the
    regulation of hepatic ODC. Adv Enzyme Regul 1985; 23:311-29.
36. Murakami Y, Hayashi S. Role of antizyme in degradation of orni-
    thine decarboxylase in HTC cells. Biochem J 1985; 226:893-6.
37. Kanamoto R, Utsunomiya K, Kameji T et al. Effects of putrescine
    on synthesis and degradation of ornithine decarboxylase in primary
    cultured hepatocytes. Eur J Biochem 1986; 154:539-44.
38. Murakami Y, Nishiyama M, Hayashi S. Involvement of antizyme
    in stabilization of ornithine decarboxylase caused by inhibitors of
    polyamine synthesis. Eur J Biochem 1989; 180:181-4.
39. Kanamoto R, Kameji T, Iwashita S et al. Spermidine-induced de-
    stabilization of ornithine decarboxylase (ODC) is mediated by ac-
    cumulation of antizyme in ODC-overproducing variant cells. J Biol
    Chem 1993; 268:9393-9.
40. Matsufuji S, Miyazaki Y, Kanamoto R et al. Analyses of ornithine
    decarboxylase antizyme mRNA with a cDNA cloned from rat liver.
    J Biochem (Tokyo) 1990; 108:365-71.
41. Miyazaki Y, Matsufuji S, Hayashi S. Cloning and characterization
    of a rat gene encoding ornithine decarboxylase antizyme. Gene 1992;
    113:191-7.
42. Murakami Y, Matsufuji S, Miyazaki Y et al. Destabilization of or-
    nithine decarboxylase by transfected antizyme gene expression in
    hepatoma tissue culture cells. J Biol Chem 1992; 267:13138-41.
43. Murakami Y, Matsufuji S, Tanaka K et al. Involvement of the
    proteasome and antizyme in ornithine decarboxylase degradation
    by a reticulocyte lysate. Biochem J 1993; 295:305-8.
44. Li X, Coffino P. Degradation of ornithine decarboxylase: Exposure
    of the C-terminal target by a polyamine-inducible inhibitory pro-
    tein. Mol Cell Biol 1993; 13:2377-83.
45. Rosenberg-Hasson Y, Bercovich Z, Ciechanover A et al. Degrada-
    tion of ornithine decarboxylase in mammalian cells is ATP depen-
    dent but ubiquitin independent. Eur J Biochem 1989; 185:469-74.
46. Bercovich Z, Rosenberg-Hasson Y, Ciechanover A et al. Degrada-
    tion of ornithine decarboxylase in reticulocyte lysate is ATP-de-

pendent but ubiquitin-independent. J Biol Chem 1989; 264: 15949-52.

47. Murakami Y, Matsufuji S, Kameji T et al. Ornithine decarboxylase is degraded by the 26S proteasome without ubiquitination. Nature 1992; 360:597-9.

48. Ghoda L, van Daalen Wetters T, Macrae M et al. Prevention of rapid intracellular degradation of ODC by a carboxyl-terminal truncation. Science 1989; 243:1493-5.

49. Ghoda L, Sidney D, Macrae M et al. Structural elements of ornithine decarboxylase required for intracellular degradation and polyamine-dependent regulation. Mol Cell Biol 1992; 12:2178-85.

50. Li X, Coffino P. Regulated degradation of ornithine decarboxylase requires interaction with the polyamine-inducible protein antizyme. Mol Cell Biol 1992; 12:3556-62.

51. Li X, Coffino P. Distinct domains of antizyme required for binding and proteolysis of ornithine decarboxylase. Mol Cell Biol 1994; 14:87-92.

52. Ghoda L, Phillips MA, Bass KE et al. Trypanosome ornithine decarboxylase is stable because it lacks sequences found in the carboxyl terminus of the mouse enzyme which target the latter for intracellular degradation. J Biol Chem 1990; 265:11823-6.

53. Matsufuji S, Matsufuji T, Miyazaki Y et al. Autoregulatory frameshifting in decoding mammalian ornithine decarboxylase antizyme. Cell 1995; 80:51-60.

54. Rom E, Kahana C. Polyamines regulate the expression of ornithine decarboxylase antizyme in vitro by inducing ribosomal frame-shifting. Proc Natl Acad Sci USA 1994; 91:3959-63.

55. Pegg AE, Williams-Ashman HG. Stimulation of decarboxylation of S-adenosylmethionine by putrescine in mammalian tissues. Biochem Biophys Res Commun 1968; 30:76-82.

56. Pegg AE. S-Adenosylmethionine decarboxylase: a brief review. Cell Biochem Funct 1984; 2:11-5.

57. Pegg AE. Evidence for the presence of pyruvate in rat liver S-adenosylmethionine decarboxylase. FEBS Letters 1977; 84:33-6.

58. Stanley BA, Pegg AE, Holm I. Site of pyruvate formation and processing of mammalian S-adenosylmethionine decarboxylase proenzyme. J Biol Chem 1989; 264:21073-9.

59. Stanley BA, Pegg AE. Amino acid residues necessary for putrescine stimulation of human S-adenosylmethionine decarboxylase proenzyme processing and catalytic activity. J Biol Chem 1991; 266:18502-6.

60. Alhonen-Hongisto L. Regulation of S-adenosylmethionine decarboxylase by polyamines in Ehrlich ascites-carcinoma cells grown in culture. Biochem J 1980; 190:747-54.

61. Mamont PS, Joder-Ohlenbusch AM, Nussli M et al. Indirect evidence for a strict negative control of S-adenosyl-L-methionine decarboxylase by spermidine in rat hepatoma cells. Biochem J 1981; 196:411-22.

62. Shirahata A, Pegg AE. Increased content of mRNA for a precursor of S-adenosylmethionine decarboxylase in rat prostate after treatment with 2-difluoromethylornithine. J Biol Chem 1986; 261: 13833-7.

63. Persson L, Khomutov AR, Khomutov RM. Feedback regulation of S-adenosylmethionine decarboxylase synthesis. Biochem J 1989; 257:929-31.

64. Shantz LM, Holm I, Jänne OA et al. Regulation of S-adenosylmethionine decarboxylase activity by alterations in the intracellular polyamine content. Biochem J 1992; 288:511-8.

65. Stjernborg L, Heby O, Mamont P et al. Polyamine-mediated regulation of S-adenosylmethionine decarboxylase expression in mammalian cells—Studies using 5'-{[(Z)-4-amino-2-butenyl] methylamino}-5'-deoxyadenosine, a suicide inhibitor of the enzyme. Eur J Biochem 1993; 214:671-6.

66. Persson L, Stjernborg L, Holm I et al. Polyamine-mediated control of mammalian S-adenosyl-L-methionine decarboxylase expression: effects of the content and translational efficiency of the mRNA. Biochem Biophys Res Commun 1989; 160:1196-202.

67. Pajunen A, Crozat A, Jänne OA et al. Structure and regulation of mammalian S-adenosylmethionine decarboxylase. J Biol Chem 1988; 263:17040-9.

68. Pulkka A, Ihalainen R, Aatsinki J et al. Structure and organization of the gene encoding rat S-adenosylmethionine decarboxylase. FEBS Lett 1991; 291:289-95.

69. Maric SC, Crozat A, Jänne OA. Structure and organization of the human S-adenosylmethionine decarboxylase gene. J Biol Chem 1992; 267:18915-23.

70. Hill JR, Morris DR. Cell-specific translation of S-adenosylmethionine decarboxylase mRNA. Regulation by the 5' transcript leader. J Biol Chem 1992; 267:21886-93.

71. Hill JR, Morris DR. Cell-specific translational regulation of S-adenosylmethionine decarboxylase mRNA. Dependence on translation and coding capacity of the cis-acting upstream open reading frame. J Biol Chem 1993; 268:726-31.

72. Ruan H, Hill JR, Fatemie-Nainie S et al. Cell-specific translational regulation of S-adenosylmethionine decarboxylase mRNA. Influence of the structure of the 5' transcript leader on regulation by the upstream open reading frame. J Biol Chem 1994; 269:17905-10.

73. Suzuki T, Kashiwagi K, Igarashi K. Polyamine regulation of S-

adenosylmethionine decarboxylase synthesis through the 5'-untranslated region of its mRNA. Biochem Biophys Res Commun 1993; 192:627-34.

74. Shantz LM, Viswanath R, Pegg AE. Role of the 5'-untranslated region of mRNA in the synthesis of S-adenosylmethionine decarboxylase and its regulation by spermine. Biochem J 1994; 302:765-72.

75. Autelli R, Stjernborg L, Khomutov AR et al. Regulation of S-adenosylmethionine decarboxylase in L1210 leukemia cells—Studies using an irreversible inhibitor of the enzyme. Eur J Biochem 1991; 196:551-6.

76. Stjernborg L, Persson L. Stabilization of S-adenosylmethionine decarboxylase by aminoguanidine. Biochem Pharmacol 1993; 45:1174-6.

77. Hölttä E, Sinervirta R, Jänne J. Synthesis and accumulation of polyamines in rat liver regenerating after treatment with carbon tetrachloride. Biochem Biophys Res Commun 1973; 54:350-7.

78. Matsui I, Wiegand L, Pegg AE. Properties of spermidine N-acetyltransferase from livers of rats treated with carbon tetrachloride and its role in the conversion of spermidine into putrescine. J Biol Chem 1981; 256:2454-9.

79. Hölttä E. Oxidation of spermidine and spermine in rat liver: purification and properties of polyamine oxidase. Biochemistry 1977; 16:91-100.

80. Bolkenius FN, Seiler N. Acetylderivatives as intermediates in polyamine catabolism. Int J Biochem 1981; 13:287-92.

81. Matsui I, Pegg AE. Increase in acetylation of spermidine in rat liver extracts brought about by treatment with carbon tetrachloride. Biochem Biophys Res Commun 1980; 92:1009-15.

82. Matsui I, Pegg AE. Effect of thioacetamide, growth hormone or partial hepatectomy on spermidine acetylase activity of rat liver cytosol. Biochim Biophys Acta 1980; 633:87-94.

83. Persson L, Pegg AE. Studies of the induction of spermidine/spermine [1]N-acetyltransferase using a specific antiserum. J Biol Chem 1984; 259:12364-7.

84. Casero RA, Celano P, Ervin SJ et al. Differential induction of spermidine/spermine [1]N-acetyltransferase in human lung cancer cells by the bis(ethyl)polyamines analogues. Cancer Res 1989; 49:3829-33.

85. Porter CW, Ganis B, Libby PR et al. Correlations between polyamine analogue-induced increases in spermidine/spermine [1]N-acetyltransferase activity, polyamine pool depletion, and growth inhibition in human melanoma cell lines. Cancer Res 1991; 51:3715-20.

86. Porter CW, Pegg AE, Ganis B et al. Combined regulation of ornithine and S-adenosylmethionine decarboxylases by spermine and the spermine analogue [1]N,[12]N-bis(ethyl)spermine. Biochem J 1990; 268:207-12.

87. Xiao L, Celano P, Mank AR et al. Characterization of a full-length cDNA which codes for the human spermidine/spermine [1]N-acetyltransferase. Biochem Biophys Res Commun 1991; 179:407-15.

88. Pegg AE, Stanley BA, Wiest L et al. Nucleotide sequence of hamster spermidine/spermine-[1]N-acetyltransferase cDNA. Biochim Biophys Acta 1992; 1171:106-8.

89. Fogel-Petrovic M, Kramer DL, Ganis B et al. Cloning and sequence analysis of the gene and cDNA encoding mouse spermidine/spermine [1]N-acetyltransferase—A gene uniquely regulated by polyamines and their analogs. Biochim Biophys Acta 1993; 1216:255-64.

90. Pegg AE, Pakala R, Bergeron RJ. Induction of spermidine/spermine [1]N-acetyltransferase activity in Chinese-hamster ovary cells by [1]N,[11]N-bis(ethyl)norspermidine and related compounds. Biochem J 1990; 267:331-8.

91. Casero Jr RA, Celano P, Ervin SJ et al. Isolation and characterization of a cDNA clone that codes for human spermidine/spermine [1]N-acetyltransferase. J Biol Chem 1991; 266:810-4.

92. Hawel L III, Tjandrawinata RR, Fukumoto GH et al. Biosynthesis and selective export of 1,5-diaminopentane (cadaverine) in mycoplasma-free cultured mammalian cells. J Biol Chem 1994; 269:7412-8.

93. Byers TL, Pegg AE. Properties and physiological function of the polyamine transport system. Am J Physiol 1989; 257:C545-53.

94. Hyvönen T, Seiler N, Persson L. Characterization of a COS cell line deficient in polyamine transport. Biochim Biophys Acta 1994; 1221:279-85.

95. Bardocz S, Duguid TJ, Brown DS et al. The importance of dietary polyamines in cell regeneration and growth. Br J Nutr 1995; 73:819-28.

96. Alhonen-Hongisto L, Seppänen P, Jänne J. Intracellular putrescine and spermidine deprivation induces increased uptake of the natural polyamines and methylglyoxal bis(guanylhydrazone). Biochem J 1980; 192:941-5.

97. Mitchell JLA, Diveley RR Jr, Bareyal-Leyser A. Feedback repression of polyamine uptake into mammalian cells requires active protein synthesis. Biochem Biophys Res Commun 1992; 186:81-8.

98. Mitchell JLA, Judd GG, Bareyal-Leyser A et al. Feedback repression of polyamine transport is mediated by antizyme in mammalian tissue-culture cells. Biochem J 1994; 299:19-22.

99. Suzuki T, He Y, Kashiwagi K et al. Antizyme protects against abnormal accumulation and toxicity of polyamines in ornithine decarboxylase-overproducing cells. Proc Natl Acad Sci USA 1994; 91:8930-4.

100. Persson L, Holm I, Ask A et al. Curative effect of DL-2-difluoromethylornithine on mice bearing mutant L1210 leukemia cells deficient in polyamine uptake. Cancer Res 1988; 48:4807-11.

101. Ask A, Persson L, Heby O. Increased survival of L1210 leukemic mice by prevention of the utilization of extracellular polyamines. Studies using a polyamine-uptake mutant, antibiotics and a polyamine-deficient diet. Cancer Lett 1992; 66:29-34.

102. Sarhan S, Knödgen B, Seiler N. The gastrointestinal tract as polyamine source for tumor growth. Anticancer Res. 1989; 9:215-24.

POLYAMINES AND NEOPLASTIC TRANSFORMATION

Uriel Bachrach

I. INTRODUCTION

One goal of current cancer research is to understand the molecular basis of the uncontrolled growth of neoplastic cells. Considerable attention has been focused on the elucidation of the mechanism of transformation, namely the process of the transition from the normal to the malignant state. Several parameters have been selected to monitor the transformation process, including contact inhibition,[1] anchorage-independent growth,[2] changes in cytoskeleton or fibronectin content,[3] actin filaments or microtubules[4] and enhanced glucose uptake.[5]

Contact inhibition can be determined by macroscopic or microscopic examination of cultured cells. Uncontrolled growth can be easily detected by the formation of foci in monolayer cultures (Fig. 4.1). Anchorage-independent growth can be established by detecting foci formation of cells grown on soft agar (Fig. 4.2). Changes in actin filaments can be observed by morphological examination of the cells. Thus in electromicrographs, transformed cells have a rounded shape and contain ruffles (Fig. 4.3) unlike the spindle-shaped normal cells.

During the past decades we have witnessed a rapid progress in molecular biology and molecular genetics. Therefore, biochemical

Polyamines in Cancer: Basic Mechanisms and Clinical Approaches, edited by Kenji Nishioka. © 1996 R.G. Landes Company.

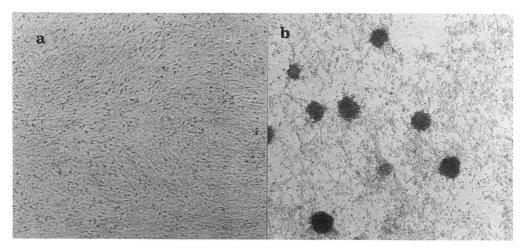

Fig.4.1. Formation of foci by transformed cultured cells. (a) Monolayers of cultured NIH 3T3 cells. (b) Foci formed by cultured ras-transformed NIH 3T3 cells (magnification x37).

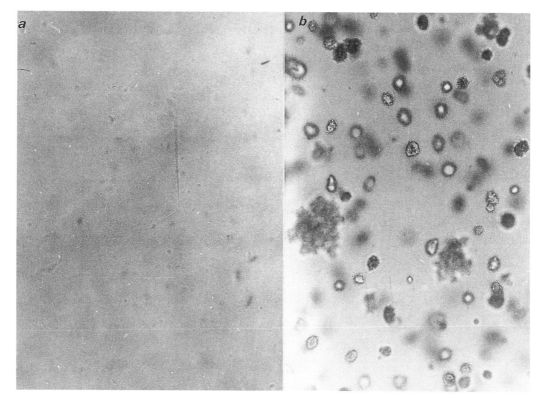

Fig. 4.2. Effect of transformation on anchorage dependence. (a) Normal NIH 3T3 cells (no foci formed in soft agar). (b) ras-transformed NIH 3T3 cells (formation of foci in soft agar). Cells were grown for 14 days.

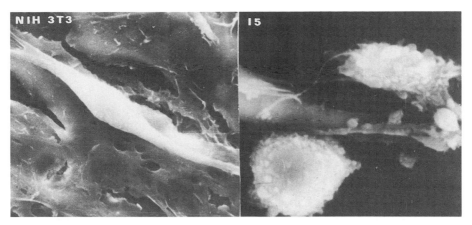

Fig. 4.3. Electron micrographs of 2-day-old cultured cells. (NIH 3T3): normal fibroblasts. (I5): ras-transformed fibroblasts. (Reprinted with permission from Shayovitz A, Bachrach U. Biochim Biophys Acta 995; 1267:107-14.)

and enzymatic markers have been added to the list of parameters by which transformation can be assessed. One of these parameters is the enzyme ornithine decarboxylase (ODC) which catalyzed the formation of the diamine putrescine from ornithine.[6] This reaction is the main limiting step in the biosynthesis of the naturally occurring polyamines spermidine and spermine.[7,8] These ubiquitous polyamines have been implicated in processes of growth,[9] differentiation[10] and tumorogenesis.[11]

The transformation process, namely the transition from the normal to the malignant state has been studied in various model systems which include:

    A. Animal Models
        1. The use of hepatoxic compounds
        2. The use of carcinogenic compounds
        3. The use of mutagenic compounds
    B. Tissue Cultures
    C. Tumor Viruses
    D. Oncogenes

II. SYSTEMS USED

A. ANIMAL MODELS

Prior to the development of cell culture technologies, malignant transformation was tested in experimental animals by transplanting cancer cells. Rosenthal and Tabor[12] found that leukocytes are rich in spermine. These cells are the main source of this polyamine in human and rodent blood. It was therefore not surprising that blood of leukemia patients was found to be rich in polyamines.[12] Specific enzymatic and chromatographic methods were subsequently used to determine the levels of polyamines in Ehrlich ascites tumor cells grown in animals.[13] This was the first reliable report on the accumulation of polyamines in neoplastic cells. Along with the detection of polyamines in tumor cells, the presence and the activity of ODC in those cells has been studied. When tumor cells were inoculated into experimental animals, tumors developed, and the activity of ODC increased in the transformed cells.[11,14,15] Moreover, it has been reported that the increase in the activity of ODC or the accumulation of polyamines correlated well with the proliferation rate of hepatomas in experimental animals,[16] cutaneous epitheliomas[17] and malignancies in the human central nervous system.[18] Levels of ODC activity were also measured in biopsy specimens of colonic mucosa and polyps from patients with familial polyposis.[19] Mucosal ODC values became increasingly higher going from morphological normal, flat mucosa from patients with polyps to dysplastic polyps, with the values for adenomatous polyps intermediate.[19] Similarly, ODC activity levels in human colon cancer were found to be higher than those of normal-appearing mucosa.[20] The relationship between tumor growth and ODC has been shown also by cytochemical studies.[21-24] More recently,[25] the relationship between ODC activity and histological findings in human hepatocellular carcinoma has been described. The increase in ODC activity during the transformation process is at least partially explained by the increase of half-life of the enzyme.[26-28] All these studies support the notion that the assay of ODC activity or protein can be employed for grading and defining the growth rate of tumors and to monitor the transformation process.[17,18]

1. The use of hepatoxic compounds

For nearly 50 years, rodent liver has been used to study chemical carcinogenesis.[29,30] Rodent liver has many advantages including the observation that nonproliferating liver cells can be stimulated to divide by carcinogens, long before overt cancer appears.[31] This in vivo model is therefore very useful for studying the mechanism of malignant transformation. Phenobarbital and anthralin were found to induce hepatic tumors, to increase ODC activity and to lead to the accumulation of polyamines in the liver.[32,33] The application of the tumor promoter 12-0-tetradecanoylphorbol-13-acetate (TPA), to the skin of experimental animals resulted in the induction of hepatic ODC with the same time course as in mouse epidermis.[34] This increase in hepatic ODC after TPA administration led to the increase in rat hepatic levels of putrescine, spermidine and spermine.[35] Diethylnitrosamine, chloroform,[36,37] 3-methylcholanthrene[38] and 2-acetylaminofluorene[39] all caused the induction of tumors in rodent liver, the activation of hepatic ODC and the accumulation of polyamines. The mechanism(s) involved in regulating ODC activity in rats treated with hepatocarcinogens were studied by injecting thioacetamide. A single injection caused a several-fold increase in both ODC protein and mRNA.[40] Since the specific activity of hepatic ODC changed during the transformation process, it has been concluded that thioacetamide deregulates ODC activities by translational post-translational mechanisms.[40] The deregulation of ODC activity after thioacetamide administration is partially explained by a decrease in ODC antizyme activity.[41] This reduction in antizyme levels could lead to the stabilization of ODC even in the presence of high levels of putrescine, which usually cause the synthesis of the antizyme. Carbon tetrachloride is another hepatoxic agent.[42] This compound enhances the interconversion of polyamines into diamines[43] by the activation of spermine/spermidine N^1-acetyltransferases (SSATs) and polyamine oxidase activities.[44] The enhanced interconversion of polyamines has also been detected during the transformation of chick embryo fibroblasts by Rous sarcoma virus[45] and in lectin-transformed lymphocytes.[46]

2. The use of carcinogenic compounds

In recent years, studies on malignant transformation have also been based on the two-stage carcinogenesis protocol of mouse skin.[47-50] Skin tumor development in mice is readily divided into two components which are named initiation and promotion. Initiation is accomplished by treating the skin with a carcinogen at a dose which is sufficiently low so that tumors develop only rarely during the animals life. Skin so treated by compounds such as urethan or 7,12-dimethylbenz[a]anthracene, appears to contain some cells that are irreversibly altered (initiated) so that application of a second agent will elicit many tumors, both malignant and benign.[31,51] It should be stressed that the second agent has the unique capability to form tumors in initiated skin but is not an effective carcinogen when applied to the skin of mice that are not initiated. The second agent, called a promoting agent, is exemplified by TPA, which was isolated from croton oil. TPA, which can also regulate the expression of oncogenes and interacts with a TPA-responsive sequence in human ODC,[52] promotes skin tumors in mice when applied twice weekly to the skin of initiated mice in the dose range of about 1 to 10 nmol. In cultured cells it causes responses at levels of 10^{-7} to 10^{-10} M. These two processes, initiation and promotion, can be regarded as part of the general malignant transformation process[31,53-56] and can serve as an important tool for studying the mechanism of transformation. While trying to elucidate the mechanism of the two-stage carcinogenesis process it has been found that the response of mouse epidermis to TPA is a typical pleiotropic response. Within two minutes, the level of cAMP and cGMP in the epidermis begins to increase.[56] Elevated levels of prostaglandins E and F are detected within 30 minutes,[57-58] and then the turnover of phosphatidyl choline is increased.[59] Since both cAMP and prostaglandins mediate the induction of ODC,[6,60] it is not surprising that 5 to 6 hours after TPA application a significant increase in ODC activity is reached.[61-64] As expected these responses are followed by increased DNA,[65] RNA and protein syntheses.[66] These changes are reversible in skin that has not been initiated, and after about three weeks there is little evidence that TPA has been applied to the skin. On the other hand, tumors arise 5 to 6 weeks after treatment of initiated mice, while the activity of ODC was increased by up to 300-fold, 4 to 5 hours after TPA application. This increase in ODC activity was followed by elevation of putrescine and spermidine levels.[61] Interesting is the finding[47] that cyclohexamide did not reduce the high levels of ODC activity in squamous papillomas of rat skin induced by the two-stage carcinogenesis. Again, these results suggest that ODC is deregulated and stabilized during the transformation process. The activity of S-adenosylmethionine decarboxylase (Ado-

MetDC) increased only by a factor of 6-7 with a peak at 9-12 hours.[17] During recent years, evidence has accumulated that ODC activity is increased at an early stage of carcinogenesis and that a variety of tumor promoters cause elevation in ODC.[66-74] It has also been proposed that the activation of ODC by carcinogens is an essential and an early step in the process of transformation.[75]

Evidence for the role of ODC in tumor promotion (and presumably in carcinogenesis) is also based on the ability of certain agents to inhibit the induction of ODC and the formation of tumors. Thus, indomethacin which inhibits cyclo-oxygenase, inhibits the TPA-dependent induction of ODC.[39] The inhibition depends on the dose of indomethacin applied to the skin two hours before TPA. The threshold for inhibition was approximately 10 nmol and inhibition was complete at 2800 nmol indomethacin. Furthermore, the inhibition could be reversed in a dose-dependent manner by prostaglandin E_2 applied at the same time as TPA.[56,76,77] The effect of indomethacin appears to be specific as it did not affect the activity of AdoMetDC.[56] Analogous results have been obtained with a number of vitamin A derivatives—retinoids. Certain retinoids inhibit ODC induction as well as the promotion of tumors by TPA.[32,35,39,69,78-81] The inhibitory effect of retinoids on the TPA-dependent induction of ODC appears to be specific, since tumor formation and ODC induction were not blocked by retinoids after treating the skin with 7,12-dimethylbenz(a)anthracene.[6] Dietary manipulations such as beta-carotenes and a fat-poor diet[82,83] or fish oil[84] also reduce ODC induction during carcinogenesis. DFMO, a specific inhibitor of ODC had a differential effect on the proliferation of Balb 3T3 and chemically transformed 3T3 cells.[85] The growth-inhibited untransformed cells resumed growth upon removal of DFMO, while transformed cells did not, unless exogenous polyamine was added. These findings confirm the involvement of polyamines in the transformation process and in neoplastic growth.

3. The use of mutagenic compounds

N-butyl-N-(4hydroxybutyl)-nitrosamine induces urinary bladder carcinogenesis in rats.[86] Administration of DFMO to mutagen-treated rats caused a significant suppression in tumor formation.[87] Nitrosomethylurea (NMU) induces mammary tumors in rats. Cells derived from these tumors grow on soft agar. Colony formation appears to depend on polyamine biosynthesis as DFMO exerted a dose-dependent inhibitory effect.[88] Dimethylnitrosamine also caused the increase in polyamine levels in rat liver and kidney.[89] The activity of the polyamine biosynthetic enzymes also increased after the administration of similar mutagens to experimental animals.[90]

B. Tissue Culture

The development of tissue culture technologies opened new possibilities for studying the mechanisms of transformation.

1. Breast cancer

The growth of N-nitrosomethylurea (NMU)-induced rat mammary tumor cells is regulated by hormones. When tumor cells are cultured in soft agar in the absence of serum, administration of estradiol, prolactin, growth hormone and progesterone stimulate tumor colony formation.[91] DFMO which inhibits polyamine synthesis exerted a dose-dependent inhibitory effect on tumor colony formation[88,91] and on murine mammary carcinogenesis.[92,93] The specificity of the DFMO effect through the polyamine pathway was supported by the ability of exogenous putrescine to reverse the DFMO effect.[88] When NMU tumors were grown on soft agar, tamoxifen—an antiestrogen—inhibited colony formation. In this case, too, the inhibitory effect was reversed by putrescine (1.0-2.5 μM) as well as by spermidine or spermine (1-100 mM) in a dose-dependent fashion.[94] Similarly, in MCF-7 breast cancer cells, grown in a liquid medium, DFMO inhibited the proliferative effect of exogenously added insulin-like growth factor-I[95] and transforming growth factor-alpha.[96] Loss of hormonal dependence in breast cancer is associated with the acquisition of an aggressive phenotype resulting in the patient's death.[91] The hypotheses to explain breast cancer transition from hormone-dependent to hormone-independent phenotype include oncogene amplification.[97] Amplification of oncogenes may lead to the induction and deregulation of ODC (see below) and thus increase cellular polyamine levels. Polyamines thus formed may circumvent the need for hormones. Evidence in literature indicates that polyamines may be functional in signal transduction processes,[98] such as regulating the activities of phospholipase C,[91] protein kinase C,[99] phosphorylation of casein[100] and other proteins.[101] It is therefore not surprising that increased intracellular polyamine levels in human cancer specimens correlated with the histological grade.[102] A positive correlation between high tumor polyamine levels and probability of recurrence within two years of mastectomy has also been reported.[102] ODC activities were high in human breast cancer tissues with high nuclear aplasia.[103] All these studies strongly suggest that polyamines are involved in cell transformation and the development of mammary tumors.

It has been suggested that drugs which inhibit polyamine synthesis could be used for the treatment of hormone-responsive breast cancer.[91] When NIH 3T3 cells were transformed with a c-Ha-*ras* oncogene, driven by a dexamethasone-responsive mouse mammary tumor virus (MMTV) promoter, transformation occurred upon the addition of the hormone. This transformation process was apparently dependent on polyamine synthesis and oncogene activation.[104] In this system too, transformation was blocked by DFMO, which caused polyamine depletion.[104] These findings are in line with the assumption that polyamines play a role in the development of mammary tumors.

2. Lymphocyte transformation

Resting lymphocytes have a very low ODC activity.[105] Stimulation of these resting cells with ligands such as concanavalin A or antigens results in an activation of ODC within minutes and a second peak within three hours.[106] The activation of AdoMetDC occurs much later and coincides with DNA synthesis.[106] Concomitant with the second rise in ODC activity, putrescine and spermidine or spermine accumulate in the stimulated lymphocytes. The interconversion of polyamines into putrescine is also activated during the early stages of lymphocyte stimulation.[107-109] Drugs which inhibit polyamine biosynthesis interfere with lymphocyte stimulation.[110] This has been demonstrated for DFMO, which inhibits ODC,[111-113] and MGBG [methylglyoxal-bis(guanylhydrazone)], which inhibits AdoMetDC,[114] all of which inhibit DNA synthesis in lectin-stimulated lymphocytes.

Friend erythroleukemia cells in culture can be induced to differentiate by compounds such as dimethyl sulfoxide and hexamethylene bisacetamide. These agents were shown to enhance polyamine synthesis.[115] Inhibitors of polyamine biosynthesis prevented the differentiation, stimulated by the inducers, and this inhibition could be reversed by exogenously added polyamines.[115] Verma and Sunkara[116] reported an enhanced polyamine synthesis during colony-stimulating factor-induced proliferation and differentiation of human granulocyte-macrophage progenitor cells. Inhibition of polyamine biosynthesis by DFMO resulted in an inhibition of differentiation which could be reversed by an exogenous supply of putrescine. Requirements for polyamines during differentiation of rabbit chondrocytes,[117] matrix induced endochondrial bone differentiation,[118] differentiation of 3T3-L1 fibroblasts into adipocytes[119] and differentiation of L6 myoblasts[120] have been reported. The differentiation of B16 melanoma cells was also inhibited by DFMO which depleted polyamines.[121]

C. Tumor Viruses

The finding that RNA and DNA viruses can induce tumors in experimental animals led to the development of in vitro systems in which cultured cells were transformed by various tumor viruses. Cultured chick embryo fibroblasts, infected with Rous sarcoma viruses (RSV), were one of the first systems studied. In the infected cultured cells, ODC was activated and polyamines accumulated.[122-125] The increase in ODC activity after infecting the chick embryo cells with RSV appears to be an early event in the process of malignant transformation.[123] The activity of AdoMetDC also increased during the transformation process, but to a lesser extent.[126] The increase in ODC activity in the transformed cells can be at least partially explained by the stabilization of the enzyme and the increase in its half-life.[26] To demonstrate that the increase in ODC activity was due to the *src* oncogene of the RSV, temperature-sensitive mutants of RSV were used. These mutants grow-readily at 42°C but cause transformation only at 37°C, the permissive temperature. It has been shown that the transformation process, and not viral growth, was responsible for the transformation, for the activation of ODC and for the accumulation of polyamines.[123,125] Rat kidney cells were also infected with a temperature-sensitive mutant of kirsten sarcoma virus (KiMSV Ts 371). Cells thus infected[104] exhibited a normal phenotype when grown at 42°C but were transformed upon temperature shift. In this system, too, the transformation process was closely linked with the activation of ODC and the increase in cellular polyamine levels.[104] Inhibiting polyamine synthesis by DFMO prevented transformation.[104] BALB/3T3 cells were also infected with mouse sarcoma viruses (MSV). This virus consists of a transforming virus and a nontransforming strain of murine leukemia virus (MuLV), which acts as a helper virus enabling the defective MSV to complete the cycle. The helper virus alone neither caused transformation, nor did it activate ODC.[127] These findings strongly suggest that the transformation process is closely associated with the activation of ODC and the accumulation of polyamines.

This phenomenon was not limited to RNA-containing retroviruses; DNA tumor viruses, such as SV40[128] or polyoma viruses,[129] also caused the increase in polyamine levels and ODC activities during the transformation process.

D. ONCOGENES

The above described experiments, in which chick embryo fibroblasts or rat kidney cells were infected with temperature-sensitive mutants of RSV or KiMSV, led to the conclusion that oncogenes are responsible for the changes in polyamine synthesis during the transformation. To demonstrate directly that oncogene can change polyamine biosynthesis, NIH 3T3 cells were transfected with plasmids containing c-Ha-*ras*.[28,130,131] These studies clearly showed that the expression of *ras* was followed by the increase in ODC activity and cellular polyamine levels. During this process, ODC is deregulated and its half-life increased.[28] Along with the accumulation of polyamines in the transfected cells, the activity of spermidine acetyltransferase also increased.[130] In another experimental model, the expression of *ras* was driven by a MMTV-LTR promoter. In this system, the hormone dexamethasone caused the transcription of *ras*. This was followed by the increase in polyamine synthesis.[104] It is of interest that the expression of *ras* and the activation of ODC also led to the transcription of the nuclear oncogenes *myc, fos* and *jun*.[131,132,144] It has been well established that more than one oncogene is required for malignant transformation[133] and the possibility that polyamines serve as a signal between the membrane and the nucleus has not been ruled out.[98,131,132]

These and other experiments also suggest that ODC could be regarded as an oncogene. These suggestions were based on the following considerations:

Several independent studies suggest that overexpression of ODC activity may cause cell transformation.[134-139] In some of the experiments, plasmid inserts that coded for ODC under the expression of a strong promoter were used to transfect NIH 3T3 cells. Clones expressing high levels of ODC showed transformed phenotype and anchorage-independent growth on soft agar. These findings and the similarity between the ODC gene and protooncogenes and oncogenes led to the hypothesis that the ODC gene can be regarded as an oncogene.[132,134,139,140] It is evident from Table 4.1 that both ODC and the nuclear oncogene *myc* can be regarded as early genes.[148,149] Both have an extremely short half-life[149,150] and are involved in proliferative processes.[151,157] They are deregulated[28,153] and elevated in tumors and activated by hormones,[154,155] by cAMP[60,160] and by lectins.[105,156] The mechanism by which polyamines cause transformation remains to be elucidated. However,

Table 4.1. Ornithine decarboxylase as an oncogene

Property	ODC	*myc*
Early genes in cell cycle	149*	148
Short half-life	149	150
Involved in proliferation	151	157
High in tumors	152	143
Deregulated in tumor cells	28	153
Stimulated by hormones	155	154
Stimulated by lectins	105	156
Phosphorylated by casein kinase	100	157
Stimulates DNA synthesis	158	159
Activated by cAMP	60	160

*Reference number

it appears that more than one oncogene is required to trigger neoplastic transformation. It has been demonstrated that polyamines enhance the transcription of *myc*,[131,141,142] *fos*[131] and *jun*.[144] In addition, the expression of the oncogenes *src*,[123,124] *neu*[145] and *ras*[28,130] lead to the increase in ODC activity. It thus appears that oncogenes stimulate the activation of ODC and the synthesis of polyamines, which on the other hand, stimulate the transcription of oncogenes. The stimulation of polyamine biosynthesis by oncogenes can be explained by several mechanisms which may include:

1. Binding of transcription factors

The *c-fos* protooncogene encodes a component of the transcription factor AP-1 which is composed of dimeric complexes between three Jun family members and four Fos family members. Both Jun and Fos components contribute to the transactivation function of the AP-1, which stimulates the transcription by binding to AP-1 elements in enhancer and promoter sequences of ODC. Recent studies[161] showed that in PC12 cells, Fos directly stimulated the transcription of the ODC gene.

2. ODC as a transcriptional target

The *c-myc* protooncogene is a key regulator of cell growth and differentiation. Constitutive c-myc expression suppresses cell cycle arrest and promotes entry into S phase. The murine ODC gene contains two potential Myc binding sites CACGTG within the first intron.[146] cMyc is a potent transactivator of ODC, apparently at the level of transcription. It is quite possible that the Myc oncoprotein dimerizes with its partner, Max, to bind DNA at the CACGTG hexanucleotide sequences which are present in p53 and ODC promoters.[148]

3. Chromatin structure

Polyamines may also enhance transformation by facilitating retroviral integration into cellular chromatin.[140,147]

III. POLYAMINES AND CANCER THERAPY

The possibility of using polyamines as targets for therapeutic intervention has been recently reviewed.[140,162] These considerations gained experimental support from the following studies:

A. Colon and Kidney Cancer

According to Luk and Baylin,[19] ODC serves as a biological marker in familial colonic polyposis. Similarly, polyamine levels are elevated in kidney tumors,[163] and DFMO affected the growth of adenocarcinoma.[164] Moreover, the radiosensitivity of cultured human colon carcinoma cells increased after inhibiting polyamine biosynthesis.[165] The growth of human or hamster pancreatic cell lines was also inhibited by DFMO[166] as was rat urinary bladder carcinogenesis.[87]

B. Melanoma

Polyamine depletion by DFMO resulted in an inhibition of growth of cultured melanoma cells as determined by growth on soft agar[167] and by colonogenic assays.[121]

C. Breast Cancer

As stated above, mammary tumor carcinogenesis is closely linked to polyamine biosynthesis. Indeed, DFMO was found to inhibit murine mammary carcinogenesis.[92,93,168,169]

D. Hematological Cancers

Polyamines were found to be essential for the proliferation of human promyelocytic leukemia cells.[170] Therefore, alterations in bone marrow and blood mononuclear cell polyamines by DFMO improved the treatment of hematological malignancies.[171] Inhibition of AdoMetDC also caused the arrest of growth of cultured human erythroid leukemia K562 cells.[172]

E. Skin Cancer

DFMO was shown to inhibit the TPA-promoted mouse skin tumor formation.[173] Methylglyoxal bis(butylamidinohydrazone), an inhibitor of polyamine biosynthesis, also exhibited an antitumor effect when tested against mouse skin tumors.[174]

F. Combined Therapy

Most of the anticancer drugs have toxic side effects and therefore cannot be used continuously. It would be of advantage to use a nontoxic cytostatic agent to prevent the proliferation of the cancer cells during the recovery from the toxic effects. DFMO is such a relatively nontoxic agent. A combination of 5-fluorouracil and DFMO was used to inhibit the growth of cultured human colon adenocarcinoma cells,[175] and DFMO and interferons were effective in treating mice bearing B16 melanoma or Lewis lung carcinomas[176] and B16 melanoma cells.[177] A combination of interferon and DFMO was also used to inhibit the growth of T47D cells.[178] The various inhibitors of polyamine biosynthesis have been described,[140] and some of those inhibitors as well as polyamine analogs are presently being studied by the National Cancer Institute as anticancer agents.[140,179]

DFMO alone or combined with methylglyoxal bis(guanylhydrazone) produced significant therapeutic response in patients with recurrent glial tumors.[179-182] Promising results were obtained in treating animals[183] and patients with prostatic adenocarcinoma with DFMO, polyamine depleted diet and intestinal antibiotics (Moulinoux, personal communication).

IV. POLYAMINES AND CANCER PREVENTION AND IN VITRO CHEMOSENSITIVITY TESTS

The above described studies suggest that DFMO greatly reduced tumor development in rodents treated with chemical carcinogens or tumor viruses. The findings that DFMO blocks the production of tumors in skin, bladder, stomach, colon and mammary glands provided a strong rationale that DFMO can be used as a chemopreventive agent.[183-189] Several clinical trials have been carried out to explore the use of DFMO as a preventive agent in high risk populations.[185-189] This aspect may provide new means to control cancer.

For the past decade attempts have been made to determine the chemosensitivity of tumor cells to anticancer drugs. These attempts failed, mainly because of the low plating efficiency of the cell isolated from patients. It has been suggested that ODC can serve as a marker for proliferation.[190] When drug-sensitive or drug-resistant mammalian cells were exposed to anticancer drugs, the activity of ODC reflected the sensitivity or the resistance of the cells to those specific drugs. Loss of activity in drug-exposed cells was interpreted as drug sensitivity, while persistence of activity meant drug resistance.[191] ODC can also be detected by immunohisto-chemical assay.[24] By this method the chemosensitivity can be detected in a small number of cells obtained by biopsy. If the validity of this approach is confirmed by testing cells from human malignancies, then new possibilities will be opened to provide better treatment for cancer patients.

Another possible application of polyamines in oncology is the use of polyamines as a marker of malignancy. This subject has been reviewed recently.[192]

V. CONCLUSIONS

The basic studies on the involvement of polyamines in neoplastic growth were quite rewarding and led to potential applications exemplified by the development of new antitumor drugs. Another promising application would be the use of polyamine inhibitors for chemoprevention of cancer and the use of polyamines for monitoring the stage and the progress of the disease. If ODC could indeed be used for the in vitro chemosensitivity assays, then new possibilities for improved treatment of cancer patients could be envisaged. All these findings provide new tools in the fight against cancer.

REFERENCES

1. Abercrombie M. Contact inhibition in tissue culture. In Vitro 1970; 6:128-42.
2. McPherson I, Montagnier L. Agar suspension culture of the selective assay of cells transformed by polyoma virus. Virology 1964; 23:291-94.
3. Mukherjee BB, Morby PM, Pena SD. Retinoic acid induces anchorage and density-dependent growth without restoring normal cytoskeleton, EGF binding, fibronectin content and ODC activity in retrovirus- transformed mouse cell lines. Exp Cell Res 1982; 138:95-107.
4. Pohjanpelto P, Virtanen I, Hölttä E. Polyamine starvation causes disappearance of actin filaments and microtubules in polyamine-auxotrophic CHO cells. Nature 1981; 293:475-77.
5. Bissell MJ. Transport as a rate-limiting step in glucose metabolism in virus-transformed cells: Studies with cytochalasin. J Cell Physiol 1976; 89:701-10.
6. Russell DH. Ornithine decarboxylase: A key regulatory enzyme in normal and neoplastic growth. Drug Metabolism Rev 1985; 16:1-88.

7. Pegg AE. Recent advances in the biochemistry of polyamines in eukaryotes. Biochem J 1986; 234:249-62.

8. Heby O, Persson L. Molecular genetics of polyamine synthesis in eukaryotic cells. Trends Biochem Sci 1990; 15:153-58.

9. Tabor CW, Tabor H. Polyamines. Ann Rev Biochem 1984; 53:749-90.

10. Heby O. Polyamines and cell differentiation. In: Bachrach U, Heimer YM, eds. The Physiology of Polyamines, Vol. 1. Boca Raton: CRC Press, 1989:83-94.

11. Russell DH, Durie BGM. Polyamines as biochemical markers of normal and malignant growth. Raven Press, 1978.

12. Rosenthal SM, Tabor CW. The pharmacology of spermine and spermidine. Distribution and excretion. J Pharmacol Exp Ther 1956; 116:131-38.

13. Bachrach U, Bekierkunst A, Abzug S. The occurrence of putrescine, spermidine and spermine in Ehrlich ascites cells. Isr J Med Sci 1967; 3:474-77.

14. Pegg AE. Polyamine metabolism and its importance in neoplastic growth and as a target for chemotherapy. Cancer Res 1988; 48:759-74.

15. Scalabrino G, Ferioli ME. Polyamines in mammalian tumors. Part 1. Adv Cancer Res 1981; 35:151-268.

16. Williams-Ashman HG, Coppoc GL, Weber G. Imbalance in ornithine metabolism of different growth rates as expressed in formation of putrescine, spermidine and spermine. Cancer Res 1972; 32:1924-32.

17. Scalabrino G, Pigatto P, Ferioli ME et al. Levels of activity of the polyamine biosynthetic decarboxylases as indicators of degree of malignancy of human cutaneous epitheliomas. J Invest Dermatol 1980; 74:122-24.

18. Scalabrino G, Modena D, Ferioli ME et al. Degrees of malignancy in human primary central nervous system tumors; ornithine decarbolylase levels as better indicators than adenosylmethionine decarboxylase levels. J Nat Cancer Inst 1982; 68:751-54.

19. Luk GD, Baylin SB. Ornithine decarboxylase as a biologic marker in familial colonic polyposis. New Engl J Med 1984; 311:80-83.

20. Rozhin J, Wilson PS, Bull AW et al. Ornithine decarboxylase activity in rat and human colon. Cancer Res 1984; 44:3226-30.

21. Dorn A, Muller M, Bernstein HG et al. Immunohistochemical localization of L-ornithine decarboxylase in developing rat brain. Int J Dev Neurosci 1987; 5:145-50.

22. Johnson LR, Tseng CC, Tipnis UR et al. Gastric mucosal ornithine-decarboxylase: Localization and stimulation by gastrin. Am J Physiol 1988; 255:G304-312.

23. Persson L, Rosengren E, Sundler F. Immunohistochemical localization of ornithine decarboxylase in the rat ovary. Histochem 1982; 75:163-67.

24. Shayovits A, Bachrach U. Immunohistochemical detection of ornithine decarboxylase in individual cells: Potential application for *in vitro* chemosensitivity assays. J Histochem Cytochem 1994; 42:607-11.

25. Tamori A, Nishiguchi S, Kuroki T et al. Relationship of ornithine decarboxylase activity and histological findings in human hepatocellular carcinoma. Hepatology 1994; 20:1179-86.

26. Bachrach U. Polyamines and neoplastic growth: Stabilization of ornithine decarboxylase during transformation. Biochem Biophys Res Commun 1976; 72:1008-113.

27. Poso H, Guha SK, Jänne J. Stabilization of ornithine decarboxylase in rat livers. Biochim Biophys Acta 1978; 524:466-73.

28. Höltta E, Sistonen L, Alitalo K. The mechanism of ornithine decarboxylase deregulation in c-Ha-ras oncogene-transformed NIH 3T3 cells. J Biol Chem 1988; 263:4500-07.

29. Pitot HC, Sirica AE. The stages of initiation and promotion in hepatocarcinogenesis. Biochim Biophys Acta 1980; 605:191-215.

30. Farber E, Cameron R. The sequential analysis of cancer development. Adv Cancer Res 1980; 31:125-226.

31. Diamond L. Tumor promoters and cell transformation. Pharmacol Ther 1984; 26:89-145.

32. Bisschop A, Van Rooijen LA, Derks HJ et al. Induction of rat hepatic ornithine decarboxylase by the tumor promotors 12-O-tetradecanoylphorbol-13-acetate and phenobarbital *in vivo*; effect of retinyl-acetate. Carcinogenesis 1981; 2:1283-87.

33. Bisschop A, Vankan PM, Uijtewaal B et al. Effect of 1,8-dihydroxy-9-anthrone (anthralin) on rat hepatic ornithine decarboxylase activity *in vivo*. Cancer Lett 1984; 23:151-57.

34. Kishore GS, Boutwell RK. Induction of mouse hepatic ornithine decarboxylase by skin application of 12-0-tetradecanoylphorbol-13-acetate. Experientia 1981; 37:179-80.

35. Van Rooijen LA, Derks HJ, Van Wijk R et al. Relation between induction of rat hepatic ornithine decarboxylase by tumor promoters 12-0-tetradecanoylphorbol-13-acetate and phenobarbital and levels of the polyamines putrescine, spermidine and spermine, *in vivo* differential effects of retinyl-acetate. Carcinogenesis 1984; 5:225-29.

36. Savage RE Jr, Westrich C, Guion C et al. Chloroform induction of ornithine decarboxylase activity in rats. Environ, Health Perspect 1982; 46:157-62.

37. Pereira MA, Savage RE Jr, Guion CW et al. Effect of chloroform on hepatic and renal DNA synthesis and ornithine decarboxylase activity in mice and rats. Toxicol Lett 1984; 21:357-64.

38. Raunio H, Pelkonen O. Effect of polycyclic aromatic compounds and phorbol esters on ornithine decarboxylase and aryl hydrocarbon hydroxylase activities in mouse liver. Cancer Res 1983; 43:782-86.

39. Bisschop A, Bakker O, Meerman JH et al. Induction of ornithine decarboxylase and augmentation of tyrosine aminotransferase activity by N-hydroxy-2-acetylaminofluorene and 2-acetylaminofluorene in rat liver. Influence of sex, retinylacetate, indomethacin, and pentachlorophenol. Cancer Invest 1984; 2:267-77.

40. Kameji T, Fujita K, Noguchi T et al. Cell-free synthesis of ornithine decarboxylase: Changes in mRNA activity in the liver of thioacetamide-treated rats. Eur J Biochem 1984; 144:35-39.

41. Scalabrino G, Ferioli ME, Modena D. Restoration of normal ornithine decarboxylase antizyme activity in rat liver after acute carcinogen treatment. Carcinogenesis 1983; 4:1663-64.

42. Poso H, Pegg AE. Effect of carbon tetrachloride on polyamine metabolism in rodent liver. Arch Biochem Biophys 1982; 217:730-35.

43. Pegg AE, Hibasami H, Matsui I et al. Formation and interconversion of putrescine and spermidine in mammalian cells. Adv Enzymc Regul 1980; 19:427-51.

44. Seiler N, Bolkenius FN, Rennert OM. Interconversion, catabolism and elimination of polyamines. Med Biol 1981; 59:334-46.

45. Bachrach U, Seiler N. Formation of acetylpolyamines and putrescine from spermidine by normal and transformed chick embryo fibroblasts. Cancer Res 1981; 41:1205-08.

46. Menashe M, Faber J, Bachrach U. Formation of N-acetylputrescine and N^1-acetylspermidine in cultured human lymphocytes. Biochem J 1980; 188:263-67.

47. Blumberg PM. *In vitro* studies on the mode of action of the phorbol esters, potent tumor promoters: Part 1. Crit Rev Toxicol 1980; 8:153-97.

48. Blumberg PM. *In vitro* studies on the mode of action of the phorbol esters, potent tumor promoters: Part 2. Crit Rev Toxicol 1980; 8:199-234.

49. Yuspa SH. Molecular and cellular basis for tumor promotion in mouse skin. Princess Takamatsu Symp 1983; 14:315-26.

50. Yuspa SH, Hennings H, Lichti U et al. Organ specificity and tumor promotion. Basic Life Sci 1983; 24:157-71.

51. Astrup EG, Boutwell RK. Ornithine decarboxylase activity in chemically induced mouse skin papillomas. Carcinogenesis 1982; 3:303-8.

52. Kim YJ, Pan H, Verma AK. Non-AP-1 tumor promoter 12-0-tetradecanoylphorbol-13 acetate responsive sequences in human ornithine decarboxylase gene. Mol Carcinogenesis 1994; 10:169-179.

53. Bourin MC, Delescluse C, Furstenberger G et al. Effect of phorbol esters on guinea pig skin *in vivo*. Carcinogenesis 1982; 3:671-76.
54. Boutwell RK, O'Brien TG, Verma AK et al. The induction of ornithine decarboxylase activity and its control in mouse skin epidermis. Adv Enzyme Regul 1978; 17:89-112.
55. Boutwell RK, Verma AK, Ashendel CL et al. Mouse skin: A useful model system for studying the mechanism of chemical carcinogenesis. Carcinog Compr Surv 1982; 7:1-12.
56. Scalabrino G, Ferioli M. Polyamine metabolism and neoplastic growth: A programmed deregulation? In: Bachrach U, Heimer YM, eds. The Physiology of Polyamines. Vol. 2. Boca Raton: CRC Press, Inc, 1989:183-217.
57. Ashendel CL, Boutwell RK. Prostaglandin E and F levels in mouse epidermis are increased by tumor-promoting phorbol esters. Biochem Biophys Res Commun 1979; 90:623-27.
58. Furstenberger G, Marks F. Early prostaglandin E synthesis is an obligatory event in the induction of cell proliferation in mouse epidermis *in vivo* by the phorbol ester TPA. Biochem Biophys Res Commun 1980; 92:749-56.
59. Rohrschneider LR, Boutwell RK. The early stimulation of phospholipid metabolism by 12-0-tetradecanoyl-phorbol-13-acetate and its specificity for tumor promotion. Cancer Res 1973; 33:1945-52.
60. Bachrach U. Cyclic-AMP-mediated induction of ornithine decarboxylase of glioma and neuroblastoma cells. Proc Natl Acad Sci, USA 1975; 72:3087-91.
61. O'Brien TG, Simsiman RC, Boutwell RK. Induction of the polyamine-biosynthetic enzymes in mouse epidermis and their specificity for tumor promotion. Cancer Res 1975; 35:2426-33.
62. O'Brien TG, Simsiman RC, Boutwell RK. Induction of the polyamine-biosynthetic enzymes in mouse epidermis by tumor-promoting agents. Cancer Res 1975; 35:1662-70.
63. O'Brien TG, Simsiman RC, Boutwell RK. The effect of colchicine on the induction of ornithine decarboxylase by 12-0-tetradecanoylphorbol-13-acetate. Cancer Res 1976; 36:3766-70.
64. O'Brien TG, Dzubow L, Dlugosz AA et al. Regulation of ornithine decarboxylase in normal and neoplastic mouse and human epidermis. Prog Clin Biol Res 1989; 298:213-31.
65. Sina JF, Bradley MO, Diamond L et al. Ornithine decarboxylase activity and DNA synthesis in primary transformed hamster epidermal cells exposed to tumor promoter. Cancer Res 1983; 43:4108-13.
66. Weber G. Enzymology of cancer cells. New Engl J Med 1977; 296:541-51.
67. Digiovianni J. Multistage carcinogenesis in mouse skin. Pharmacol Therap 1992; 54:63-128.

68. Baird WM, Sedgwick JA, Boutwell RK. Effects of phorbol and four diesters of phorbol on the incorporation of tritiated precursors into DNA, RNA, and protein in mouse epidermis. Cancer Res 1971; 31:1434-39.

69. Dawson MI, Chao WR, Helmes CT. Inhibition by retinoids of anthralin-induced mouse epidermal ornithine decarboxylase activity and anthralin-promoted skin tumor formation. Cancer Res 1987; 47:6210-15.

70. Feo F, Garcea R, Pascale R et al. The variations of S-adenosyl-L-methionine content modulate hepatocyte growth during phenobarbital promotion of diethylnitrosamine-induced rat liver carcinogenesis. Toxicol Pathol 1987; 15:109-14.

71. Gilmour SK, Aglow E, O'Brien TG. Heterogeneity of ornithine decarboxylase expression in 12-0-tetradecanoylphorbol-13-acetate-treated mouse skin and in epidermal tumors. Carcinogenesis 1986; 7:943-47.

72. Gilmour SK, O'Brien TG. Regulation of ornithine decarboxylase gene expression in normal and transformed hamster embryo fibroblasts following stimulation by 12-0-tetradecanoylphorbol-13-acetate. Carcinogenesis 1989; 10:157-62.

73. Gilmour SK, Robertson FM, Megosh L et al. Induction of ornithine decarboxylase in specific subpopulations of murine-epidermal cells following multiple exposures to 12-0-tetracanoylphorbol-13-acetate, mezerein and ethyl phenylpropriolate. Carcinogenesis 1992; 13:51-56.

74. Mufson RA, Fischer SM, Verma AK et al. Effects of 12-0-tetradecanoylphorbol-13-acetate and mezerein on epidermal ornithine decarboxylase activity, isoproterenol-stimulated levels of cyclic adenosine 3':5'-monophosphate, and induction of mouse skin. Cancer Res 1979; 39:4791-95.

75. O'Brien TG. The induction of ornithine decarboxylase as an early, possibly obligatory, event in mouse skin carcinogenesis. Cancer Res 1976; 36:2644-53.

76. Furstenberger G, Richter H, Fusenig NE et al. Arachidonic acid and prostaglandin E2 release and enhanced cell proliferation induced by the phorbol ester TPA in a murine epidermal cell line. Cancer Lett 1981; 11:191-98.

77. Verma AK, Rice HM, Boutwell RK. Prostaglandins and skin tumor promotion: Inhibition of tumor promoter-induced ornithine decarboxylase activity in epidermis by inhibitors of prostaglandin synthesis. Biochem Biophys Res Commun 1977; 79:1160-66.

78. Verma AK, Slaga TJ, Wertz PW et al. Inhibition of skin tumor promotion by retinoic acid and its metabolite 5,6-epoxyretinoic acid. Cancer Res 1980; 40:2367-71.

79. Verma AK, Boutwell RK. Intracellular calcium and skin tumor promotion: Calcium regulation of the induction of epidermal ornithine decarboxylase activity by the tumor promoter 12-0-tetradecanoylphorbol-13-acetate. Biochem Biophys Res Commun 1981; 101:375-83.

80. Boutwell RK, Verma AK. The influence of retinoids on polyamine and DNA synthesis in mouse epidermis. Ann NY Acad Sci 1981; 359:275-80.

81. Kensler TW, Verma AK, Boutwell RK et al. Effects of retinoic acid and juvenile hormone on the induction of ornithine decarboxylase activity by 12-0-tetradecanoylphorbol-13-acetate. Cancer Res 1978; 38:2896-99.

82. Rao CV, Reddy BS. Modulating effect of amount and types of dietary fat on ornithine decarboxylase, tyrosine protein kinase and prostaglandin production during colon carcinogenesis in male F344 rats. Carcinogenesis 1993; 14:1327-33.

83. Phillips RW, Kikendall JW, Luk GD et al. β-Carotene inhibits rectal mucosal ornithine decarboxylase activity in colon cancer patients. Cancer Res 1993; 53:3723-25.

84. Nigro ND, Bull AW, Boyd ME. Inhibition of intestinal carcinogenesis in rats: effect of difluoromethylornithine with piroxicam or fish oil. J Natl Cancer Inst 1986; 77:1309-13.

85. Medrano EE, Goldemberg SH, Algranati ID. Differential effect of alpha-difluoromethyl-ornithine on the proliferation of Balb 3T3 and chemically transformed 3T3 cells. J Cell Physiol 1983; 117:141-47.

86. Fukushima S, Murasaki G, Hirose M et al. Histopathological analysis of pre-neoplastic changes during N-butyl-N-(4-hydroxybutyl)-nitrosamine-induced urinary bladder carcinogenesis in rats. Acta Pathol Jpn 1982; 32:243-50.

87. Homma Y, Kakizoe T, Samma S et al. Suppression of rat urinary bladder carcinogenesis by alpha-difluoromethylornithine. J Urol 1989; 141:1454-57.

88. Manni A, Wright C. Effect of tamoxifen and alpha-difluoromethylornithine on clones of nitrosomethylurea-induced rat mammary tumor cells grown in soft agar culture. Cancer Res 1983; 43:1084-86.

89. Bardocz S, Varvolgyi C, Rady P et al. Effect of dimethylnitrosamine on the concentration of polyamines in rat liver and kidney. Anticancer Res 1982; 2:309-14.

90. Garcea R, Pascale R, Daino L et al. Variations of ornithine decarboxylase activity and S-adenosyl-L-methionine and 5'-methylthioadenosine contents during the development of diethylnitrosamine-induced liver hyperplastic nodules and hepatocellular carcinoma. Carcinogenesis 1987; 8:653-58.

91. Manni A. The role of polyamines in the hormonal control of breast cancer cell proliferation. In: Dickson R, Lippman M, eds. Mammary Tumorogenesis and Malignant Progression. Boston: Kluwer Academic Publishers, 1994:209-25.

92. Thompson HJ, Herbst EJ, Meeker LD et al. Effect of D,L-alpha-diluoromethylornithine on murine mammary carcinogenesis. Carcinogenesis 1984; 5:1649-51.

93. Thompson HJ, Meeker LD, Herbst EJ et al. Effect of concentration of D,L-2-difluoromethylornithine on murine mammary carcinogenesis. Cancer Res 1985; 45:1170-73.

94. Manni A, Wright C. Reversal of the antiproliferative effect of the antiestrogen tomaxifen by polyamines in breast cancer cells. Endocrinology 1984; 114:836-39.

95. Glikman PL, Manni A, Bartholomew M et al. Polyamine involvement in basal estradiol-stimulated insulin-like growth factor 1, secretion and action in breast cancer cells in culture. J Steroid Biochem Mol Biol 1990; 37:1-10.

96. Kim I, Manni A, Lynch J et al. Polyamine involvement in the secretion and action of TGF-alpha in hormone sensitive human breast cancer cells in culture. Breast Cancer Res Treat 1991; 18:83-91.

97. Kasid A, Lippman ME, Papageorge AG et al. Transfection of v-ras[H] DNA into MCF-7 human breast cancer cells bypasses dependence on estrogen for tumorigenicity. Science 1985; 228:725-28.

98. Mustelin T, Poso H, Lapinjoki SP et al. Growth signal transduction: Rapid activation of covalently bound ornithine decarboxylase during phosphatidylinositol breakdown. Cell 1987; 49:171-76.

99. Butler AP, Cohn WB, Mar PK et al. Regulation of ornithine decarboxylase mRNA by phorbol esters and insulin in normal and c-kinase-deficient rat hepatoma cells. J Cell Physiol 1991; 147:256-64.

100. Meggio F, Flamigni F, Caldarera CM et al. Phosphorylation of rat heart ornithine decarboxylase by type-2 casein kinase. Biochem Biophys Res Commun 1984; 122:997-1004.

101. Combest WL, Gilbert LI. Polyamines modulate multiple protein phosphorylation pathways in the insect prothoracic gland. Mol Cell Endocrinol 1992; 83:11-19.

102. Kingsnorth AN, Wallace HM, Bundred NJ et al. Polyamines in breast cancer. Br J Surg 1984; 71:352-56.

103. Glikman P, Manni A, Demers L et al. Polyamines involvement in the growth of hormone-responsive and resistant human breast cancer cells in culture. Cancer Res 1989; 49:1371-78.

104. Bachrach U, Tabib A. Polyamine biosynthesis and ras oncogene. In: Dowling RH, Folsch VR, Loser C, eds. Polyamines in the

Gastrointestinal Tract. London, Boston: Kluwer Academic Publishers, 1992:105-19.

105. Seiler N, Atanassov CL. The natural polyamines and the immune system. In: Jucker E, ed. Progress in Drug Research. Basel: Birkhauser Verlag, 1994; 43:87-141.

106. Korpela H, Höltta E, Hovi T et al. Response of enzymes involved in the metabolism of polyamines to phytohaemagglutinin-induced activation of human lymphocytes. Biochem J 1981; 196:733-38.

107. Seiler N. Functions of polyamine acetylation. Can J Physiol Pharmacol 1987; 65:2024-35.

108. Bachrach U, Menashe M, Faber J et al. Polyamine biosynthesis and metabolism in transformed human lymphocytes. In: Caldarera CM, Zappia V, Bachrach U, eds. Adv. Polyamine Res. Vol. 3, New York: Raven Press, 1981:259-74.

109. Matsui-Yuasa I, Otani S, Morisawa S. Role of protein kinase in phytohemagglutinin-stimulated induction of spermidine/spermine N^1 acetyltransferase. Biochem Inter 1987; 15:997-1003.

110. Seyfried CE, Morris DR. Relationship between inhibition of polyamine biosynthesis and DNA replication in activated lymphocytes. Cancer Res 1979; 39:4861-67.

111. Höltta E, Jänne J, Hovi T. Suppression of the formation of polyamines and macromolecules by D,L-alpha-difluoromethylornithine and methylglyoxal-bis-(guanylhydrazone) in phytohemagglutinin-activated human lymphocytes. Biochem J 1979; 178: 109-17.

112. Höltta E. Polyamine requirement for polyribosome formation and protein synthesis in human lymphocytes. In: Selmecci L, Brosnan ME, Seiler N, eds. Recent Progress in Polyamine Research. Budapest: Akademiai Kiado, 1985:137-50.

113. Elitsur Y, Strom J, Luk GD. Inhibition of ornithine decarboxylase activity decreases polyamines and suppresses DNA synthesis in human colonic *lamina propria* lymphocytes. Immunopharmacol 1993; 25:253-60.

114. Kay JE, Pegg AE. Effect of inhibition of spermidine formation on protein and nucleic acid synthesis during lymphocyte activation. FEBS Lett 1973; 29:301-04.

115. Gazitt Y, Friend C. Polyamine biosynthesis snzymes in the induction and inhibition of differentiation in Friend erythroleukemia cells. Cancer Res 1980; 40:1727-32.

116. Verma DS, Sunkara PS. An essential role for polyamine biosynthesis during human-granulopoietic differentiation. Cancer Res 1982; 42:3046-49.

117. Takano T, Takigawa M, Suzuki F. Role of polyamines in expression of the differentiated phenotype of chondrocytes in culture. Med Biol 1981; 59:423-27.

118. Rath NC, Reddi AH. Changes in polyamines, RNA synthesis and cell proliferation during matrix-induced cartilage, bone and bone marrow development. Dev Biol 1981; 82:211-16.

119. Bethell DR, Pegg AE. Polyamines are needed for the differentiation of 3T3-L1 fibroblasts into adipose cells. Biochem Biophys Res Commun 1981; 102:272-78.

120. Erwin BG, Ewton DZ, Florini JR et al. Polyamine depletion inhibits the differentiation of L6 myoblast cells. Biochem Biophys Res Commun 1983; 114:944-49.

121. Sunkara PS, Chang CC, Prakash NJ et al. Effect of inhibition of polyamine biosynthesis by DL-alpha-difluoromethylornithine on growth and melanogenesis of B16 melanoma *in vitro* and *in vivo*. Cancer Res 1985; 45:4067-70.

122. Bachrach U, Don S, Wiener H. Polyamines in normal and in virus-transformed chick embryo fibroblasts. Cancer Res 1974; 34:1577-80.

123. Don S, Wiener H, Bachrach U. Specific increase in polyamine levels in chick embryo cells transformed by Rous sarcoma virus. Cancer Res 1975; 35:194-98.

124. Haddox MK, Magun BE, Russell DH. Ornithine decarboxylase induction during B1 progression of normal and Rous sarcoma virus-transformed cells. Cancer Res 1980; 40:604-08.

125. Hölttä E, Vartio T, Jänne J et al. Temperature-dependent and transformation-associated changes in polyamine metabolism in normal and Rous sarcoma virus-infected chick embryo fibroblasts. Biochim Biophys Acta 1981; 677:1-6.

126. Bacharch U, Wiener H. Increase in S-adensoyl-L-methionine decarboxylase activity during the transformation of chick embryo fibroblasts by Rous sarcoma virus. Int J Cancer 1980; 26:75-78.

127. Gazdar AF, Stull HB, Kilton LJ et al. Increased ornithine decarboxylase activity in murine sarcoma virus infected cells. Nature 1976; 262:696-98.

128. Lembach KJ. Regulation of growth *in vitro*. I. Control of ornithine decarboxylase in untransformed and transformed mouse fibroblasts by serum. Biochim Biophys Acta 1974; 354:88-100.

129. Goldstein DA, Heby O, Marton LJ. Biphasic stimulation of polyamine biosynthesis in primary mouse kidney cells by infection with polyoma virus. Proc Natl Acad Sci, USA 1976; 73:4022-26.

130. Pakala R, Kreisel M, Bachrach U. Polyamine metabolism and interconversion in NIH 3T3 and *ras*-transfected NIH 3T3 cells. Cancer Res 1988; 48:3336-40.

131. Tabib A, Bachrach U. Activation of the protooncogene c-*myc* and c-*fos* by c-*ras*: Involvement of polyamines. Biochem Biophys Res Commun 1994; 202:720-27.

132. Bachrach U, Tabib A. Activation of nuclear protooncogenes by polyamines. In: Caldarera CM, Clo C, Moruzzi MS, eds. Polyamines: Biological and Clinical Aspects. Bologne, CLUEB, 1994:17-22.

133. Hunter T. Cooperation between oncogenes. Cell 1991; 64:249-70.

134. Auvinen M, Paasinen A, Andersson LC et al. Ornithine decarboxylase activity is critical for cell transformation. Nature 1992; 360:355-58.

135. Moshier JA, Dosescu J, Skunca M et al. Transformation of NIH/3T3 cells by ornithine decarboxylase overexpression. Cancer Res 1993; 53:2618-22.

136. Hölttä E, Auvinen M, Paasinen A et al. Ornithine decarboxylase-induced cellular transformation: The involvement of protein tyrosine kinase(s) and pp130. Biochem Soc Trans 1994; 22:853-59.

137. Shantz LM, Pegg AE. Overproduction of ornithine decarboxylase caused by relief of translational repression is associated with neoplastic transformation. Cancer Res 1994; 54:2313-16.

138. Hibshoosh H, Johnson M, Weinstein IB. Effect of overexpression of ornithine decarboxylase (ODC) on growth control and oncogene-induced cell transformation. Oncogene 1991; 6:739-43.

139. Hölttä E, Auvinen M, Andersson LC. Polyamines are essential for cell transformation by pp60v-src: delineation of molecular events relevant for the transformed phenotype. J Cell Biol 1993; 122:903-14.

140. Marton LJ, Pegg AE. Polyamines as targets for therapeutic intervention. Ann Rev Pharmacol Toxicol 1995; 35:55-91.

141. Celano P, Baylin SB, Giardiello FM et al. Effect of polyamine depletion on c-myc expression in human colon carcinoma cells. J Biol Chem 1988; 263:5491-94.

142. Celano P, Baylin SB, Casero Jr RA. Polyamines differentially modulate the transcription of growth-associated genes in human colon carcinoma cells. J Biol Chem 1989; 264:8922-27.

143. Tonin PN, Yeger H, Stallings RI et al. Amplification of N-myc and ornithine decarboxylase genes in human neuroblastoma and hydroxyurea-resistant hamster cell lines. Oncogene 1989; 4:1117-21.

144. Sistonen L, Hölttä E, Makela TP et al. The cellular response to induction of the p21 cHa-ras oncoprotein includes stimulation of jun gene expression. EMBO J 1989; 8:815-22.

145. Sistonen L, Hölttä E, Lehvaslaiho H et al. Activation of the neu tyrosine kinase induces fos/jun transcription factor complex, the glucose transporter and ornithine decarboxylase. J Biol Chem 1989; 109:1911-19.

146. Bello-Fernandez C, Packham G, Cleveland J. The ornithine decarboxylase gene is a transcriptional target of c-Myc. Proc Natl Acad Sci, USA 1993; 90:7804-08.

147. Pryciak PM, Muller HP, Varmus HE. Simian virus 40 mini-chromosomes as targets for retroviral integration *in vivo*. Proc Natl Acad Sci, USA 1992; 89:9237-41.

148. Amati B, Littlewood TD, Evan GI. The c-Myc protein induces cell-cycle progression and apoptosis through dimerization with Max. EMBO J 1993; 12:5083-87.

149. Russell DH, Snyder SH. Amine synthesis in regerating rat liver: Extremely rapid turnover of ornithine decarboxylase. Mol Pharmacol 1969; 5:253-62.

150. Dani C, Mechti N, Piechaczyk M et al. Increased rate of degradation of *c-myc* mRNA in interferon-treated Daudi cells. Proc Natl Acad Sci, USA 1985; 82:4896-99.

151. Shayovits A, Bachrach U. Ornithine decarboxylase: an indicator for growth of NIH 3T3 fibroblasts and their c-Ha-ras transformants. Biochim Biophys Acta 1995; 1267:107-14.

152. LaMuragila GM, Lacaine F, Malt RA. High ornithine decarboxylase activity and polyamine levels in human colorectal neoplasia. Ann Surg 1986; 204:89-93.

153. Nau MM, Brooks BJ Jr, Carney DN et al. Human small-cell lung cancers show amplification and expression of the N-*myc* gene. Proc Natl Acad Sci, USA 1986; 83:1092-96.

154. Rozengurt E, Stroobant P, Waterfield MD et al. Platelet-derived growth factor elicits cyclic AMP accumulation in Swiss 3T3 cells: Role of prostaglandin production. Cell 1983; 34:265-72.

155. Bachrach U. Physiological aspects of ornithine decarboxylase. Cell Biochem Function 1984; 2:6-10.

156. Kelly K, Cochran BH, Stiles CD et al. Cell specific regulation of the c-myc gene by lymphocyte mitogens and platelet derived growth factor. Cell 1983; 35:603-10.

157. Marcu KB, Bossone SA, Patel AJ. *myc* function and regulation. Ann Rev Biochem 1992; 61:809-60.

158. Brewer EN, Rusch HP. Control of DNA replication: Effect of spermine on DNA polymerase activity in nuclei isolated from *Physarum polycephalum*. Biochem Biophys Res Commun 1966; 25:579-84.

159. DePamphilis ML. Transcriptional elements as components of eukaryotic origins of DNA replication. Cell 1988; 52:635-38.

160. Ran W, Dean M, Levine RA et al. Induction of c-fos and c-myc mRNA by epidermal growth factor or calcium ionophore is cAMP dependent. Proc Natl Acad Sci, USA 1986; 83:8216-20.

161. Wrighton C, Busslinger M. Direct transcriptional stimulation of the ornithine carboxylase gene by Fos in PC12 cells but not in fibroblasts. Mol Cell Biol 1993; 13:4657-69.

162. McCann PP, Pegg AF. Ornithine decarboxylase as an enzyme for therapy. Pharmacol Therap 1992; 54:195-215.

163. Dunzendorfer U, Russel DH. Altered polyamine profile in prostatic hyperplasia and in kidney tumors. Cancer Res 1978; 38:2321-24.

164. Kingsnorth AN, McCann PP, Diekema KA et al. Effects of alpha-difluoromethylornithine on growth of experimental Wilm's tumor and renal adenocarcinoma. Cancer Res 1983; 43:4031-34.

165. Arundel CM, Nishioka K, Tofilon PJ. Effects of alpha-difluoromethylornithine-induced polyamine depletion on the radiosensitivity of a human colon carcinoma cell line. Radiat Res 1988; 114:634-40.

166. Chang BK, Black O Jr, Gutman R. Inhibition of growth of human or hamster pancreatic cancer cell lines by alpha-difluoromethylorthinine alone and combined with cis-diamminedichloroplatinum(II). Cancer Res 1984; 44:5100-04.

167. Bregman MD, Meyskens Jr FL. Difluoromethylornithine enhances inhibition of melanoma cell growth in soft agar by dexamethasone, clone A interferon and retinoic acid. Int J Cancer 1986; 37:101-7.

168. Manni A, Badger B, Glikman P et al. Individual and combined effects of alpha-difluoromethylornithine and ovariectomy on the growth and polyamine millieu of experimental breast cancer in rats. Cancer Res 1989; 49:3529-34.

169. Fozard JR, Prakash NJ. Effects of DL-alpha-difluoromethylornithine, an irreversible inhibitor of ornithine decarboxylase, on the rat mammary tumor induced by 7,12-dimethylbenz[a]anthracene. Naunyn Schmiedebergs Arch Pharmacol 1982; 320:72-77.

170. Luk GD, Civin CI, Weissman RM et al. Ornithine decarboxylase: essential in proliferation but not differentiation of human promyelocytic leukemia cells. Science 1982; 216:75-77.

171. Maddox AM, Freireich EJ, Keating MJ et al. Alterations in bone marrow and blood mononuclear cell polyamine and methylglyoxal bis(guanylhydrazone) levels: phase 1 evaluation of alpha-difluoromethylornithine and methylglyoxal bis(guanylhydrazone) treatment of human hematological malignancies. Cancer Res 1988; 48: 1367-73.

172. Hibasami H, Tsukada T, Maekawa S et al. Antitumor effect of methylglyoxal bis(3-aminopropylamidinohydrazone), a new inhibitor of S-adenosylmethionine and ornithine decarboxylases, on human erythroid leukemia K562 cells. Cancer Chemother Pharmacol 1988; 22:187-90.

173. Takigawa M, Verma AK, Simsiman RC et al. Inhibition of mouse skin tumor promotion and of promoter-stimulated epidermal polyamine biosynthesis by alpha-difluoromethylornithine. Cancer Res 1983; 43:3732-38.

174. Hibasami H, Tsukada T, Maekawa S et al. Inhibition of mouse

skin tumor promotion and of promoter-induced epidermal polyamine biosynthesis by methylglyoxal bis(butylamidino-hydrazone). Carcinogenesis 1988; 9:199-202.

175. Kingsnorth AN, Russell WE, McCann PP et al. Effects of alpha-difluoromethylornithine and 5-fluorouracil on the proliferation of human colon adenocarcinoma cell line. Cancer Res 1983; 43:4035-38.

176. Sunkara PS, Bowlin TL, Rosenberger AL et al. Effects of murine alpha-, beta, and gamma interferons in combination with alpha-difluoromehthylornithine as inhibitor of B16 melanoma and Lewis lung carcinoma in mice. J Biol Response Mod 1989; 8:170-79.

177. Sunkara PS, Rosenberger AI. Antimetastatic activity of DL-alpha-difluoro-methyl-ornithine, an inhibitor of polyamine biosynthesis in mice. Cancer Res 1987; 47:933-35.

178. Kyriakidis DA, Kortsaris A. Effects of human interferon and al-pha-difluoromethylornithine on T47D cells. J Interferon Res 1986; 6:527-33.

179. Abeloff MD, Slavik M, Luk GD et al. Phase I trial and pharmaco-kinetic studies of alpha-difluoromethylornithine—an inhibitor of polyamine biosynthesis. J Clin Oncol 1984; 2:124-30.

180. Levin VA, Chamberlain MC, Prados MD et al. Phase I-II study of eflornithine and mitoguazone combined treatment in recurrent brain tumors. Cancer Treat Rep 1987; 71:459-64.

181. Levin VA, Prados MD, Jung WK et al. Treatment of recurrent gliomas with eflornithine. J Natl Cancer Inst 1992; 84:1432-37.

182. Prados M, Rodriguez L, Chamberlain M et al. Treatment of recurrent gliomas with 1,3-bis (2-chloroethyl)-l-nitrosourea and alpha-difluoromethylornithine. Neurosurgery 1989; 24:806-09.

183. Cipolla B, Guille F, Moulinoux J-P et al. Polyamines and prostatic carcinoma: Clinical and therapeutic implications. Eur Urol 1993; 24:124-31.

184. Kelloff GJ, Boone CW, Crowell JA et al. Chemopreventive drug development: Perspectives and progress. Cancer Epidemiol Biomarker Rev 1994; 3:85-89.

185. Kulkarni N, Zang E, Kelloff G et al. Effect of chemopreventive agents piroxicam and D,L-alpha-difluoromethylornithine on inter-mediate biomarkers of colon carcinogenesis. Carcinogenesis 1992; 13:995-1000.

186. Love RR, Carbone PP, Verma AK et al. Randomized phase 1 chemoprevention dose-seeking study of alpha-difluoromethyl orni-thine. J Nat Cancer Inst 1993; 85:732-37.

187. Creaven PJ, Pendyala L, Peterili NJ. Evaluation of alpha-difluoromethylornithine as a potential chemopreventive agent: Tol-erance to daily oral administration in humans. Cancer Epidemiol Biomarkers Rev 1993; 2:243-47.

188. Loprinzi CI, Messing EM. A prospective clinical trial of difluoro-methylornithine (DFMO) in patients with resected superficial bladder cancer. J Cell Biochem Suppl 1992; 161:153-55.

189. Sharma S, Stutzman JD, Kelloff GJ et al. Screening of potential chemopreventive agents using biochemical markers of carcinogenesis. Cancer Res 1994; 54:5848-55.

190. Bachrach U, Shayovitz A, Marom Y et al. Ornithine decarboxylase—a predictor for tumor chemosensitivity. Cell Mol Biol 1994; 40:957-64.

191. Assaraf YG, Drori S, Bachrach U et al. Determination of multidrug resistance levels in cultured mammalian cells using ornithine decarboxylase activity. Analyt Biochem 1994; 216:97-109.

192. Bachrach U. Polyamines as markers of malignancy. In: Jucker E, ed. Progress In Drug Research. Basel, Bikhauser Verlag, 1992:9-33.

CHAPTER 5

GENETIC ENGINEERING OF POLYAMINE METABOLISM IN TRANSGENIC RODENTS

Juhani Jänne, Leena Alhonen, Maria Halmekytö, Leila Kauppinen and Riitta Sinervirta

I. INTRODUCTION

Although studied for several decades, the function(s) of the polyamines still remains by large unsolved. The metabolism of the polyamines putrescine, spermidine and spermine is most closely linked to the proliferation of animal cells as revealed by the use of highly specific inhibitors of their synthesis. A chemically-induced depletion of cellular putrescine and spermidine pools invariably results in growth arrest of mammalian cells, a phenomenon that has already been applied to cancer chemotherapy.[1] However, owing to the power and great complexity of the regulatory machinery responsible for the control of the polyamine pools, an efficient depletion of the polyamines is difficult to achieve. Similarly, an enhanced accumulation of the polyamines as resulted from a stimulation of ornithine decarboxylase (ODC) activity has been implied to be causally related to malignant transformation. This is exemplified by recent findings indicating that cultured cells over-expressing ODC as a result of transfection of its gene appear to undergo malignant transformation.[2-4] Elevated ODC activity has

Polyamines in Cancer: Basic Mechanisms and Clinical Approaches, edited by Kenji Nishioka. © 1996 R.G. Landes Company.

been considered as a risk factor in some human neoplasia, such as colorectal cancer.[5] In addition to the growth processes, the polyamines are also believed to be involved in neuronal degeneration in response to excitotoxic or ischemic insults,[6] possibly through an interaction with the N-methyl-D-aspartate (NMDA) receptor.[7] However, the experiments conducted with cultured and immortalized cells or with experimental animals exposed to various pathophysiological conditions do not necessarily reflect the situation in vivo.

During the past few years, we have generated a number of transgenic rodent lines with aberrant expression of some of the biosynthetic enzymes of the polyamines. As summarized in this chapter, experimental data collected with the aid of these animals are not always in complete agreement with the widely expressed views of the putative functions of the polyamines.

II. OVEREXPRESSION OF ORNITHINE DECARBOXYLASE IN TRANSGENIC RODENTS

We have generated several independent transgenic mouse lines overexpressing the human ODC gene to a varying extent. The gene construct used was human genomic ODC with all the exons and introns together with about 800 nucleotides of the 5' flanking and 1000 nucleotides of the 3' flanking sequence.[8] With the exception of one single line out of eight transgenic mouse lines all the animals displayed very high ODC activity practically in all of the tissues studied.[9]

Not only was ODC overexpressed in the tissues of the transgenic mice, but there was also a close correlation between the number of integrated gene copies and the level of the transgene expression in testis and brain but not in kidney.[9] The tissue distribution, as regarding the transgene-derived ODC activity, was strikingly different from that found in syngenic mice. Normal mice display very high ODC activity in kidney whereas the highest ODC activity in the transgenic mice was found in testis.[9] While ODC activity in normal mice is barely detectable in tissues such as brain and muscle, the enzyme activity in the transgenic animals was elevated up to 100-fold. Interestingly, transgenic mice harboring the bacterial chloramphenicol acetyltransferase (CAT) reporter gene operationally fused with mouse ODC promoter displayed almost superimposable tissue distribution of the transgene-derived CAT activity as did the mice harboring the human ODC gene.[9] In striking contrast to the endogenous enzyme activity that is very high in kidney, no CAT activity was found in this tissue of the transgenic animals.[9]

The reasons for the aberrant overexpression and distorted tissue distribution of the transgenes in comparison with the endogenous ODC are not known. Position-independent and gene copy number-dependent expression of transgenes is commonly attributed to the presence of so-called matrix attachment elements or locus control regions, i.e., specific sequences around the transgene rendering the expression of the gene independent of the surrounding genetic environment.[10,11] However, typical to these elements appears to be tissue-specific expression[10,11] that apparently is not true in case of the ODC transgenes. Moreover, the matrix attachment elements are usually located at far 5' or 3' flanking regions of the gene. The human ODC construct used to generate transgenic animals contained only about 800 nucleotides of 5' and 1000 nucleotides of the 3' flanking regions,[8] making the presence of the elements unlikely. It is, however, possible that the ODC gene contains some silencer elements not included in the transgene constructs. Even this possibility is rendered somewhat unlikely as we have generated transgenic mice with human ODC gene construct containing 8,000 nucleotides of the 5' flank.[12] These animals likewise showed aberrant ODC expression in their tissues just like those mice harboring the shorter promoter sequence (unpublished observations). Interestingly, the same human ODC gene construct with the 800 nucleotide promoter when used in transfection experiments yielded a large number of Chinese hamster ovary cell clones stably expressing the gene, yet there was no correlation between the number of integrated gene copies and the rate of expression as judged by the level of enzyme activity or the amount of ODC-specific mRNA.[13] These observations may imply that the gene copy number-dependent expression of the transgene had been achieved during the embryonic development.

III. REGULATION OF THE TRANSGENE-DERIVED ODC EXPRESSION

Even though ODC is highly regulated and one of the most inducible mammalian enzymes, surprisingly little is known about the exact mechanisms involved in the control of its expression. Experimental data accumulated over the past few years, especially after the cloning of ODC, indicate that there are only a few instances where the regulation of the expression is unambiguously and solely attributable to the transcriptional level. In fact, transfection experiments carried out with various heterologous gene constructs have emphasized the importance of the coding region, and peculiarly not the promoter region, in the expression of mammalian ODC.[14]

As outlined below, our own experiments with transgenic mice harboring the human ODC gene or mouse ODC promoter-driven reporter gene likewise distinctly support the importance of a posttranscriptional control mode as a major regulatory element in the regulation of mammalian ODC expression. We employed three different experimental conditions known to greatly enhance ODC activity in different tissues and transgenic mice either carrying the intact human ODC gene or mouse ODC promoter-driven CAT reporter gene. These included testosterone-induced ODC stimulation in female kidney, induction of epidermal ODC in response to phorbol esters and finally stimulation of ODC activity following partial hepatectomy.[12] ODC activity was strikingly enhanced in the appropriate tissues in response to any of these stimuli, yet the mouse ODC promoter-driven CAT reporter gene was completely insensitive under any of the treatment conditions.[12] This is especially puzzling as the used promoter (-1658 to +13 relative to the transcription start site) has been shown to possess full promoter activity in transfection experiments.[15] This may be understood in terms that the promoter alone, without the coding region or/and introns, is unable to respond to these stimuli. Similarly, the human transgene-derived ODC activity in the kidney was entirely insensitive to testosterone, whereas the epidermal transgene-derived ODC responded to the phorbol ester, yet with slower kinetics than the endogenous one.[12] Both endogenous and transgene-derived ODC activities were stimulated in the regenerating mouse liver in very much similar fashion. Interestingly, this stimulation of the enzyme activity apparently did not involve any enhanced accumulation of mRNA.[12] These results are in line with the notion that the promoter region of mammalian ODC gene may be of minor importance for the regulation of the expression. However, the fact remains the promoter region of the ODC gene is ultimately required for the expression as we have also generated transgenic mice harboring a truncated, promoterless human ODC gene and found no evidence whatsoever of the presence of human-specific ODC mRNA in any of the tissues of these animals.[8]

IV. CHANGES IN POLYAMINE METABOLISM IN TRANSGENIC MICE OVEREXPRESSING ODC

Although the ODC activity in tissues of the transgenic mice was up to 100-fold higher than that of their syngenic littermates resulting sometimes in a massive putrescine accumulation, these changes were not reflected in the sizes of the pools of the higher polyamines spermidine and spermine, i.e., in most tissues putrescine was not converted further into spermidine and spermine.[16] Testicular tissue represented an exception of this rule as the content of spermidine was moderately increased in most of the transgenic animals. However, almost all of the tissues of the transgenic animals showed a significant elevation in the molar ratio of spermidine to spermine.[16] There were large discrepancies between the ODC activity in a given tissue and the tissue level of putrescine. This is exemplified by the observation that, for instance, in transgenic animals testicular tissue displayed an ODC activity of nearly 700 nmol/g of tissue per hour, yet the steady-state level of putrescine was only about 400 nmol/g of tissue, i.e., at this ODC activity the manufacturing of such a putrescine pool would have required not more than a couple of hours.[17] This discrepancy can be taken as evidence that the transgene-derived ODC does not operate under optimal conditions in vivo. This view is supported by earlier observations indicating that in most mouse tissues the level of L-ornithine, the substrate of ODC, appears to be well below the Km value for ODC.[18] The major consumer of tissue L-ornithine is ornithine transaminase, an enzyme involved in shunting the amino acid into the oxidative metabolism of glutamate. An inhibition of ornithine transaminase by the ornithine analog 5-fluoromethyl-ornithine is known to strikingly expand ornithine pools in most of the mouse tissues and give rise to an enhanced putrescine accumulation.[18,19] A treatment of transgenic mice overexpressing ODC with 5-fluoromethylornithine indeed increased the tissue accumulation of putrescine[17] as exemplified by the changes of the brain polyamine pools in Figure 5.1. As shown in the figure, brain putrescine levels were practically undetectable in nontransgenic animals regardless of the treatment whereas they were some 15 times higher in the transgenic animals and were further substantially elevated in response to the treatment with 5-fluoromethylornithine. However, the pools of brain spermidine and spermine displayed only insignificant changes (Fig. 5.1). Similar changes took place also in other tissues in response to 5-fluoromethylornithine treatment, yet none of the tissues studied led the enhanced accumulation of putrescine to a rise in spermidine or spermine concentrations.[17]

The transgenic mice overexpressing ODC were subsequently subjected to in depth analyses in order to elucidate the nature of the apparent block between putrescine and spermidine. An assay of the activities of all the enzymes involved in the metabolism of the polyamines did not reveal any changes that could explain the peculiar accumulation of putrescine but not of the higher polyamines.[16] Figure 5.2 displays the testicular activities of the enzymes involved in the biosynthesis and catabolism of the polyamines in transgenic and syngenic animals. Although the activities of the biosynthetic enzymes AdoMetDC, spermidine and spermine synthases showed some increase in testis of transgenic animals (Fig. 5.2), the changes in other tissues were either insignificant or inconsistent. Interestingly, there was no sign of a possible activation of the backconversion pathway of the polyamines in the transgenic animals. As shown in Figure 5.2, spermidine/spermine N^1-acetyltransferase (SSAT) activity that is the rate-controlling enzyme remained unchanged in all tissues of the transgenic animals. Similarly, the activity of polyamine oxidase converting the higher polyamines ultimately into putrescine was not altered in any of the tissues of transgenic mice overexpressing ODC.[16] These findings apparently indicate that the lack of an enhanced accumula-

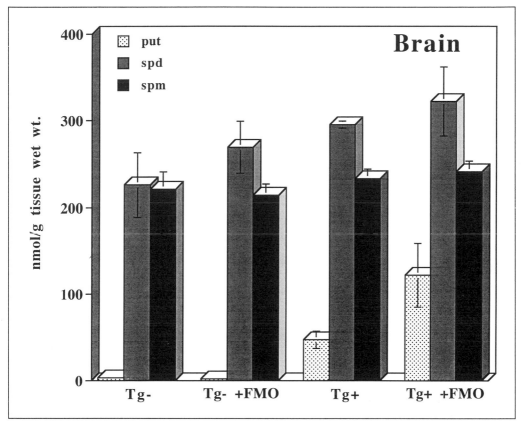

Fig. 5.1. Brain polyamine concentrations in syngenic (Tg-) and transgenic (Tg+) mice overexpressing ODC without or with 5-fluoromethylornithine (FMO) treatment. put, putrescine; spd, spermidine; spm, spermine. The vertical bars represent standard deviations. Data adapted from ref. 17.

tion of the higher polyamines in spite of strikingly expanded putrescine pools in the transgenic animals was not explainable by an accelerated catabolism of spermidine and spermine.

As indicated in Figure 5.3 only minor and insignificant differences were found between transgenic and syngenic animals with regards to the urinary excretion of the polyamines. The fact that the urinary excretion of N^1-acetylspermidine remained unaltered in the transgenic animals likewise supports the notion that the backconversion pathway was not activated in response to ODC overexpression.

Based on these results it appears obvious that mammalian tissues can tolerate remarkably high concentrations of putrescine

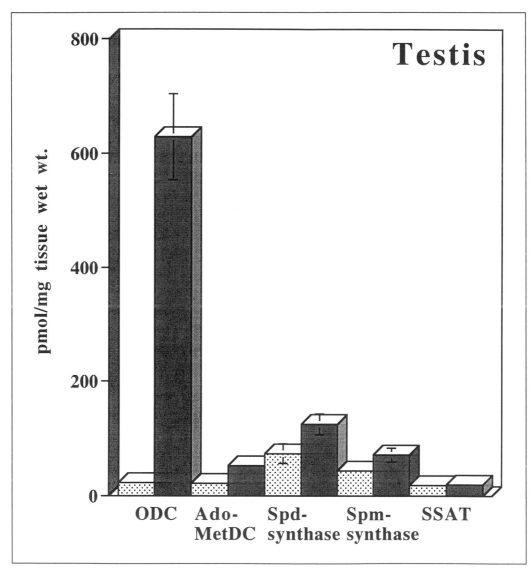

Fig. 5.2. Activities of the polyamine metabolizing enzymes in the testis of syngenic (light columns) and transgenic (dark columns) mice overexpressing ODC. AdoMetDC, S-adenosylmethionine decarboxylase; Spd, spermidine; Spm, spermine; SSAT, spermidine/spermine N^1 acetyltransferase. The vertical bars represent standard deviations. Data adapted from ref. 16.

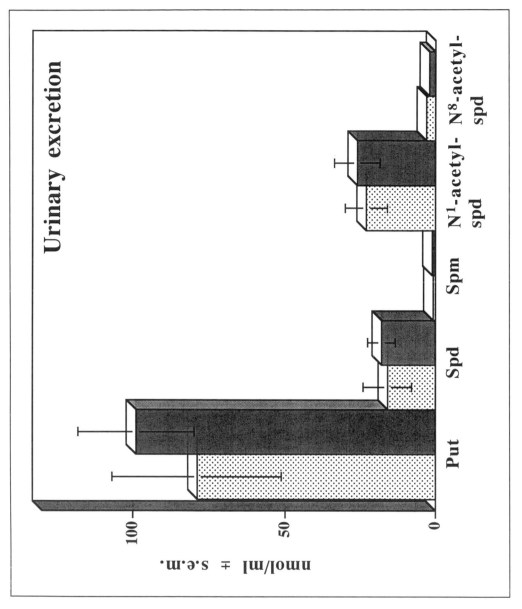

Fig. 5.3. Urinary excretion of polyamines and their acetylated derivatives in syngenic (light columns) and transgenic (dark columns) mice overexpressing ODC. Put, putrescine; Spd, spermidine; Spm, spermine. The vertical bars represent standard errors of the means. Data adapted from ref. 17.

resulting from the overexpression of ODC. However, it also seems evident that there exist powerful regulatory mechanism that prevent any overaccumulation of spermidine and spermine in nondividing cells. These mechanisms may include an enhanced excretion of the polyamines in response to L-ornithine load as demonstrated currently[18] or a decrease in AdoMetDC together with a prolonged metabolic half-life of putrescine as shown to occur during hypo-osmotic stress.[20,21] However, none of these mechanisms appears to be operative in transgenic mice overexpressing ODC.

V. PHENOTYPIC CHANGES ASSOCIATED WITH PUTRESCINE OVERPRODUCTION

Regardless of the level of ODC expression, the transgenic animals did not show any overt physical or behavioral abnormalities nor was their life-span changed in comparison with syngenic littermates. Among the tissues of the transgenic animals testis and brain, both displaying exceptionally high ODC activity and putrescine accumulation, appear to be the most interesting with regards to overt phenotypic changes.

A. TESTIS

Among the first transgenic founding animals there was a male that soon was found to be infertile. An analysis of the ODC activity of a number of tissues revealed that testicular tissue exhibited a dramatically (more than 100-fold in comparison with nontransgenic animals) increased enzyme activity.[8] Histological examination of the testis of the transgenic founding male revealed striking morphological changes in comparison with normal males. The amount of germinal epithelium was greatly reduced, the spermatogenesis was completely halted and the number of Leydig cells was increased. The sperm count was decreased to almost zero and the few spermatozoa found were frequently malformed and immotile.[8] Interestingly, also male members of other transgenic lines with only moderately (up to 20-fold) elevated ODC activity showed similar, yet much milder, changes, most notably moderately reduced sperm count.[8] The infertile founding male with very high tissue ODC activity also showed macroscopic and microscopic changes in the preputial gland that was grossly enlarged due to an increase in the glandular tissue together with the thickening of metaplastic ductal epithelium.[8] The reasons for these changes are unknown.

A detailed analysis of male members of two transgenic mouse lines, K2 displaying 20 to 30 times and K15 displaying 70 times higher testicular ODC activity than in syngenic animals, revealed that the enhanced enzyme activity and putrescine accumulation stimulated mitotic DNA synthesis in seminiferous tubuli whereas meiotic DNA synthesis was either unaltered (K2) or significantly depressed (K15).[22] Moreover, unlike syngenic animals, in which testicular ODC activity decreased upon aging, the transgene-derived activity tended to increase up to the age of 12 months.[22] This was probably reflected as a reduced number of meiotic and particularly postmeiotic cells in aged males of the K15 line.[22]

It is not known for certain whether the toxic effects on the testicular tissue ultimately leading to complete sterility of the transgenic males were related to the very high ODC activity and excessive putrescine accumulation or whether these effects would be attributable to small but consistently found significant increases in testicular spermidine concentration.[16,22] The latter view, i.e., elevated spermidine pools being responsible for the observed effects on the testicular function, is indirectly supported by the data depicted in Figure 5.4. The figure displays a testicular polyamine pattern of nontransgenic rats and that of members of three transgenic rat lines overexpressing the human ODC gene. Male descendants of the line UkuR2 showed normal reproductive performance whereas founding UkuR4 and homozygous males of the UkuR6 line were infertile. If one looks at the testicular polyamine patterns of the males of the line UkuR2, it's obvious that apart from the distinctly increased putrescine level the contents of spermidine and spermine as well as the amount of total polyamines were similar to those of the control animals. In the founding animal UkuR4 and members of the UkuR6 line, the concentration of spermidine was more than doubled in comparison with the control animals, and the amount of total polyamines was distinctly elevated in both lines (Fig. 5.4). One may also notice that in the founding male UkuR4 the molar ratio of spermidine to spermine was dramatically changed (Fig. 5.4).

Based on the present results it appears that a moderate overexpression of ODC in testicular tissue may have a beneficial effect on the development of the sperm cells, but an excessive enzyme activity and putrescine accumulation ultimately lead to a complete sterility. It is entirely possible, however, that a sufficiently high putrescine level leads to a leakage of the block between putrescine and spermidine in such a way that toxic concentrations of spermidine will gradually accumulate.

B. BRAIN

Brain also occupies a special position among the tissues of transgenic mice overexpressing ODC as the enzyme activity in this

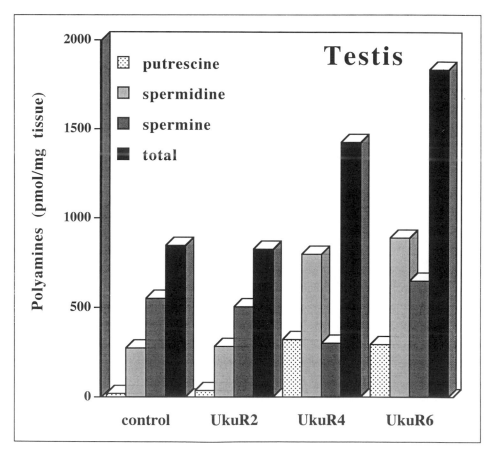

Fig. 5.4. Testicular polyamines in syngenic (control) and transgenic (UkuR2, UkuR4 and UkuR6) rats overexpressing ODC.

tissue was increased by a factor ranging from 50 to more than 200.[8] Prior to any functional studies, we subjected the transgenic animals to nuclear magnetic resonance (NMR) spectroscopy in order to elucidate possible transgene-related changes of brain energy metabolism and intracellular pH. In connection with these studies we found that the level of brain free Mg^{2+} was significantly reduced by about 40% in the transgenic animals.[23] The decrease in free Mg^{2+} was not attributable to altered intracellular pH or changes in cellular high-energy metabolites.[23] The reason for the lowering of free Mg^{2+} concentration in the presence of high concentrations of putrescine remains to be elucidated. Relatively little if anything is known about the interaction between the polyamines and Mg^{2+} ions. Magnesium ions appear to interact with the polyamine transport system in cultured cells, yet at relatively high concentrations.[24] More relevant to the brain functions may be the finding indicating that Mg^{2+} acts as a physiological blocker for glutamate-mediated excitatory currents at the NMDA receptor.[25] Thus the lowering of brain free Mg^{2+} in the transgenic animals would be expected to sensitize the NMDA receptor to excitotoxic stimuli and hence to render the animals prone to neuronal degeneration. As shown below, this apparently is not the consequence of putrescine overproduction. A subsequent NMR analysis of brain metabolites, such as N-acetyl aspartate, glutamate and gamma-aminobutyric acid (GABA), did not reveal any differences between syngenic and transgenic animals.[26]

Brain ODC is known to be greatly induced in response to a number of stimuli ultimately leading to neuronal degeneration, and this stimulation and the subsequent enhanced accumulation of brain putrescine is believed to be causally related to the development of neuronal damage.[6] It is, however, remarkable that the transgenic animals constitutively expressed ODC at a level fully comparable to or even higher than that reported as a consequence of ischemic episodes[27,28] or of an application of excitotoxic stimuli.[29] The polyamines act as agonists at the NMDA receptor, and they have their own recognition site at the receptor, the occupation of which enhances the binding of glycine and glutamate to the receptor.[30] Thus one would expect that an enhanced accumulation of the polyamines would predispose the animals to excitotoxic or ischemic conditions.

To elucidate the possible consequences of putrescine overproduction to functions of the central nervous system, transgenic mice (line K2) were subjected to a number of tests measuring proneness to epileptic seizures, spatial learning and memory. An analysis of several brain regions revealed that the transgenic animals had grossly elevated (up to 20-fold) putrescine in all brain regions (cortex, striatum, hippocampus and cerebellum) analyzed.[26] The transgenic animals showed a significantly elevated seizure threshold to electrical stimuli. This applied to both clonic and tonic seizures.[26] Apparently a further protection against electroshock-induced seizures was provided by the increase in brain putrescine with the aid of 5-fluoromethylornithine.[26] This together with the fact that the concentrations of the major neurotransmitter amino acids, namely glutamate and GABA, remained unaltered in the transgenic mice strongly suggest that the excessive accumulation of putrescine was causally related to the changes found. The transgenic animals were similarly protected against pentylenetetrazol-induced seizures as indicated by an increased minimal seizure threshold.[26] Transgenic animals and their syngenic littermates were likewise subjected to the water maze test mainly measuring spatial learning and memory. In this test the nontransgenic animals performed significantly better than their transgenic littermates indicating that the overproduction of putrescine in brain could impair spatial learning and memory.[26]

The experimental evidence obtained from the studies described above appears to point to the direction that the expanded putrescine pools in the brain of transgenic animals influence the functions of the NMDA receptor. Increased seizure threshold and impaired spatial learning are clearly indicative of a partial blockade of the receptor and hence imply that putrescine would be a physiological antagonist of the NMDA receptor. In any event, these results certainly do not support the widely expressed views[6,27,28] that a stimulation of ODC activity and the subsequent accumulation of brain putrescine are causally related to neuronal degeneration triggered by excitotoxic stimuli.

The studies with the transgenic animals were subsequently extended to involve cerebral ischemia in response to bilateral occlusion of the common carotid arteries.[31] These studies revealed that both the endogenous and transgene-derived ODC activity responded to the incomplete forebrain ischemia generated. It is noteworthy that the accumulation of putrescine in the brains of transgenic animals at 12 to 24 hours after the ischemia reached a level that was 50-fold greater than the basal level in syngenic mice, yet histological examination did not reveal any difference between the two animal groups.[31] Neuronal necroses were found in the hippocampus in both syngenic and transgenic animals at identical frequency.[31] These results clearly indicate that the stimulation of ODC activity and an enhanced putrescine accumulation in response to ischemic insults reflect an adaptive response rather than being a direct cause-effect sequence to neuronal damage. This view is further strongly supported by the observation that a life-long constitutive overexpression of ODC in the brains of transgenic mice did not lead to any accelerated neuronal degeneration.[32]

C. GENERAL TUMORIGENESIS

The metabolism of the polyamines is, often with good reasons, closely linked to cell proliferation in general and malignant transformation in particular. ODC has even been considered as an oncoprotein with full or partial transforming capacity.[24] The members of the transgenic mice harboring 24 ODC gene copies (line K2) displayed an epidermal ODC activity that was about 20 times higher than that in their syngenic littermates[33] and hence were excellent tools to elucidate the possible contribution of high ODC activity to skin tumorigenesis. A single topical application of the tumor promoter 12-O-tetradecanoylphorbol-13-acetate (TPA) induced a much more profound and longer lasting stimulation of the transgene-derived ODC activity in comparison with endogenous enzyme activity.[33] Transgenic animals and their syngenic littermates treated with a single topical application dimethylbenz[a]antracene followed by twice weekly application of TPA started to develop skin papillomas seven weeks after the initiation of the tumorigenesis.[33] At the time of the termination of the experiment, 11 weeks after the beginning of the treatments, the number of papillomas in transgenic animals was almost twice as high as in the syngenic animals. However, initiation or promotion alone did not induce papilloma formation in either of the animal groups, and none of the papillomas in any of the animals was malignant.[33] These results indicate that high epidermal ODC activity apparently confers a growth advantage on benign skin tumors but do not support the view that ODC would be critically involved in malignant transformation.

A group of the same transgenic animals together with their syngenic littermates were subjected to a long-term follow up. After an observation period of two years, which already represents the very edge of mouse life-span, 6 of 10 transgenic and 4 of 10 syngenic animals were still alive.[32] At the age of two years the tissue ODC activity was 20 to 50 (brain) times higher than in their syngenic littermates. Macroscopic and microscopic analyses of altogether 45 tissue samples taken from each animal did not reveal any difference in general tumor incidence between the transgenic and syngenic animals.[32] A comparison of the hematological values of peripheral blood revealed that the only difference between syngenic and transgenic mice was a significantly higher hemoglobin value in the latter animals.[32] It is also noteworthy that in spite of the 20 times higher ODC activity in the bone marrow of the transgenic animals, no blast cells were found in any of the animals.[32] These results indicate that a life-long overexpression of ODC in tissues of transgenic mice is not a risk factor for the development of spontaneous tumors.

VI. OVEREXPRESSION OF SPERMIDINE SYNTHASE IN TRANSGENIC MICE

We also generated transgenic mice overexpressing the human chromosome 1-derived spermidine synthase gene.[34] Members of one line, designated K43, were studied in greater detail.[35] Moreover, hybrid animals overexpressing both ODC and spermidine synthase were likewise generated. The transgenic animals expressed human spermidine synthase-derived mRNA in all tissues studied, and they displayed a tissue spermidine synthase activity that was 2 to 6 times higher than that in their syngenic littermates.[35] Interestingly, quantitation of the mRNA levels from several tissues did not reveal any correlation between the level of the message and the enzyme activity suggesting that the expression of spermidine synthase might be regulated post-transciptionally. Indeed, it has been recently shown that the 5' untranslated region of the spermidine synthase mRNA plays a crucial role in the regulation of the translation of the message.[36] As shown in Figure 5.5 depicting enzyme activities involved in polyamine metabolism in testis, the only change in comparison with syngenic animals was a greatly enhanced spermidine synthase activity. Typical to the tissue polyamine pattern of the transgenic animals was the absence of putrescine with no changes in the concentrations of spermidine and spermine.[35] When animals of the line K43 (overexpressing the spermidine synthase gene) were cross-bred with those overexpressing ODC (line K2), the tissue polyamine pattern closely resembled that of those overexpressing ODC alone as demonstrated in Figure 5.6. It is noteworthy that combined overexpression of both ODC and spermidine synthase did not result in any significant changes in tissue levels of spermidine and spermine (Fig. 5.6). This can be attributable to the fact that not spermidine synthase but AdoMetDC is the rate-controlling step in the synthesis of the higher polyamines. However, our recent experiments in which we employed transgenic animals overexpressing rat AdoMetDC gene did not reveal any marked changes in the concentrations of spermidine and spermine even after cross-breeding the animals with ODC overproducer (unpublished results). It thus appears that an extremely powerful machinery exists in mammalian cells aimed to prevent any overaccumulation of the higher polyamines.

VII. CONCLUDING REMARKS

In spite of active research for several decades, the exact physiological functions of the natural polyamines are and still remain uncovered. The metabolism of the polyamines appears to be closely related to the growth of animal cells, and their undisturbed synthesis is required for cell proliferation to occur as unambiguously demonstrated by the use of specific inhibitors of their biosynthesis.[1] Very little is likewise known about the roles of individual polyamines in the growth processes of animal tissues. A specific inhibition of ODC results in a gradual and profound depletion of putrescine and spermidine, but not spermine, that is closely associated with growth arrest of animal cells. On the other hand, specific inhibition of AdoMetDC efficiently depletes spermidine and

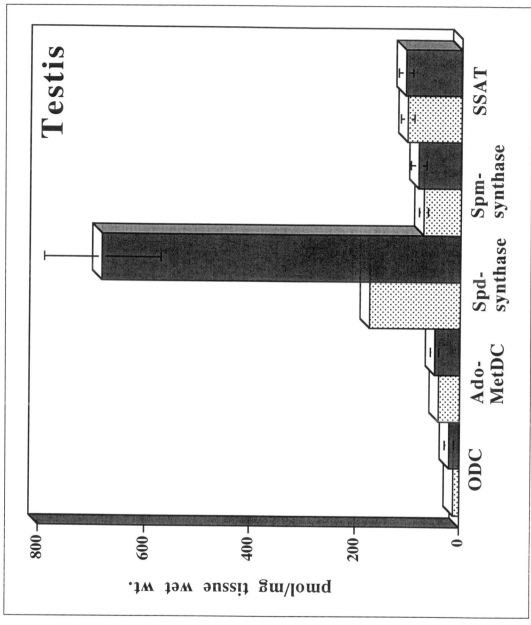

Fig. 5.5. Activities of the polyamine metabolizing enzymes in the testis of syngenic (light columns) and transgenic (dark columns) mice overexpressing spermidine synthase. Ado-MetDC, S-adenosylmethionine decarboxylase; Spd, spermidine; Spm, spermine; SSAT, spermidine/spermine N¹-acetyltransferase. The vertical bars represent standard deviations. Data adapted from ref. 35.

spermine and causes a massive overaccumulation of putrescine.[1] Interestingly, this situation is also incompatible with cell proliferation. Taken together, it thus appears that spermidine plays a crucial role in cell growth, putrescine and spermine being dispensable in this respect. With regards to the importance of the overproduction of the polyamines, the situation is vastly more complex. High levels of polyamines are traditionally linked to both compensatory

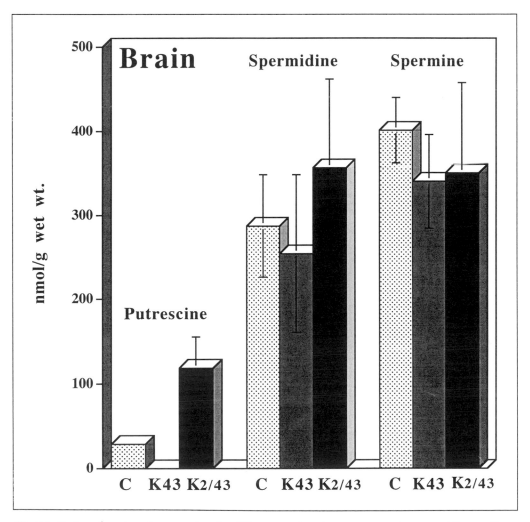

Fig. 5.6. Brain polyamines in syngenic mice (C), transgenic mice overexpressing spermidine synthase (K43) and in hybrid mice overexpressing both ODC and spermidine synthase (K2/43). The vertical bars represent standard deviations. Data adapted from ref. 35.

and malignant cell growth, yet there are only a few instances, especially regarding malignant growth, where this really is apparent. Enhanced activity of ODC has widely been considered as a marker of rapid growth. While this in most cases is obvious, the significance of the phenomenon is still far from solved. The elucidation of the role of ODC, however, is of central importance as it appears to have considerable practical applications. These include the widely expressed notion that enhanced ODC activity may be a risk factor for tumor development and could be an indication for chemopreventive measures in humans.[5] This view has recently been substantiated by a number of studies proposing an oncoprotein role for ODC.[2-4] In this respect, the present results demonstrate the power of transgenic techniques. They clearly indicate that under physiological settings a strikingly elevated ODC activity associated with massive tissue putrescine accumulation can be tolerated by most tissues for a life-long period without any overt phenotypic changes. This especially applies to the role of ODC stimulation and putrescine accumulation in response to a variety of stimuli known to lead to neuronal degeneration and brain damage. Not only was the level of ODC activity in the brain of the transgenic animals fully comparable with that observed after various neurotoxic stimuli,[6] but this expression continued constitutively for the whole life-span of the animals with apparently no harmful effects. Testicular tissue appears to be the only exception of this general rule. However, it is not proven on present evidence that high ODC activity and excessive putrescine levels are responsible for the observed disturbances of the male reproductive performance. It is by no means excluded that the small increases in spermidine concentration found in the transgenic males would be the primary cause responsible for the toxic effect on germ cell development. This brings us to the most important issue emerging from the present results. Why and how is the overaccumulation of spermidine prevented under conditions where ODC activity may be 100-fold and putrescine concentration 20-fold higher than in normal animals? As indicated, this is not explainable by any alterations of the biosynthetic or catabolic enzymes nor by an enhanced excretion of the polyamines. There appears to exist a powerful machinery, the nature of which is entirely unknown presently. It is, however, sufficiently strong to prevent an overaccumulation of spermidine in nondividing tissues at very high levels of ODC expression. It is not before the nature of this regulation has been solved that we can have access to the real functions of the polyamines.

REFERENCES

1. Jänne J, Alhonen L, Leinonen P. Polyamines: from molecular biology to clinical applications. Ann Med 1991; 23:241-259.
2. Hibshoosh H, Johnson M, Weinstein B. Effects of overexpression of ornithine decarboxylase (ODC) on growth control and oncogene-induced cell transformation. Oncogene 1991; 6:739-743.
3. Auvinen M, Paasinen A, Andersson LC et al. Ornithine decarboxylase activity is critical for cell transformation. Nature 1992; 360:355-358.
4. Moshier JA, Dosescu J, Skunca M et al. Transformation of NIH/3T3 cells by ornithine decarboxylase overexpression; Cancer Res 1993; 53:2618-2622.
5. O'Brien MJ, O'Keane JC, Zauber A et al. Precursors of colorectal carcinoma. Cancer 1992; 70:1317-1327.
6. Paschen W. Polyamine metabolism in different pathological states of the brain. Mol Chem Neuropathol 1992; 16:241-271.
7. Romano C, Williams K, Molinoff PB. Polyamines modulate the binding of [^{3}H]MK-801 to the solubilized N-methyl-D-asparatate receptor. J Neurochem 1991; 57:811 -818.
8. Halmekytö M, Hyttinen J-M, Sinervirta R et al. Transgenic mice aberrantly expressing human ornithine decarboxylase gene. J Biol Chem 1991; 266:19746-19751.
9. Halmekytö M, Alhonen L, Wahlfors J et al. Position-independent, aberrant expression of the human orntihine decarboxylase in transgenic mice. Biochem Biophys Res Commun 1991; 180: 262-267.
10. Phi-Van L, Strätling WH. The matrix attachment regions of the chicken lysozyme gene co-map with boundaries of the chromatin domain. EMBO J 1988; 7:655-664.
11. Stief A, Winter DM, Strätling WH et al. A nuclear DNA attachment element mediates elevated and position-independent gene activity. Nature 1989; 341:343-345.
12. Halmekytö M, Hyttinen J-M, Sinervirta R et al. Regulation of the expression of human ornithine decarboxylase gene and ornithine decarboxylase promoter-driven reporter gene in transgenic mice. Biochem J 1993; 292:927-932.

13. Hölttä E, Hirvonen A, Wahlfors J et al. Human ornithine decarboxylase(ODC)-encoding gene: cloning and expression in ODC-deficient CHO cells. Gene 1989; 83:125-135.

14. van Daalen Wetters T, Brabant M, Coffino P. Regulation of mouse ornithine decarboxylase activity by cell growth, serum and tetradecanoyl phorbol acetate is governed primarily by sequences within the coding region of the gene. Nucleic Acids Res 1989; 17:9843-9860.

15. Palvimo JJ, Eisenberg LM, Jänne OA. Protein-DNA interactions in the cAMP responsive promoter region of the mouse ornithine decarboxylase gene. Nucleic Acids Res 1991; 19:3921-3927.

16. Halmekytö M, Alhonen L, Wahlfors J et al. Characterization of a transgenic mouse line over-expressing the human ornithine decarboxylase gene. Biochem J 1991; 278:895-898.

17. Halmekytö M, Alhonen L, Alakuijala L et al. Transgenic mice over-producing putrescine in their tissues do not convert the diamine into higher polyamines. Biochem J 1993;291:505-508.

18. Seiler N, Daune G, Bolkenius FN et al. Ornithine aminotransferase activity, tissue ornithine concentrations and polyamine metabolism. Int J Biochem 1989; 21:425-432.

19. Daune G, Gerhart F, Seiler N. 5-Fluoromethylornithine, an irreversible and specific inhibitor of L-ornithine: 2-oxo-acid aminotransferase. Biochem J 1988; 253:481488.

20. Käpyaho K, Jänne J. Regulation of putrescine metabolism in Ehrlich ascites carcinoma cells exposed to hypotonic medium. Biochem Biophys Acta 1982; 714:93-100.

21. Poulin R, Wechter RS, Pegg AE. An early enlargement of the putrescine pool is hypoosmotic press required for growth in L1210 mouse leukemia cells under hypoosmotic press. J Biol Chem 1991; 266:6142-6151.

22. Hakovirta H, Keiski A, Toppari J et al. Polyamines and regulation of spermatogenesis: selective stimulation of late spermatogonia in transgenic mice overexpressing the human ornithine decarboxylae gene. Mol Endocrinol 1993; 7:1430-1436.

23. Kauppinen RA, Halmekytö M, Alhonen LJ et al. Nuclear magnetic resonance spectroscopy study on energy metabolism, intracellular pH, and free Mg^{2+} concentration in the brain of transgenic mice overexpressing human ornithine decarboxylase gene. J Neurochem 1992; 58:831-836.

24. Seppänen P, Alhonen-Hongisto L, Jänne J. Relation of the antiproliferative action of methylglyoxal bis(guanylhydrazone) to the natural polyamines. Eur J Biochem 1980; 110:7-12.

25. Stanfield PR. Intracellular Mg^{2+} may act as a co-factor in ion channel function. Trends Neurosci 1988; 11:475-477.

26. Halonen T, Sivenius J, Miettinen R et al. Elevated seizure threshold and impaired spatial learning in transgenic mice with putrescine overproduction in the brain. Eur J Neurosci 1993; 5:1233-1239.

27. Muller M, Cleef M, Röhn G et al. Ornithine decarboxylase in reversible cerebral ischemia: an immunohistochemical study. Acta Neuropathol 1991; 83:39-45.

28. Paschen W, Csiba L, Röhn G et al. Polyamine metabolism in transient focal ischemia of rat brain. Brain Res 1991; 566:354-357.

29. Martinez E, de Vera N, Artigas F. Differential response of rat brain polyamines to convulsant agents. Life Sci 1991; 48:77-84.

30. Williams K, Romano C, Molinoff PB. Effects of polyamines on the binding of [³H]MK-801 to the N-methyl-D-aspartate receptor: pharmacological evidence for the existence of a polyamine recognition site. Mol Pharmacol 1989; 36:575-581.

31. Lukkarinen J, Kauppinen RA, Koistinaho J et al. Cerebral energy metabolism and immediate early gene induction following severe incomplete ischaemia in transgenic mice overexpressing the human ornithine decarboxylase gene: Evidence that putrescine is not neurotoxic in vivo. Eur J Neurosci 1995; 7:1840-1849.

32. Alhonen L, Halmekytö M, Kosma V-M et al. Life-long over-expression of ornithine decarboxylase (ODC) gene in transgenic mice does not lead to generally enhanced tumorigenesis or neuronal degeneration. Int J Cancer 1995; 63:401-404.

33. Halmekytö M, Syrjänen K, Jänne J et al. Enhanced papilloma formation in response to skin tumor promotion in transgenic mice overexpressing the human ornithine decarboxylase gene. Biochem Biophys Res Commun 1992; 187:493-497.

34. Myöhänen S, Kauppinen L, Wahlfors J et al. Human spermidine synthase gene: Structure and chromosomal localization. DNA Cell Biol V 10:467-474.

35. Kauppinen L, Myöhänen S, Halmekytö M et al. Transgenic mice over-expressing the human spermidine synthase gene. Biochem J 1993; 293:513-516.

36. Kauppinen L. Regulation of the human spermidine synthase mRNA translation by its 5'untranslated region. FEBS Lett 1995; 365:61-65.

CHAPTER 6

An Overview of the Known and Suspected Mechanisms for Control of Apoptosis by Polyamines and Their Metabolites

Ralph E. Parchment

I. APOPTOSIS: A NATURAL PROCESS FOR REMOVING SPECIFIC CELLS AT SPECIFIC TIMES

The fact that cells in both adult and embryonic tissues of many organisms, from mammals to *C. elegans,* die independently of toxic xenobiotics has been known for about a century.[1-13] This naturally-occurring type of cell death in healthy tissues is called apoptosis.[10-13] It is an important biological process, specifically eradicating redundant or spent cell types during development to prevent ectopic tissues;[14-18] removing embryonic tissues to generate the morphology of the adult (e.g., between the prospective digits in the developing hand and foot);[19-20] balancing mitosis in renewing tissues to regulate tissue mass and selecting clones during lymphocyte maturation;[3,10-12,18,21-29] and removing genetically damaged cells

---

Polyamines in Cancer: Basic Mechanisms and Clinical Approaches, edited by Kenji Nishioka. © 1996 R.G. Landes Company.

to prevent oncogenesis.[30-34] The term apoptosis describes the morphological appearance of the dying cell; it means falling away as leaves from a tree in autumn.[10,12,13] During apoptosis, the cytoplasm and chromatin condense (pyknosis), and the plasma membrane contracts and withdraws the dying cell away from its neighbors except at points of adhesive plaques; yet most, if not all, of the intracellular organelles, including mitochondria and lysosomes, remain active.[3,13,22,35] Then the nucleus, containing the condensed chromatin fragments and surrounded by condensed cytoplasm, pinches off to form vesicles which are called apoptotic bodies. Near the end, dying cells and apoptotic bodies can be phagocytized by adjacent cells and destroyed in lysosomes.[22] Although there are molecular markers in some model systems that can be used to monitor apoptosis, there appears to be no universal molecular marker at this time. Degradation of genomic DNA into nucleosome-sized fragments, activation of a Ca^{++}, Mg^{++}-dependent endonuclease, flip-flop of phosphatidyl serine to the outer leaflet of the plasma membrane, and up-regulation of cell surface receptors for vitronectin and cell surface transglutaminases have all been proposed as markers of apoptosis.[2,3,14,31,36-45]

These cytological features easily distinguish apoptosis from a second process of cell death called necrosis, in which the dying cell shows swollen cytoplasm and mitochondria, clumped chromatin, and nuclear membrane and plasma membrane rupture, although late-stage apoptosis in the absence of phagocytosis and lysosomal degradation can resemble necrosis.[2,3,11-14,46] Perhaps the most important distinction between apoptosis and necrosis is a biological one: apoptosis is a controlled process which keeps intracellular substances contained within membranes at all times and therefore does not culminate with an inflammatory reaction, while necrosis results in cytolysis and an inflammatory reaction which can often cause serious tissue damage.[2,10-13,47] Especially in the renewing epithelial tissues of the adult,[48] apoptotic cells can be found completely surrounded by differentiated or proliferating cells.

This precise control of apoptosis, i.e., the regularity, predictability, and localized nature, led to the notion of an intracellular, genetically programmed pathway which kills a cell from within, and hence the term programmed cell death.[3,5,8,21] The presence of isolated dead cells in the midst of a milieu of viable cells did not seem explainable unless there was a mechanism for such cellular suicide,[2,21] and suicide is a reasonable explanation for the lack of adverse effects upon neighboring cells. However, extracellular substances, such as tumor necrosis factor and monoclonal antibodies against epitopes on T and B cells, trigger apoptosis, and in the murine blastocyst, extracellular H_2O_2 triggers apoptosis of a few cells expressing a developmental program that is no longer needed but spares the majority (Section II.A).[14-17,30,36,49-59] These data prove that death from within (suicide) is not required to obtain an isolated apoptotic cell in the midst of living cells; it can also be due to exposure of all of the cells to an extracellular trigger of apoptosis (murder).[14,15] Therefore, this talk considers not only direct versus indirect mechanisms, but also extra- versus intracellular mechanisms.

The broad scope of this monograph reflects the important roles of polyamines in many facets of development, tissue homeostasis, and neoplasia. Studies of polyamines and studies of apoptosis are separate bodies of knowledge. The purpose of this chapter is to describe the known and most likely intersections of these two rather large bodies of knowledge. There has been only a small amount of intentional research at this intersection. What is known in each field suggests many possible levels of control of apoptosis by polyamines—both direct and indirect. Since necrosis and apoptosis have little in common, and the mechanisms and causes of necrosis constitute yet a third body of knowledge, the control of necrosis by polyamines and their metabolites will not be considered here.

II. INDIRECT MECHANISMS FOR CONTROL OF APOPTOSIS BY POLYAMINES

In this section, all of the substances that are generated during polyamine biosynthesis, interconversion and breakdown are considered as possible triggers of apoptosis or regulators of the cell death program. Since they require metabolism to be produced, the polyamines can be viewed as inert storehouses of these substances which can be mobilized to produce them upon demand, and therefore they have been grouped together as indirect mechanisms of polyamine control of apoptosis. Some of these compounds, like H_2O_2, are short-lived and reactive, putting selective pressure on nature to develop a way to have them available at any time but present only when needed. The direct influence of the polyamines themselves upon apoptosis will be covered in the following section.

A. APOPTOSIS IN COMMITTED PROGENITORS TRIGGERED BY EXTRACELLULAR H₂O₂ FROM POLYAMINE OXIDATION

The blastocyst is the developing embryo at 3.5-4.5 days in the mouse.[60-67] It is a relatively simple cellular system containing three cell types that produce a spherical body with an outer layer of cells surrounding an inner layer of cells and a fluid-filled cavity (the blastocele cavity). The inner cell mass is the aggregate of inner cells which produces all the tissue lineages during the blastulation process. This aggregate is positioned eccentrically inside the cavity of the sphere to lie directly underneath a specialized subpopulation of the outer cell layer called the polar trophectoderm. The polar trophectoderm cells are produced by the differentiation of a few of the underlying inner cell mass cells and then differentiation into mural trophectoderm, which is the specialized outer layer of epithelial cells actively pumping fluid to fill the blastocele cavity. After the blastocele cavity has maximally expanded with fluid, the inner cell mass can no longer produce polar trophectoderm but instead produces a new population of cells called primitive endoderm, which migrates over the inner cell mass and along the inner face of the trophectodermal wall. This marks the beginning of the embryonic germ layers that will give rise to the embryo proper and make contributions to extraembryonic membranes.

During this process, apoptosis occurs for the first time in the mouse in the redundant cells within the inner cell mass.[14-17,50,52,64-70] Detectable at the mid-blastula stage by light and electron microscopic observation, 6-8 inner cell mass cells (10%) show the cytological and biochemical characteristics of apoptosis. Inner cell masses isolated from early embryos regenerate a trophectodermal layer within 24-36 hours and re-expand with fluid, thereby producing a smaller yet structurally correct blastocyst. In contrast, inner cell masses from late-stage blastocysts do not regenerate trophectoderm. Instead, they form embryoid bodies of inner cell mass covered by a layer of primitive endoderm. Thus, the inner cell mass loses its potential to regenerate trophectoderm concomitant with the appearance of apoptotic cells. These observations are consistent with the idea that apoptosis eliminates certain cells from the inner cell mass after they are no longer needed, i.e., those inner cell mass cells with trophectodermal potential (ICM-T), and thereby prevents ectopic trophectoderm formation within the germ layers. This is an example of histogenetic apoptosis,[14,15] i.e., cell death that permanently affects the phenotypic composition of a tissue. It will be interesting to determine if indeed there is any developmental consequence of blocked apoptosis of ICM-T cells, for inactivation of *C. elegans* or murine genes required for apoptosis does not cause any pathology unless the host is predisposed to the related disease.[9,71,72]

Nearly 50% of malignant ICM-T cells, in the form of an embryonal carcinoma cell line called ECa 247, undergo apoptosis in the blastocyst.[50,52-54,73-77] The 50% survivors are not resistant to the mechanism in the blastocele fluid, as a 44% death rate among populations grown from survivors and re-exposed to this microenvironment indicates (unpublished data). Note that neither polar nor mural trophectodermal cells are killed even though exposed to blastocele fluid, so it seems likely that the constant ratio of apoptotic to surviving ECa 247 cells is related to stages of differentiation. Perhaps only committed progenitors of the trophectodermal lineage are sensitive to the factor in blastocele fluid, but not stem cells or mature functional end cells. ICM cells destined to form the embryonic germ layers ("ICM-E")[50,73,78,79] should also be resistant. If so, then the sensitivity to apoptosis should be developmentally regulated as part of the differentiation program of ICM-T and ICM-E cells to assure destruction of the former but survival of the latter. This developmental program might be expression of glutathione-dependent protective mechanisms in ICM-E but not ICM-T cells, since depletion of intracellular glutathione pools in ICM-E cells increased their sensitivity to the apoptosis-inducing factor in blastocele fluid to a level equal to that of ICM-T cells.[53,54,77]

A soluble, extracellular substance was discovered in the blastocele fluid that triggers apoptosis in both normal and malignant ICM-T cells, but not in ICM-E cells or malignant caricatures of ICM-E cells.[14,15,50,54,77] Thus, this soluble, extracellular activity caused the same specific apoptosis that occurs during blastulation. The normal blastocyst contains only 1 nl of blastocele fluid,[80] so the embryoid bodies of a third embryonal carcinoma were used as an alternative source for biochemical purification of the active substance.[53,54,81] These embryoid bodies suppressed colony formation by micro-injected ICM-T but not ICM-E cells, and blastocele-like fluid isolated from the bodies induced apoptosis preferentially in ICM-T over ICM-E cells.[53,54,77] There were concentrations which killed 50% of ICM-T cells but 0% of the ICM-E cells, and ICM-E but not ICM-T cells were sensitized to the cytotoxic activity by glutathione depletion.[53,54] It was concluded that this blastocele-like fluid contained the substance present in the blastocyst which triggers apoptosis of ICM-T cells.

A role for glutathione was interesting in light of its known detoxification of H_2O_2 and acrolein, both of which are generated during oxidation of polyamines and histamine,[82-100] and the suggestion that H_2O_2 and/or acrolein generated during enzymatic oxidation of spermine and spermidine is the trigger for apoptosis in the developing limb bud was also interesting.[14,15,51] The amine oxidase family of enzymes utilizes molecular oxygen to oxidize polyamines or polyamine derivatives to the corresponding lower order amine:[90]

$$R\text{-}CH_2\text{-}NHR + O_2 + H_2O \rightarrow R\text{-}CHO + NH_2R + H_2O_2(O_2^-)$$

The nature of the polyamine substrate varies with the specific amine oxidase, and can range from putrescine, histamine, and other diamines for diamine oxidase, to spermine and spermidine for serum amine oxidases, and to N^1-acetylspermine and -acetylspermidine for flavin polyamine oxidases. All amine oxidases generate H_2O_2, sometimes superoxide anion as well,[83] and some form of an aminoaldehyde.[87] Both peroxide and aminoaldehydes are cytotoxic and mutagenic, the latter by decomposition into acrolein; the peroxide is more toxic than the aldehyde at 37°C, but the reverse is true at elevated temperatures.[88,91,92] The direct toxicity of the N-acetylated aminoaldehydes has not been examined.

There were two types of amine oxidases in the in vitro assay of the C44 fluid: one derived from the fetal bovine serum in the culture medium and a second flavin-dependent one derived from the C44 blastocele fluid, which also contained substrates for both of these enzymes.[51,54,86,89,95-98] Using specific enzyme inhibitors, the serum-derived amine oxidase was shown to be responsible for the selective cytotoxic activity of C44 blastocele fluid toward ICM-T cells, and no other apoptotic activity was detectable in the C44 fluid.[53,54] Furthermore, the apoptotic substance in the fluid partitioned into the low molecular weight fraction, and exogenously added spermine and H_2O_2 reproduced the selective toxicity for ICM-T cells, so we concluded that either H_2O_2 or acrolein triggers apoptosis in the blastocele.[53,54]

This conclusion raised two important questions. First, which amine oxidase generated the H_2O_2 in the blastocele fluid? C44 fluid did not contain diamine or serum amine oxidases (unpublished data), but it did contain a polyamine oxidase (PAO), similar to the flavin enzyme that oxidizes acetylated spermine and spermidine in rat liver,[89,96] is secreted by macrophages,[95] and is present in the developing limb at the time of interdigital apoptosis.[51] However, unequivocal proof of the extracellular enzyme that generates the H_2O_2 in the blastocele fluid is lacking,[14,15] and several other oxidase systems have not yet been assayed in the C44 fluid, in particular xanthine oxidase and its substrates, which gain access to extracellular fluids.[101,102] It should be noted that in vitro cultured tumor cells generate high levels of extracellular H_2O_2 even during treatment with combinations of inhibitors of xanthine oxidase, amine oxidases and cytochrome P-450.[103]

Second, was the cytotoxic species in the blastocele fluid acrolein or H_2O_2? It was exclusively H_2O_2, based on results showing that co-injection of catalase blocks completely the apoptosis of ICM-T cells micro-injected into the blastocyst[77] and that H_2O_2 added to culture media recapitulated the activity of the blastocele fluid for ICM-T but not ICM-E.[54] That extracellular H_2O_2 can be a physiological trigger of apoptosis is perhaps not surprising given the fact that physiological concentrations of peroxide are known to cause apoptosis in vitro[31,32,104,105] and that H_2O_2 causes sister chromatid exchange, the rate of which is higher during blastulation.[70,106]

Although functions for reaction products from polyamine metabolism have sporadically appeared in the literature, the results in the blastocyst model provide the first proof of a physiologic function for the H_2O_2 metabolite of polyamine catabolism. It is possible that this same mechanism triggers apoptosis and balances mitosis in renewing epithelial tissues like gut and skin in which committed progenitors are exposed to H_2O_2 from polyamine oxidation during differentiation and in which death of some but not all cells of a population might be equivalent biologically to inhibition of proliferation.[14,15,18,50] In the epidermis, apoptotic cells are evident not only in the corneum as a result of terminal differentiation but also in the cell layer immediately superficial to the basal cell layer. Polyamines, amine oxidases, free radical detoxification systems and glutathione peroxidases are present in the skin, and DFMO influences keratinocyte proliferation.[107-111] Furthermore, dendritic cells that influence suprabasal development were recently shown to produce H_2O_2.[112] The model of programmed cell death in the blastocyst[14,15] suggests that the H_2O_2 is generated in the dendritic cells by amine oxidases and that it is responsible for the apoptosis that occurs in some but not all of the suprabasal cells. Suprabasal cells that survive might be the basal cells which slowly down-regulate the high level of expression of superoxide dismutase in the basal layer,[113] or another antioxidant protective mechanism, as part of the differentiation program.[108,111] The apoptotic cells might repress superoxide dismutase (SOD) expression much faster. It is interesting that a relationship between SOD and keratinocyte proliferation has been proposed.[114]

How would polyamine oxidation regulate tissue mass in the renewing epidermis?[14,15] Terminally differentiating keratinocytes release polyamines, especially spermidine, into the extracellular space and increase the level of cell surface transglutaminase which conjugates polyamines to cell surface proteins (Sec. III.E).[115-117] However, some of these polyamines likely escape conjugation, or are released by proteolysis, and diffuse through the epidermal layers. Greater numbers of keratinizing cells would produce more polyamines for amine oxidase-dependent generation of H_2O_2 in the dendritic cells and increase the death rate of basal cell progeny in the suprabasal layer. Conversely, an insufficient mass of keratinizing cells would decrease the amount of H_2O_2 generated by dendritic cells in the suprabasal layer and permit a greater fraction of basal cell progeny to survive and differentiate, restoring epidermal mass. In this regard, it is intriguing that psoriatic lesions contained elevated levels of conjugated polyamines;[115-117] in the proposed model this would result in decreased levels of free polyamines in the dendritic layer, decreased H_2O_2 and increased and superfluous keratinocyte production. It is also intriguing that the spermidine content of keratinocytes dramatically falls during Ca^{2+}-induced differentiation, but putrescine content falls less dramatically, and spermine content does not fall at all,[115] indicating precise regulation of polyamine release and conjugation in the different layers of the epidermis.

This model proposes that the H_2O_2-polyamine system exhibits many of the characteristics of chalones in renewing tissues of the adult; it regulates tissue mass via a feedback mechanism between the differentiated and renewing compartments and balances cell loss via cell death with cell gain via proliferation.[14,15] However, there is a subtle point; neither the H_2O_2 nor the polyamines per se are the chalones, because polyamines are the diffusible substance but only the storehouse for the active principle, yet H_2O_2 is the chalone which is not diffusible (because of its reactivity) and which is generated in situ only at the site where tissue mass is regulated (progenitor level). If the epidermal chalone is H_2O_2 from polyamine oxidation, one can easily understand why it has been so difficult to purify; H_2O_2 is too reactive to purify and too nonspecific in assays, but polyamines are only the precursor for the chalone and are, therefore, inactive in vitro in chalone bioassays. The investigators of many years ago who implied that isolated chalones were "contaminated" by polyamines[118-120] might have been closer to the truth than any of their numerous critics realized.

Regardless of what the enzymatic source ultimately turns out to be, extracellular H_2O_2 triggers apoptosis in inner cell mass cells with trophectodermal potential during blastulation to prevent ectopic formation of trophectoderm within the embryonic germ layers. The data show that the specificity of apoptosis in the embryo is due to the biochemical status of the exposed cell rather than the nature of the signal, and that programmed cell death is murder rather than suicide. Target cell specificity results from developmental regulation of a glutathione-dependent protective mechanism. The life or death fate of an ICM cell depends not upon its exposure to the apoptotic trigger, as all ICM cells are presumably exposed in situ, but rather upon its ability to defend itself against free radical damage—a "survival of the fittest" mechanism to be sure. Although the presence of apoptotic cells in the midst of viable neighboring cells was accepted as evidence for cellular suicide or death from within, the results in the blastocyst indicate how incorrect intuition can be. This mechanism might pertain not only to a novel model of programmed cell death in the embryo but also to tissue renewal in the adult.[14,15]

Polyamines are ubiquitously involved in control of differentiation and proliferation in renewing tissues, including the embryo, but their exact mechanisms of action have been difficult to pinpoint.[121-123] The data from our studies suggest a novel function for polyamines: nontoxic storehouses of extracellular H_2O_2 equivalents. There have been hints from other laboratories that extracellular H_2O_2 from polyamine oxidation plays a physiologic role. For example, DFMO- and putrescine-induced alterations in clonal growth of tumor cells and hematopoietic cells requires extracellular amine oxidase activity.[104,124-126] In addition, inhaled spermidine is selectively toxic to Clara cells in the lung,[127] and it will be interesting to determine if these cells contain high levels or a specific type of amine oxidase. Although H_2O_2 is directly cytotoxic and murders cells developmentally programmed for apoptosis, the cell death could be triggered through signal transduction pathways.[101,128-139]

B. Apoptosis Induced by Intracellular H_2O_2 from Polyamine Oxidation

There are data indicating that intracellular H_2O_2 can also trigger apoptosis, including internucleosomal DNA degradation.[32,105,140] Although in many cases, xenobiotics are used to generate intracellular H_2O_2, these data implicate any intracellular enzyme system which generates H_2O_2 in a regulated fashion as an initiator of apoptosis. There is only limited evidence that intracellular oxidation of polyamines by amine oxidases can induce apoptosis. Micro-injection of diamine or serum amine oxidase into the cytoplasm of intact cells results in cell death.[141] Although they are not the only intracellular enzyme sources of H_2O_2, diamine oxidase and flavin PAOs are candidate triggers of apoptosis. In addition to amine oxidases, the amino acid oxidases, xanthine oxidase, arginine oxidase, lipoxygenases, plasma membrane oxidoreductases, flavin oxidases and unidentified systems are all candidate sources.[94,102,103,142-148]

Apoptosis could also be controlled via regulation of the levels of enzymes that detoxify intracellular oxyradicals. Intracellular oxidation of spermine is most cytotoxic when glutathione levels are depleted.[85] Although SOD also generates H_2O_2 during metabolism of O_2-,[138,149-151] in general it protects cells against oxyradical-dependent apoptosis.[152-156] Apoptosis could also be regulated by changes in availability of intracellular polyamines brought about by alterations in polyamine uptake.[157]

How might H_2O_2 trigger apoptosis? One target of intracellular H_2O_2 is a plasma membrane Ca^{2+}-ATPase that is responsible for pumping calcium out of the cell to maintain low cytoplasmic calcium levels, and the activity of this enzyme depends upon a thiol group from a cysteine that can be oxidized by peroxides.[158] A role for calcium in apoptosis has been deduced from the inhibition of cell death in some models by inhibiting Ca^{2+} influx or chelating cytoplasmic Ca^{2+} and the activation of the apoptosis program with calcium ionophores, implicating activation of protein kinase-C and a Ca^{2+}, Mg^{2+}-dependent endonuclease already present in the nucleus of some cells.[44,45,55,59,159-164] The potential inactivation of this Ca^{2+} pump via oxidation of the critical thiol is particularly interesting in light of the key role discovered for glutathione-dependent pathways during apoptosis in the blastocyst. Apoptosis induced by direct DNA damage seems unlikely given the low reactivity of H_2O_2 with DNA.

Tumor necrosis factor is a physiologic substance that induces apoptosis via production of oxyradicals, which is modulated by the intracellular activity of manganous SOD.[56,151-156,165,166] In addition, the level of endogenous Mn^{2+}-SOD is induced by tumor necrosis factor (TNF) exposure,[154] explaining why inhibitors of transcription and protein translation were required for the early bioassays of TNF activity. These data indicate that TNF-induced apoptosis is triggered directly by superoxide anion, or by the more toxic hydroxyl radical (OH) or H_2O_2 that can be generated nonenzymatically.[167-170] The intracellular source of these TNF-induced oxyradicals has not been identified, but PAOs are candidates; TNF exposure induces ODC and elevates polyamine levels, while DFMO pre-treatment renders cells insensitive to TNF-induced apoptosis.[166] In addition to TNF, interleukin-1 induces superoxide anion and/or H_2O_2 in various cell types, and also induces increased expression of MnSOD.[156,171-174] Since the generation of oxyradicals plays an important role in the pathogenesis of chronic inflammation, an examination of the role of amine oxidases in this process might provide clinical impact for polyamine regulation. An oxyradical mechanism based on polyamine oxidation might also be involved in tissue atrophy upon trophic factor withdrawal (see Section III.B).

Like TNF, glucocorticoids induce apoptosis in murine thymocytes,[36,59] and exogenously added spermine prevents DNA laddering and karyorrhexis.[175] Both ODC and N^1-acetyltransferase activity (but not N^8-acetyltransferase activity) are induced early in the process, but intracellular polyamine levels decrease after 2-4 hours and spermine pools are depleted by 12 hours. Increased polyamine synthetic enzymes accompanied by depletion of intracellular polyamine levels prior to internucleosomal cleavage of chromatin is consistent with an involvement of polyamine oxidase-derived H_2O_2 or other by-products during thymocyte apoptosis. Also like TNF, ODC is induced in thymocytes stimulated to proliferate by Con-A, but the induction is more sustained and intracellular polyamine levels are increased out to 12 hours.[175] Intracellular oxidation is a requirement for glucocorticoid-induced apoptosis in thymocytes, and increased antioxidant capacity within the thymocytes inhibits apoptosis.[176]

C. REGULATION OF APOPTOSIS BY INTRA- OR EXTRACELLULAR ACROLEIN AND OTHER BY-PRODUCTS OF POLYAMINE METABOLISM

Acrolein is a well-accepted and direct-acting trigger of apoptosis based on data from direct assays of extracellular acrolein as well as from the decomposition of activated cyclophosphamide.[87,91,177-182] Acrolein is a by-product of polyamine metabolism, resulting from the relatively slow decomposition of the aminopropyl aldehyde generated during the catabolism of spermine and spermidine by serum amine oxidases[97,91,92] and possibly from decomposition of the N-acetylpropyl aldehyde generated during catabolism of acety-lated spermine and spermidine by flavin PAO[89,95-97] after N-de-acetylation. Acrolein is detoxified in large part by aldehyde dehy-drogenase,[183,184] and this enzyme is required in combination with catalase to achieve complete protection of cells against amine oxi-dase-dependent spermine cytotoxicity.[91,92] One important aldehyde dehydrogenase (ALDH) might be ALDH class-3, because over-expression of this isozyme protects against cyclophosphamide cy-totoxicity and its inhibition potentiates drug toxicity, even though the enzyme does not oxidize the aldophosphamide intermedi-ate.[185-187] There are additional ALDHs that confer resistance.[188] Acrolein can also be detoxified in part by glutathione-dependent mechanisms,[189] although there are systems resistant to acrolein in spite of reduced glutathione-dependent detoxification.[183] The au-thor could not find any citations in Medline addressing the role of acrolein or ALDH in apoptosis under physiologic situations.

It is interesting that compounds which induce spermine/spermi-dine-N^1-acetyltransferase, the rate-limiting enzyme in production of the substrates of polyamine oxidase and, therefore, the genera-tion of intracellular H_2O_2, cause cytotoxicity,[190] but it is not known whether enzyme induction in the absence of its acetylated polyamine substrates would also be cytotoxic. This mechanism is yet one more theoretical pathway for regulating apoptosis: the in-duction of rate limiting enzymes that produce the substrates for H_2O_2 equivalents.

There are other intracellular biochemicals generated during polyamine synthesis and interconversion which conceivably could trigger apoptosis or influence the cell death program, including 5-methylthioadenosine and $^1\Delta$-pyrroline. Although some of these compounds have been studied,[191,192] it is too early to speculate on their role in controlling apoptosis.

III. DIRECT MECHANISMS FOR CONTROL OF APOPTOSIS BY POLYAMINES

This section considers substantiated and suspected mechanisms whereby the polyamines per se could trigger apoptosis or influence the process. Intracellular mechanisms are discussed first, because of the historical assumption that polyamines function primarily intracellularly. The mechanisms by which extracellular polyamines can directly influence apoptosis are covered toward the end of this section.

A. SPECIFIC CONTROL OF APOPTOSIS-INDUCING GENES BY INTRACELLULAR POLYAMINES

The first genes to be studied in detail that control the process of apoptosis were identified as programmed cell death genes during development of *C. elegans* and named *ced-3*, *ced-4* and *ced-9*.[9] The *ced-3* and *ced-4* genes are involved in the destruction of the cell and are required for apoptosis, while the *ced-9* gene protects against apoptosis and dysfunction of the gene resulting in apoptosis of cells that normally survive during development. In mammals, the *bcl-2* gene family seems to be a functional analog of *ced-9*.[193-197] The *bcl-2* gene product is a mitochondrial protein,[23] perhaps a G protein,[24,25] that decelerates the programmed cell death in hematopoietic cells following growth factor deprivation[23] and in lymphocytes,[71] keratinocytes[198] and in cells exposed to cyclophosphamide.[199] Ectopic expression of *bcl-2* in transgenic mice blocks apoptosis of developing lymphocytes in lymph nodes, resulting in follicular hyperplasia, especially in lymphoma-prone strains.[71,72] In humans, it is associated with follicular lymphoma.[194] Another mammalian gene known as interleukin-1beta converting enzyme ("ICE") and its genetic relatives are homologs of *ced-3* and are required for apoptosis in mice.[200-210] This gene encodes a cytoplasmic protease that probably degrades key intracellular proteins during apoptosis and is required for processing of interleukin-1beta from the precursor to secreted active species.[207,211-216]

Regulation of expression of endonuclease genes and the activity of the enzymes, in particular the Ca++, Mg++ endonuclease first implicated in apoptosis using the murine thymocyte model, should also be important in the control of apoptosis.[32,36,44,59,159-161] Polyamines modulate activity of enzymes involved in excision-repair of DNA[217] and affect the susceptibility of chromatin to nuclease digestion.[218] In fact, spermine, but not spermidine or putrescine, prevents glucocorticoid- and Ca^{2+} ionophore-induced DNA fragmentation and apoptosis in thymocytes, and blocks the activity of the Ca++, Mg++-dependent endonuclease in liver nuclei by modifying chromatin structure.[219]

The modulation of the expression of these apoptosis genes and the function of the proteins by polyamines needs investigation; because polyamines are implicated in apoptosis following trophic factor withdrawal (Section III.B), these apoptosis-control genes are functionally interconnected to oncogene expression that is regulated by polyamines, and polyamines are general regulators of gene expression.[220-231] The role of cytotoxic by-products from polyamine interconversion is also important to consider, because *bcl-2* activity decreases the cellular generation of oxyradicals and decreases toxicity,[232] and decreased levels of *bcl-2* accompany the apoptosis triggered by acrolein.[233] There are cDNA libraries from cells and tissues undergoing apoptosis[234-242] that are available for probing for these key enzymes of polyamine metabolism and response.

B. Intracellular Polyamine Regulation of Apoptosis upon Trophic Factor Withdrawal: The Mitosis-Apoptosis Decision

Many cell types are dependent upon the continued presence of trophic factors for survival, and withdrawal of these trophic factors triggers apoptosis.[26,40,243-247] The induction of ODC and other early response genes associated historically with proliferation accelerates apoptosis when it occurs in the absence of growth factor signal transduction, e.g., induction of ODC activity by c-*myc* after failure of the normal mechanism to down-regulate *c-myc* in response to trophic factor withdrawal, or direct overexpression of ODC to by-pass transcriptional regulation by *c-myc*.[227,248-254] These results are consistent with a proposal made several years ago that intracellular polyamine levels are tightly controlled in all organisms from prokaryotes to higher mammals to prevent cytotoxicity.[255] Although a mechanism was not proposed at the time, this idea seems to be closely related to the more recent discovery that there are mechanisms to synchronize the phases of the cell cycle, and if these are uncoupled or "dys-synchronized", apoptosis will result.[256-262] The accelerated apoptosis resulting from ODC induction in the absence of trophic factor stimulation might be due to this dys-synchronization mechanism.

Furthermore, ODC is one of several normally mitogenic signals required for TNF-induced apoptosis[166] and is also induced in thymocytes undergoing glucocorticoid-induced apoptosis.[175] In the thymocyte system, the drop in intracellular polyamine levels is a requirement for apoptosis, because exogenously added spermine prevents DNA laddering and karyorrhexis.[175,219,263] ODC induction also occurs in thymocytes stimulated to proliferate by Con-A; the decision to commit to mitosis rather than apoptosis is associated with a prolonged induction of ODC, and increased levels of intracellular polyamines out to 12 hours after the signal.[175] TNF and IL-1 usually induce ODC and there is often a cellular decision to commit to mitosis or apoptosis following exposure.[264-268] Transforming growth factor-β (TGF-β), in contrast, suppresses ODC levels when inducing apoptosis.[269,270]

The decision between proliferation and apoptosis might be influenced by polyamine metabolites rather than polyamines per se. In the blastocyst model of H_2O_2-induced apoptosis, lower oxidant levels at a different developmental time point stimulate differentiation and mitosis instead.[271] In other cellular models, low level exposure to H_2O_2 is accompanied by ODC induction and increased polyamine levels within three hours; higher level exposure that induces apoptosis was associated with a similarly rapid inhibition of ODC but depletion of the intracellular polyamine pool, and preventing these changes with phorbol esters blocked apoptosis.[105]

C. REGULATION OF APOPTOSIS VIA MODULATION OF CALCIUM CHANNEL ACTIVITY BY INTRACELLULAR POLYAMINES

Calcium triggers apoptosis in several cell types, as evidenced by the induction of apoptosis by calcium ionophores and other treatments that elevate cytoplasmic calcium for sustained time periods.[45,55,59,159-161,164] This calcium-induced apoptosis might also be viewed in the same way as ODC induction: either signal in the absence of a second confirmatory proliferative signal results in apoptosis, while the presence of this second confirmatory signal results in mitosis. Regulation of calcium channel activity can be related to apoptosis by increased calcium influx through a voltage-operated L-type Ca++ channel[272-274] and through R-type calcium channels.[275] Putrescine, but not spermine or spermidine, increases currents through L-type but not T-type calcium channels by increasing the frequency of prolonged channel openings.[274] The inhibition of L-type Ca++ channels by putrescine likely involves intracellular binding sites.[274] This effect of putrescine on calcium influx would be exacerbated by inactivation of the plasma membrane Ca-ATPase by H_2O_2 from polyamine oxidation (Section II.B). Although it is has been assumed that Ca++ directly triggers apoptosis by activating endonuclease activity,[45,59,161] some data suggest instead that intracellular levels of bound Zn++ suppress apoptosis and activate mitosis.[163,164,246] Ca++ influx induces apoptosis by displacing Zn++ from these apoptosis-inhibiting binding sites, including the Ca++, Mg++-dependent endonuclease.[276-278]

D. REGULATION OF APOPTOSIS BY MODULATION OF EXCITATORY NEUROTRANSMISSION BY INTRA- AND EXTRACELLULAR POLYAMINES

The NMDA receptor is a well-characterized system that can trigger excitatory ligand-dependent neuronal cell death. In some but not all areas of the brain, spermine and spermidine modulate ligand binding by this receptor, its associated ion channel, and the rate to equilibrium and affinity by binding at a stereoselective site, while putrescine antagonizes spermine even though it is nearly inactive itself.[279-290] Polyamine binding is ligand- and voltage-dependent.[291,292] Like Mg++, polyamines preferentially enhance the affinity of antagonists by binding to a site that is distinct from a second polyamine binding site identified by ligand competition experiments.[293,294] Mg++ and spermine modulation can be distinguished developmentally,[295] and putrescine and spermidine-modulated effects are not responsible for the developmental difference in NMDA receptor sensitivity to Mg++ antagonism.[296]

Polyamine modulation of ligand binding can range from enhancement to non-competitive antagonism, depending upon the concentration.[280,281,296-302] It is possible to develop spermine and spermidine analogs which are pure antagonists[301] or which don't exhibit the switch from agonist to antagonist as concentration increases,[298] consistent with the conclusion that the stimulatory and inhibitory polyamine binding sites are distinct.[299,300,302] A key question to be answered is whether the polyamine binding site(s) resides on the intracellular or extracellular domain of the receptor complex. Some data indicate an intracellular site,[281] while other data show modulation of NMDA-induced cell death by extracellular but not intracellular polyamine levels and the unimportance of NMDA induction of ODC levels, consistent with an extracellular modulatory site.[303] However, some studies have shown the pre-existent receptor state-dependency of spermine activity, implying very complex data analysis issues that depend on receptor status in the preparation used to assess binding.[304,305]

In vitro systems employing cultured neurons or cell lines that express the receptor have been used to model this neurotoxicity. Studies on intact cells have shown that exogenously added spermine and spermidine (but not putrescine) potentiate NMDA-induced cell death and that exogenous glutathione prevents receptor-mediated cytotoxicity[306] by circumventing the inhibition of cystine uptake and resulting increase in sensitivity to free radical damage.[307,308] NMDA stimulation induces ODC in neurons but not glia, but there is conflicting data on the impact of inhibiting ODC with DFMO upon neurotoxicity.[303,309] In addition, there might be an artifactual role played by the serum amine oxidase in the culture medium used for the ex vivo experiments; because serum is required for cytotoxicity even at high agonist concentrations,[310] glutamate or kainate induces in vitro neurotoxicity in cells lacking functional glutamate and kainate receptors,[311,312] and monoamine substrates of the serum amine oxidase might be released into the medium in response to ligand. When stimulated by agonists, neurons with NMDA receptors also produce nitric oxide radical, which diffuses to target cells and triggers apoptosis,[313] but inhibitors of nitric oxide synthetase do not completely protect cultured cells against the toxicity of kainate,[314] leaving open the possibility of a contribution by serum amine oxidase.

Other binding sites in brain for diamines and polyamines with K_D values in the physiologic range have been reported.[315] In vivo, systemic treatment with an agonist (kainate) of a related excitatory neuroreceptor class results in ODC fluctuations and increased activity of the N^1-acetyltransferase but increases in acetylspermine and acetylspermidine only if a selective inhibitor of polyamine oxidase is co-administered,[316-318] implying that there is a high level of H_2O_2 production by PAO in the normal absence of enzyme inhibitors.

E. REGULATION OF APOPTOSIS BY MODULATION OF TRANSGLUTAMINASE UTILIZATION OF EXTRACELLULAR POLYAMINES

Tissue transglutaminases covalently attach polyamines to γ-glutamine groups in proteins,[319-323] and transglutaminase activity parallels tissue polyamine content—especially putrescine—in skin, gut, liver and several malignancies[324-328] but not prostate,[329] or liver and kidney during pregnancy-induced fluctuations.[330] This enzyme is linked to apoptosis[38,115-117,331,332] and the inhibition of cell proliferation.[333] It is also intriguing that intracellular levels of putrescine and/or spermidine, but not spermine, regulate the level of transglutaminase activity.[334] Transglutaminase regulation during apoptosis and by polyamines might be important not only for the dying cell but also for controlling the amount of unconjugated polyamines that diffuse back to the suprabasal layer to trigger apoptosis (Section II.A). This idea superimposes a layer of regulation on the level of diffusible polyamines via the control of transglutaminase activity in the differentiated compartment.

IV. IN SITU LOCALIZATION STUDIES AND THE CONTROL OF APOPTOSIS BY POLYAMINES

Molecular and biochemical studies utilize tissue extracts from a mixture of different cell types and from various stages of differentiation for a particular cell type. These studies can easily correlate molecular and cellular changes, but they cannot prove that the biochemical changes occur in the responding cell. Dramatic changes in enzyme levels within a small but important subpopulation of cells can be completely missed using biochemical measurements on tissue extracts.[335]

At the current time, there are only a few probes available for histochemical localization of polyamines and the enzymes that control their levels. Antibodies against ODC[336-340] and the polyamines[341-344] have been reported, as have nucleic acid probes for in situ localization of ODC mRNA.[345,346] A cerium-based histochemical technique has been developed for in situ detection of H_2O_2 production,[347-354] which has been used to localize serum amine oxidase,[355] flavin-dependent PAO,[356,357] diamine oxidase[358,359] and monoamine oxidase[360-364] at the cellular and subcellular levels.

The following sections attempt to coalesce the data from localization studies within the epidermis and gastrointestinal mucosa with the mechanisms proposed in the preceding sections to control apoptosis in these two tissues. The gastrointestinal mucosa and the epidermis are emphasized exclusively, because differentiation and apoptosis are neatly compartmentalized into discrete anatomic locations within the tissue. A comprehensive picture in a single species is not possible at this time, and results from one species cannot be assumed to extrapolate to a second one.[363]

A. EPIDERMIS

In situ localization of ODC protein and mRNA in the murine epidermis under homeostatic conditions was unsuccessful,[337,345,346] and immunohistochemical staining for ODC protein was negative after a single treatment with TPA, which is known to induce enzyme activity by 200-fold.[337] In these studies, ODC became detectable in epidermal cells after pre-malignant changes had been induced by ultraviolet light or chronic TPA treatment. Although one study failed to detect ODC protein in normal human epidermis,[338] a second immunohistochemical study demonstrated constitutive levels of ODC protein in all cell layers of the epidermis, with the highest levels of expression in the basal layer and the corneal layer.[340] The cell layers with high ODC levels are also the layers found previously to contain high polyamine levels,[365] but immunolocalization data for polyamines in the epidermis are not available.[342] In vitro, the highest ODC protein levels are found in the smallest-sized keratinocytes which are thought to represent the proliferative compartment.[340] Of the amine oxidases, only monoamine oxidase has been studied with the cerium capture technique, and it could not be detected in any cell layer of the epidermis.[361] Although unrelated to polyamine metabolism, xanthine oxidase is demonstrable in the corneal and granular layers of the rat epidermis, with less intense staining in the spinal layer, while the basal and immediately suprabasal layers are negative.[361]

The localization studies to date support the previously proposed[14,15] mechanism of paracrine control of apoptosis in the epidermis (Section II.A). Both ODC and polyamines exist at high levels in the stratum corneum, a layer composed of apoptotic cells dying as part of the terminal differentiation program. Why would the dying cell re-express ODC which had been repressed since the basal cell stage? The model predicts that ODC is re-expressed to generate the polyamines that will diffuse back to the suprabasal layer and modulate the incidence of apoptosis among epidermal progenitors. When combined with the known restriction of SOD expression to the basal cell layer,[113] the data also suggest that maturing keratinocytes are exposed to an increasing gradient of free radicals as they mature, which might control apoptosis during terminal differentiation. However, the free radicals in this gradient would have to be present at a lower level than in the dendritic cells, or be an oxyradical other than H_2O_2 (superoxide?), since keratinocytes in all cellular layers were negative in the study that identified constitutive H_2O_2 production exclusively in dendritic cells of the suprabasal layer.[112] Is it conceivable that H_2O_2 controls apoptosis in the progenitor pool, while superoxide controls terminal differentiation (squamation) in the corneal layer? This notion is not that different from the H_2O_2-mediated apoptosis of ICM-T cells in the blastocyst, a tissue which nevertheless requires oxyradicals for proper maturation.[271] Since the histochemical localization studies did not detect monoamine and xanthine oxidases in dendritic cells, the enzymatic source of peroxide in this cell type remains an open question. The cellular localization of diamine and polyamine oxidase in the epidermis will be important in proving or disproving the apoptosis hypothesis (Section II.A).

B. GASTROINTESTINAL MUCOSA

The cellular distribution of polyamines and the enzymes of polyamine metabolism have been studied most thoroughly in the small bowel, and less extensively in the large bowel and stomach.[366] In the mucosa of the small bowel, in which DFMO treatment inhibits the activity of trophic factors, ODC is detectable in both enterocytes and crypt cells under normal conditions.[366,367] In the fasted state, however, ODC is only expressed in the crypt cells; the mature enterocytes no longer express ODC. Upon refeeding, ODC re-appears in the enterocytes and is maintained in the crypt cells. In fasted rats, the trophic factors epidermal growth factor (EGF) and gastrin increase the expression of ODC just in the crypt cells, while luminal glycine increases ODC just in the mature enterocytes. PAO localizes exclusively to the peroxisomes at the apical side of the enterocytes, but it is not detectable in the crypt cells, and there is considerable intervillous variability in the amount of PAO.[357] Enterocytes also contain diamine oxidase, which like PAO is not detectable in the crypt cell population.[359] In contrast to PAO, the subcellular location of diamine oxidase is the baso-lateral face. Monoamine oxidase activity has also been found within enterocytes but not in crypt cells.[361-363] It should be noted that xanthine oxidase, D-amino acid oxidase and NADH oxidoreductase are also detected in enterocytes,[361,362,368-370] so amine oxidases are not the only source of oxygen radicals and by-products of amine oxidation in the small bowel mucosa.

Similar findings were obtained during studies in the mucosa of the colon.[359,361,363,364,366,371] ODC is found in both enterocytes and crypt cells in animals fed ad libitum. Only the crypt cells are positive for ODC in fasted animals, but refeeding induces ODC in enterocytes without altering ODC in crypt cells. As in small bowel, EGF and gastrin increase ODC only in the crypt cells. PAO has not been localized to a particular cell type in colonic mucosa. Diamine and monoamine oxidases localize in the large bowel[359,363,364] exactly as they do in the small bowel mucosa with two exceptions: all colonic enterocytes in the rat are negative for monoamine oxidase,[363] and enterocytes on the tip of the villus are negative for diamine oxidase in most species,[359] leaving enterocytes on the sides of the villus as the only diamine oxidase positive cells in colonic mucosa. As in small bowel, amine oxidases are not the only source of oxyradicals in the colonic mucosa.[361]

Cytological studies in gastric mucosa have included the localization of the polyamines in addition to some of the enzymes. An anti-spermine antibody heavily stains the chief cells in the gastric glands, while surface mucous cells and cells in the isthmus of the glands stained less intensely.[342] Since mitotic activity in gastric glands has been localized primarily to the surface mucous cells in the foveolae and the neck mucous cells,[372] it can be concluded that spermine and mitotic figures do not co-localize. Unfortunately, putrescine has not been immunolocalized in this tissue. ODC is detectable in the cells at the base of the oxyntic gland in fasted animals, and the trophic factor gastrin increases ODC content in these cells.[335,366] Thus, constitutive ODC in the renewing cell populations of the small and large bowel and stomach mucosa behave in a similar fashion. However, the lower 20% of the antral mucosa is positive for ODC and fails to exhibit any change when exposed to gastrin.[335,366] Polyamine and diamine oxidases have not been localized in the stomach, but monoamine oxidase is present in the parietal cells (except in the rat), but not the chief cells, of the gastric glands.[363] In a striking similarity to the cornifying epidermis, the cornified layer of the forestomach contains xanthine oxidase,[361] again consistent with an involvement of oxyradicals in terminal squamous differentiation.

V. SUMMARY

There is considerable data to implicate polyamines, and the biochemicals generated enzymatically during their interconversion, in the regulation of apoptosis (Table 6.1). Discoveries in a variety of biological systems reveal several themes in polyamine regulation in addition to direct control: biologically active (extracellular) H_2O_2, glutathione and/or thiol regulation of cellular survival, and polyamines as storehouses for peroxide or other by-products of oxidation. There is substantial data proving that H_2O_2 is the trigger of apoptosis of a subpopulation of inner cell mass cells in the murine blastocyst and implicating extracellular acetylated polyamines as the nontoxic storehouse for this trigger. This extracellular location of the active polyamine species suggests that paracrine controls operate within the tissues: the cell that produces and secretes the polyamines and the cell that responds to them are different.

The idea that extracellular polyamines play important paracrine roles in tissue renewal already exists within a different context in the proposal of Johnson and colleagues that regulation of growth of gastrointestinal mucosa by trophic factors and dietary stimuli involves paracrine effects of enterocyte-derived polyamines upon crypt cell proliferation.[366] In this model, enterocytes synthesize and secrete polyamines that diffuse back to the crypts, where they

Table 6.1. Mechanisms of polyamine control over apoptosis

Trigger	Cell Specificity	Model System	Description	Evidence
Extracellular H_2O_2	GSH levels	Blastocyst (murine) Epidermis	Section II.A Section II.A	Substantiated Speculative
Intracellular H_2O_2	Antioxidant levels	Microinjected cells Cultured cells Thymocytes	Section II.B Section II.B Section II.B	Circumstantial Substantiated Speculative
Aminoaldehydes	GSH, ALDH levels	Cultured cells	Section II.C	Circumstantial
Inhibition of apoptosis-inducing enzymes	Levels of enzymes, polyamines, and cytokine signals	Thymocytes Hepatocytes	Section III.A Section III.A	Circumstantial Circumstantial
Trophic factor withdrawal	Cytokines and second messengers	Myeloid cells Thymocytes	Section III.B Section III.B	Substantiated Substantiated
Calcium influx class	Calcium channel	Thymocytes	Section III.C	Circumstantial
NMDA agonists	NMDA receptor GSH levels	Neurons	Section III.D	Substantiated
Oxygen radicals	Transglutaminase Amine oxidases Antioxidants	Epidermis GI mucosa	Section III.E Sections IV.A, IV.B	Speculative Speculative

Substantiated in this table means that there are experimental data which support the proposed mechanism that have been obtained during experiments designed to study the mechanism. In contrast, circumstantial means that there are data which support the proposed mechanism that have been obtained during experiments designed to study other topics. Note that the specificity of most of these mechanisms originates in an intracellular site of action such that surrounding cells are not exposed to the control mechanism. However, these examples illustrate how apoptosis does not necessarily result from cellular suicide but rather from murder: the sensitization of a few cells of a target population to an apoptosis trigger to which all cells of the tissue are exposed. Paracrine control via polyamines is also evident in this table. GSH, glutathione; ALDH, aldehyde dehydrogenase; NMDA, N-methyl-D-aspartate.

modulate proliferation. In fact, biochemical studies have suggested that PAO rather than ODC is the predominant source of putrescine in the small bowel under certain conditions.[373] The theory of apoptosis espoused in the present paper could be viewed as a second pathway of paracrine control over tissue renewal that is superimposed over, or complements and balances, this previously proposed mechanism of control of crypt cell proliferation. The high ODC expression in enterocytes and the corneum of the epidermis suggests that the production of polyamines by terminally differentiated cells is a recurring theme in renewing tissues. If so, current data point to a purpose for these polyamines: the paracrine control of tissue renewal. Amine oxidases in the gut mucosa (and other oxidases in gut mucosa and epidermis and their substrates) are positioned to receive the extracellular polyamines and generate H_2O_2 that controls how many progenitors die, or live to replace senescent cells.[14,15] Polyamines not used in this way diffuse into the stem cell compartment, where they stimulate proliferation.[366] Thus, proliferation, apoptosis and terminal differentiation are all balanced to maintain homeostasis in tissue mass. Paracrine effects of polyamines can stimulate tissue production in the stem cell compartment and balance this by stimulating apoptosis in the progenitor pool or increasing the rate of terminal differentiation. These processes are balanced because they are controlled by the same factors. Once completed, histological localization of all of the key enzymes will make possible some conclusions either in support of or against this paracrine model. Oxyradical mediators of tissue renewal also provide an explanation why homeostatic tissue factors have been so difficult to measure and purify ex vivo.

Of note is the consistent absence of oxyradical producing enzymes, including amine and xanthine oxidases, in the regions of tissues where mitotic figures are common and the levels of antioxidant enzymes are high. In renewing tissues, nature seems to have gone to great lengths to protect stem cells from oxyradical damage, while at the same time evolving a multiplicity of controllable enzymatic systems for the production of free radicals in the progenitor and differentiating compartments. The elucidation of these potential regulatory pathways is of considerable biomedical importance, especially in oncology, to understand how polyamine analogs both induce and protect against apoptosis,[374,375] and how best to take advantage of drugs that modulate polyamine levels, the activities of the enzymes of polyamine metabolism and the generation of the cytotoxic by-products. Other physiological radicals, such as nitric oxide, should not be forgotten, because polyamines exert influence over many of these as well.[376]

REFERENCES

1. von Szily A. Ueber die einleitenden Vorgange bei der ersten Enstehung der Nervenfasen im n. opticus. v Graefes Arch Ophthal 1912; 81:67.
2. Ucker DS. Death by suicide: one way to go in mammalian cellular development? New Biologist 1991; 3:103-9.
3. Bowen ID, Bowen SM. Programmed Cell Death in Tumors and Tissues. New York: Chapman and Hall, 1990.
4. Saunders Jr JW. Death in embryonic systems. Science 1966; 154:604-12.
5. Glucksmann A. Cell deaths in normal vertebrate ontogeny. Biol Rev Cambridge Philos Soc 1951; 26:59-86.
6. Lockshin RA. Programmed cell death: Activation of lysis by a mechanism involving the synthesis of protein. J Insect Physiol 1969; 15:1505-16.
7. Lockshin RA. Programmed cell death: Nature of the nervous signal controlling breakdown of intersegmental muscles. J Insect Physiol 1971; 17:149-58.
8. Lockshin RA, Beaulaton J. Programmed cell death. Life Sci 1974; 15:1549-65.
9. Hengartner MO, Horvitz HR. Programmed cell death in Caenorhabditis elegans. Curr Opin Genet Dev 1994; 4:581-86.
10. Wyllie AH, Kerr JF, Currie AR. Cell death: The significance of apoptosis. Int Rev Cytol 1980; 68:251-306.
11. Searle J, Kerr JF, Bishop CJ. Necrosis and apoptosis: Distinct modes of cell death with fundamentally different significance. Pathol Annu 1982; 17 Pt 2:229-59.
12. Kerr JFR, Wyllie AH, Currie AR. Apoptosis: A basic biological phenomenon with wide-ranging implications in tissue kinetics. Br J Cancer 1972; 26:239-57.
13. Wyllie AH. Cell death: A new classification separating apoptosis from necrosis. In: Bowen, Lockshin RA eds. Cell Death in Biology and Pathology. 1981:9-34.
14. Parchment RE. Programmed cell death (apoptosis) in murine blastocysts: Extracellular free-radicals, polyamines, and other cytotoxic agents. In Vivo 1991; 5:493-500.

15. Parchment RE. The implications of a unified theory of programmed cell death, polyamines, oxyradicals and histogeneis in the embryo. Int J Dev Biol 1993; 37:75-83.

16. Pierce GB, Lewellyn AL, Parchment RE. Mechanism of programmed cell death in the blastocyst. Proc Natl Acad Sci USA 1989; 86:3654-58.

17. El-Shershaby AM, Hinchliffe JR. Cell redundancy in the zona-intact preimplantation mouse blastocyst. J Embryology Exp Morph 1974; 31:643-54.

18. Pierce GB, Gramzinski RA, Parchment RE. Amine oxidases, programmed cell death, and tissue renewal. Philos Trans Roy Soc Lond B 1990; 327:67-74.

19. Parchment RE, Pierce GB. Polyamine oxidation, programmed cell death, and regulation of melanoma in the murine embryonic limb. Can Res 1989; 49:6680-86.

20. Goel SC. Role of cell death in the morphogenesis of the amniote limbs. In: Fallon JF, Caplan AL eds. Limb Development and Regeneration, Part A. New York: Alan R. Liss, 1983:175-82.

21. Sen S. Programmed cell death: Concept, mechanism and control. Biol Rev Camb Philos Soc 1992; 67:287-319.

22. Kerr JFR, Searle J, Harmon BV et al. Apoptosis. In Potten CS ed. Perspectives on Mammalian Cell Death. New York: Oxford, 1987: 93-128.

23. Hockenbery D, Nunez G, Milliman C et al. Bcl-2 is an inner mitochondrial membrane protein that blocks programmed cell death. Nature 1990; 348:334-36.

24. Haldar S, Beatty C, Croce CM. BCL-2 alpha encodes a novel small molecular weigh GTP binding protein. Adv Enzyme Regul 1990; 3:145-53.

25. Monica K, Chen-Levy Z, Cleary ML. Small G proteins are expressed ubiquitously in lymphoid cells and do not correspond to Bcl-2. Nature 1990; 346:189-91.

26. Sandford NL, Searle JW, Kerr JF. Successive waves of apoptosis in the rat prostate after repeated withdrawal of testosterone stimulation. Pathol 1984; 16:406-10.

27. Bennett RE, Harrison MW, Bishop CJ et al. The role of apoptosis in atrophy of the small gut mucosa produced by repeated administration of cytosine arabinoside. J Pathol 1984; 142:259-63.

28. McCarthy NJ, Smith CA, Williams GT. Apoptosis in the development of the immune system: Growth factors, clonal selection and bcl-2. Cancer Metastasis Rev 1992; 11:157-78.

29. Howie SE, Harrison DJ, Wyllie AH. Lymphocyte apoptosis—mechanisms and implications in disease. Immunol Rev 1994; 142:141-56.

30. Barry MA, Behnke CA, Eastman A. Activation of programmed cell death (apoptosis) by cisplatin other anticancer drugs, toxins and hyperthermia. Biochem Pharm 1990; 40:2353-62.

31. Sellins KS, Cohen JJ. Gene induction by irradiation leads to DNA fragmentation in lymphocytes. J Immunol 1987; 139:3199-206.

32. McConkey DJ, Hartzell P, Nicotera P et al. Stimulation of endogenous endonuclease activity in hepatocytes exposed to oxidative stress. Toxicol Lett 1988; 42:123-130.

33. McConkey DJ, Jondal M, Orrenius S. Cellular signaling in thymocyte apoptosis. Seminar Immunol 1992; 4:371-77.

34. Lennon SV, Martin SJ, Cotter TG. Dose-dependent induction of apoptosis in human tumour cell lines by widely diverging stimuli. Cell Prolif 1991; 24:203-14.

35. Allen TD. Ultrastructural aspects of cell death. In: Potten CS, ed. Perspectives on Mammalian Cell Death. New York: Oxford, 1987:39-65.

36. Wylie AH. Glucocorticoid-induced thymocyte aopotosis is associated with endogenous endonuclease activation. Nature 1980; 284:555-56.

37. Fadok V. Signals on the apoptoic lymphocyte cell surface triggering recognition and removal by macrophages. Boulder: University of Colorado, 1991 (thesis).

38. Fesus L, Thomazy V, Falus A. Induction and activation of tissue transglutaminase during programmed cell death. FEBS Lett 1987; 224:104-8.

39. Savill J, Dransfield I, Hogg N et al. Vitronectin receptor-mediated phagocytosis of cells undergoing apoptosis. Nature 1990; 343: 170-73.

40. Kyprianou N, English HF, Davidson NE et al. Programmed cell death during regression of the MCF-7 human breast cancer following estrogen ablation. Can Res 1991; 51:162-66.

41. Devlin TM. Biological membranes: structure and membrane transport. In: Devlin TM ed. Textbook of Biochemistry with Clinical Corrrelations. 1986:177-209.

42. Fadok VA, Voelker DR, Campbell PA et al. Exposure of phosphatidylserine on the surface of apoptotic lymphocytes triggers specific recognition and removal by macrophages. J Immunol 1992; 148:2207-16.

43. Fadok VA, Savill JS, Haslett C et al. Different populations of macrophages use either the vitronectin receptor or the phosphatidylserine receptor to recognize and remove apoptotic cells. J Immunol 1992; 149:4029-35.

44. Bicknell GR, Cohen GM. Cleavage of DNA to large kilobase pair fragments occurs in some forms of necrosis as well as apoptosis. Biochem Biophys Res Commun 1995; 207:40-7.

45. McConkey DJ, Hartzell P, Nicotera P. Calcium-activated DNA fragmentation kills immature thymocytes. FASEB J 1989; 3: 1843-49.

46. Fawthrop DJ, Boobis AR, Davies DS. Mechanisms of cell death. Arch Toxicol 1991; 65:437-44.

47. Rao MS, Yeldandi AV, Subbarao V et al. Role of apoptosis in copper deficiency-induced pancreatic involution in the rat. Am J Pathol 1993; 142:1952-57.

48. Benedetti A, Mancini R, Marucci R et al. Alimentary tract and pancreas: Quantitative study of apoptosis in normal rat gastroduodenal mucosa. J Gastroenterol Hepato 1990; 5:369-74.

49. Ijiri K, Potten CS. Cell death in cell hierarchies in adult mammalian tissues. In: Potten CS ed. Perspectives on Mammalian Cell Death. New York: Oxford, 1987: 326-56.

50. Pierce GB, Lewellyn AL, Parchment RE. Mechanism of programmed cell death in the blastocyst. Proc Natl Acad Sci USA 1989; 86:3654-58.

51. Parchment RE, Pierce GB. Polyamine oxidation, programmed cell death, and regulation of melanoma in the embryonic limb. Can Res 1989; 49:6680-86.

52. Pierce GB, Gramzinski RA, Parchment RE. Programmed cell death in the blastocyst. Ann NY Acad Sci 1989; 567:182-86.

53. Parchment RE, Gramzinski RA, Pierce GB. Neoplastic embryoid bodies of embryonal carcinoma C44 as a source of blastocele-like fluid. Differentiation 1990; 43:51-58.

54. Gramzinski RA, Parchment RE, Pierce GB. Evidence linking programmed cell death in the blastocyst to polyamine oxidation. Differentiation 1990; 43:59-65.

55. McConkey DJ, Hartzell P, Duddy SK et al. 2,3,7,8-Tetrachlorodibenzo-p-dioxin kills immature thymocytes by Ca^{2+} mediated endonuclease activation. Science 1988; 242:256-59.

56. Laster SM, Wood JG, Gooding LR. Tumor necrosis factor can induce both apoptic and necrotic forms of cell lysis. J Immunol 1988; 141:2629-34.

57. Mercep M, Weissman AM, Frank SJ et al. Activation-driven programmed cell death and T-cell receptor zeta eta expression. Science 1989; 246:1162-65.

58. Kohler HR, Dhein J, Alberti G et al. Ultrastructural analysis of apoptosis induced by the monoclonal antibody anti-APO-1 on a lymphoblastoid B cell line. Ultra Pathol 1990; 14:513-18.

59. Cohen JJ, Dale RC. Glucocorticoid activation of a calcium-dependent endonuclease in thymocyte nuclei leads to cell death. J Immunol 1984; 132:38-42.

60. Slack JMW. From Egg to Embryo. 1983; 138:139-47.

61. Pratt HPM. Isolation, culture and manipulation of pre-implantation mouse embryos. In: Mammalian Development, A Practical Approach 1987:13-42.

62. Beddington R. Isolation, culture and manipulation of post-implantation mouse embryos. In: Mammalian Development, A Practical Approach 1987:43-69.

63. Damjanov I et al. Production to teratocarcinomas from embryos transplanted to extra-uterine sites. In: Teratocarcinomas and Embryonic Stem Cells, A Practical Approach 1987:1-18.

64. Hogan B, Tilly R. Cell interactions and endoderm differentiation in cultured mouse embryos. J Embryol Exp Morph 1981; 62:379-94.

65. Handyside AH. Time of commitment of inside cells isolated from preimplantation mouse embryos. J Embryol Exp Morph 1978; 45:37-53.

66. Hogan B, Tilly R. In vitro development of inner cell masses, isolated immunosurgically from mouse blastocysts. J Embryol Exp Morph 1978; 45:93-105.

67. Pierce GB, Arechaga J, Muro C et al. Differentiation of ICM cells into trophectoderm. Am J Pathol 1988; 132:356-64.

68. El-Shershaby AM, Hincliffe JR. Epithelial autolysis during implantation of the mouse blastocyst: An ultrastructural study. J Embryol Exp Morph 1975; 33:1067-80.

69. Handyside AH, Hunter S. Cell division and death in the mouse blastocyst before implantation. Roux's Arch Dev Biol 1986; 195:519-26.

70. El-Hage S, Singh SM. A 5-fold reduction in sister-chromatid exchange following implantation of mouse embryos is not directly related to the expression of embryonic genes responsible for oxygen radical metabolism. Mutat Res 1990; 232:217-26.

71. Secord EA, Edington JM, Thorbecke GJ. The Emu-bcl-2 transgene enhances antigen-induced germinal center formation in both BALB/c and SJL mice but causes age-dependent germinal center hyperplasia only in the lymphoma-prone SJL strain. Am J Pathol 1995; 147:422-33.

72. Linette GP, Hess JL, Sentman CL et al. Peripheral T-cell lymphoma in lckpr-bcl-2 transgenic mice. Blood 1995; 86:1255-60.

73. Pierce GB, Speers WC. Tumors as caricatures of the process of tissue renewal: prospects for therapy by directing differentiation. Can Res 1988; 48:1996-2004.

74. Lehman JM, Speers WC, Swartzendruber DE et al. Neoplastic differentiation: Characteristics of cell lines derived from a murine teratocarcinoma. J Cell Physiol 1974; 84:13-28.

75. Pierce GB, Arechaga J, Jones A et al. The fate of embryonal carci-

noma cells in mouse blastocysts. Differentiation 1987; 33:247-53.

76. Pierce GB, Lewis SH, Miller GJ et al. Tumorigenicity of embryonal carcinoma as an assay to study control of malignancy by the murine blastocysts. Proc Natl Acad Sci USA 1979; 76:6649-51.

77. Pierce GB, Parchment RE, Lewellyn AL. Hydrogen peroxide as a mediator of programmed cell death in the blastocyst. Differentiation 1991; 46:181-86.

78. McBurney MW, Rogers BJ. Isolation of male embryonal carcinoma cells and their chromosome replication patterns. Devel Biol 1982; 89:503-08.

79. Mintz B, Illmensee K. Normal genetically mosaic mice produced from malignant teratocarcinoma cells. Proc Natl Acad Sci USA 1975; 72:3585-89.

80. Pierce GB. The cancer cell and its control by the embryo. Amer Assoc Pathol 1983; 113:117-24.

81. Monzo M, Andres X, Ruano-Gilet D. Etude morphologique d' une population homogene de cellules de terato-carcinome. Bulletin L'Association Des Anatomists 1983; 67:315-22.

82. Tabor CW et al. The aldehyde products of the oxidation of spermine and spermidine by purified plasma amine oxidase. J Biol Chem 1964; 239:2194-203.

83. Gaugas JM, Dewey DL. Oxygen-dependent free radicals in spermine oxidation cytostasis and chemiluminescene and the role of superoxide dismutase. Br J Cancer 1980; 41:946-54.

84. Blaschko H, Friedman PJ, Hawes R et al. The amine oxidases of mammalian plasma. J Physiol 1959; 145:384-404.

85. Brunton VG, Grant MH, Wallace HM. Spermine toxicity and glutathione depletion in BHK-21/C13 cells. Biochem Pharmacol 1990; 40:1893-1900.

86. Gahl WA, Pitot HC. Polyamine degradation in foetal and adult bovine serum. Biochemical J 1982; 202:603-11.

87. Gaugas JM, Dewey DL. Evidence for serum binding of oxidized spermine and its potent G_1-phase inhibition of cell proliferation. Br J Cancer 1979; 39:548-57.

88. Henle KJ, Moss AJ, Nagle WA. Mechanism of spermidine cytotoxicity at 37°C and 43°C in Chinese hamster ovary cells. Can Res 1986; 46:175-82.

89. Holtta E. Polyamine oxidase (rat liver). Methods Enzymol 1983; 94:306-11.

90. Yasunobu KT, Ishizaki H, Minamiura N. The molecular, mechanistic and immunological properties of amine oxidases. Molec Cellul Biochem 1976; 13:3-29.

91. Averill-Bates DA, Agostinelli E, Przybytkowski E et al. Aldehyde dehydrogenase and cytotoxicity of purified bovine serum amine

oxidase and spermine in Chinese hamster ovary cells. Biochem Cell Biol 1994; 72:36-42.

92. Agostinelli E, Przybytkowski E, Mondovi B et al. Heat enhancement of cytotoxicity induced by oxidation products of spermine in Chinese hamster ovary cells. Biochem Pharmacol 1994;48:1181-86.

93. Buffoni F, Blaschko H. Benzylamine oxidase and histaminase: Purification and crystallization of an enzyme from pig plasma. Proc Royal Soc London Series B 1964; 161:153-67.

94. Hampton Jr JK, Rider LJ, Goka TJ et al. The histaminase activity of ceruloplasmin. Proc Soc Exptl Biol Med 1972; 141:974-77.

95. Morgan DML, Ferulga J, Allison AC. Polyamine oxidase and macrophage function. In: Gaugas JM ed. Polyamines in Biomedical Research. New York: John Wiley & Sons, 1980:303-8.

96. Morgan DML. Polyamine oxidases. In: Gaugas JM ed. Polyamines in Biomedical Research. New York: John Wiley & Sons, 1980: 285-302.

97. Gahl WA, Vale AM, Pitot HC. Separation of putrescine oxidase and spermidine oxidase in foetal bovine serum with the aid of a specific radioactive assay of spermidine oxidase. Biochem J 1980; 187:197-204.

98. Gahl WA, Pitot HC. Putrescine-oxidase activity in adult bovine serum and fetal bovine serum. In Vitro 1979; 15:252-57.

99. Pettersson G. Plasma amine oxidase. In: Bruno Mondovi ed. Structure and Functions of Amine Oxidases. Boca Raton: CRC Press, 1985:105-210.

100. Agostinelli E, Riccio P, Mucigrosso J et al. Amine oxidases as biological regulators. In: Perin A, Scalabrino G, Sessa A, Ferioli ME eds. Perspectives in Polyamine Research. Italy: Wichtig Editore, 1988:11-15.

101. Stirpe F, Higgins T, Tazzari PL et al. Stimulation by xanthine oxidase of 3T3 swiss fibroblasts and human lymphocytes. Exp Cell Res 1991; 192:635-38.

102. Ellis LC. Free radicals in tissue culture. In: Art to Science. Logan, UT: Hyclone, 1990; 9(3):1-6, 9(4):1-7, 10(1):1-5.

103. Szatrowski TP, Nathan CF. Production of large amounts of hydrogen peroxide by human tumor cells. Can Res 1991; 51:794-98.

104. Ali-Osman F, Mauer HR. Stimulation of clonal tumor cell growth in vitro by inhibiting the serum polyamine oxidase activity. J Can Res Clin Oncol 1983; 106:17-20.

105. Dypbukt JM, Ankarcrona M, Burkitt M et al. Different prooxidant levels stimulate growth, trigger apoptosis, or produce necrosis of insulin-secreting RINm5F cells. The role of intracellular polyamines. J Biol Chem 1994; 269:30553-60.

106. Tachon P. Intracellular iron mediated the enhancing effects of his-

tidine on the cellular killing and clastogenicity induced by H_2O_2. Mutat Res 1990; 228:221-28.

107. Koza RA, Megosh LC, Palmieri M et al. Constitutively elevated levels of ornithine and polyamines in mouse epidermal papillomas. Carcinogenesis 1991; 12:1619-25.

108. Reiners Jr JJ, Thai G, Pavone A et al. Modulation of catalase activities in murine epidermal cells as a function of differentiation and exposure to 12-O-tetradecanoylphorbol-13-acetate. Carcinogenesis 1990; 11:957-63.

109. Carraro C, Pathak MA. Characterization of superoxide dismutase from mammalian skin epidermis. J Invest Dermatol 1988; 90:31-6.

110. Perchellet EM, Maatta EA, Abney NL et al. Effects of diverse intracellular thiol delivery agents on glutathione peroxidase activity, the ratio of reduced/oxidized glutathione, and ornithine decarboxylase induction in isolated mouse epidermal cells treated with 12-O-tetradecanoylphorbol-13-acetate. J Cellul Physiol 1987; 131:64-73.

111. Perchellet JP, Perchellet EM, Orten DK et al. Decreased ratio of reduced/oxidized glutathione in mouse epidermal cells treated with tumor promoters. Carcinogenesis 1986; 7:503-6.

112. Ledger PW, Klarich BL, Cormier M. Oxidative activity associated with a network of dendritic cells in the human epidermis. Arch Dermatol Res 1991; 283:474-5.

113. Kobayashi T, Matsumoto M, Iizuka H et al. Superoxide dismutase in psoriasis, squamous cell carcinoma and basal cell epithelioma: an immunohistochemical study. Brit J Dermatol 1991; 124:555-9.

114. Ohkuma N, Kajita S, Iizuka H. Superoxide dismutase in epidermis: its relation to keratinocyte proliferation. J Dermatol 1987; 14:562-8.

115. Piacentini M, Farrace MG, Imparato M et al. Polyamine-dependent post-translational modification of proteins in differentiating mouse epidermal cells. J Invest Dermatol 1990; 94:694-9.

116. Martinet N, Beninati S, Nigra TP et al. N^1N^8-Bis(γ-glutamyl) spermidine cross-linking in epidermal-cell envelopes. Biochem J 1990; 271:305-8.

117. Piacentini M, Martinet N, Beninati S et al. Free and protein-conjugated polyamines in mouse epidermal cells. J Biol Chem 1988; 263:3790-4.

118. Patt LM, Barrantes DM, Houck JC. Inhibition of lymphocyte DNA-synthetic responses by spermine-derived polycations. Biochem Pharmacol 1982; 31:2353-60.

119. Rijke EO, Ballieux RE. Is thymus-derived lymphocyte inhibitor a polyamine? Nature 1978; 274:804-5.

120. Dewey DL. Melanocytes, chalones, and polyamines. In: Gaugas JM, ed. Polyamines in Biomedical Research. New York: Wiley-Interscience, 1980: 309-20.

121. Pegg AE, McCann PP. Polyamine metabolism and function in mammalian cells and protozoans. ISI Atlas of Science: Biochemistry 1988; 11-8.

122. Heby O. Role of polyamines in the control of cell proliferation and differentiation. Differentiation 1981; 19:1-20.

123. Boynton AL, Whitfield JF, Walker PR. The possible roles of polyamines in prereplicative development and DNA synthesis: A critical assessment of the evidence. In: Gaugas JM, ed. Polyamines in Biomedical Research. New York: Wiley-Interscience, 1980: 63-79.

124. Heston WDW, Lazan DW, Fair WR. Aminoguanidine reversal of the inhibitory effects of ornithine analogs on the in vitro clonogenic survival of the R3327AT prostate-derived tumor. Cancer Lett 1981; 11:323-30.

125. Niskanen E, Kallio A, McCann PP et al. The role of polyamine biosynthesis in hematopoietic precursor cell proliferation in mice. Blood 1983; 61:740-5.

126. Niskanen E, Wharton III WW. Diamine oxidase is important in assessment of polyamine effects on hemopoietic cell proliferation in vitro. In Vitro Cell Devel Biol 1987; 23:257-60.

127. Foster JR, Smith LL, Hext PM et al. Target cell toxicity of inhaled spermidine in rat lungs. Int J Exp Pathol 1990; 71:617-30.

128. Birnboim HC, Kanabus-Kaminska M. The production of DNA strand breaks in human leukocytes by superoxide anion may involve a metabolic process. Proc Natl Acad Sci USA 1985; 82:6820-4.

129. Cerutti P, Krupitza G, Larsson R et al. Physiological and pathologic effects of oxidants in mouse epidermal cells. Ann NY Acad Sci 1988; 551:75-82.

130. Borek C. Oncogenes, hormones, and free-radical processes in malignant transformation *in vitro*. Ann NY Acad Sci 1988; 551:95-101.

131. Birnboim HC. Superoxide anion may trigger DNA strand breaks in human granulocytes by acting at a membrane target. Ann NY Acad Sci 1988; 551:83-94.

132. Heffetz D, Bushkin I, Dror R et al. The insulinomimetic agents H_2O_2 and vanadate stimulate protein tyrosine phosphorylation in intact cells. J Biol Chem 1990; 265:2896-902.

133. Link EM. Enzymic pathways involved in cell response to H_2O_2. Free Rad Res Comms 1990; 11:89-97.

134. Nose K, Shibanuma M, Kikuchi K et al. Transcriptional activation of early-response genes by hydrogen peroxide in a mouse osteoblastic cell line. Eur J Biochem 1991; 201:99-106.

135. Alcaín FJ, Burón MI, Rodríguez-Aguilera JC et al. Ascorbate free radical stimulates the growth of a human promyelocytic leukemia cell line. Can Res 1990; 50:5887-91.

136. Wenner CE, Cutry AF. The stimulation of cell growth by extracellular oxidants. In: Crane FL, Morré DJ, Löw HE, eds. Oxidoreduction at the Plasma Membrane: Relation to Growth and Transport. Boca Raton: CRC Press, 1990:131-9.

137. Gozález-Quevedo M, Alcaín FJ, González-Reyes JA et al. Growth patterns of the HL-60 human promyelocytic cell line stimulated by ascorbate free radical. Can J 1991; 4:262-6.

138. Amstad P, Peskin A, Shah G et al. The balance between Cu,Zn-superoxide dismutase and catalase affects the sensitivity of mouse epidermal cells to oxidative stress. Biochem 1991; 30:9305-13.

139. Schreck R, Rieber P, Baeuerle PA. Reactive oxygen intermediates as apparently widely used messengers in the activation of the NF-kappa B transcription factor and HIV-1. EMBO J 1991; 10: 2247-58.

140. Baier-Bitterlich G, Fuchs D, Murr C et al. Effect of neopterin and 7,8-dihydroneopterin on tumor necrosis factor-alpha induced programmed cell death. FEBS Lett 1995; 364:234-8.

141. Bachrach U, Ash I, Abu-Elheiga L et al. Fusion-mediated microinjection of active amine and diamine oxidases into cultured cells: Effect on protein and DNA synthesis in chick embryo fibroblasts and in glioma cells. J Cell Physiol 1987; 131:92-8.

142. White RE, Coon MJ. Oxygen activation by cytochrome P-450. Ann Rev Biochem 1980; 49:315-56.

143. Meagher RC, Salvado AJ, Wright DG. An analysis of the multilineage production of human hematopoietic progenitors in long-term bone marrow culture: Evidence that reactive oxygen intermediates derived from mature phagocytic cells have a role in limiting progenitor cell self-renewal. Blood 1988; 72:273-81.

144. McCall TB, Boughton-Smith NK, Palmer RMJ et al. Synthesis of nitric oxide from L-arginine by neutrophils. Biochem J 1989; 261:293-6.

145. Tada M, Fukui K, Momoi K et al. Cloning and expression of a cDNA encoding mouse kidney D-amino acid oxidase. Gene 1990; 90:293-7.

146. Löw H, Crane FL, Morré DJ et al. Oxidoreductase enzymes in the plasma membrane. In: Crane FL, Morré DJ, Löw HE, eds. Oxidoreduction at the Plasma Membrane: Relation to Growth and Transport. Boca Raton: CRC Press, 1990: 29-65.

147. Ziegler DM. Unique properties of the enzymes of detoxication. Drug Metab Dispos 1991; 19:847-52.

148. Chiricolo M, Tazzari PL, Abbondanza A et al. Cytotoxicity of, and DNA damage by, active oxygen species produced by xanthine oxidase. Fed Eur Biochem Soc 1991; 291:173-6.

149. Pluthero FG, Shreeve M, Eskinazi D et al. Purification of an inhibitor of erythroid progenitor cell cycling and antagonist to interleukin 3 from mouse marrow cell supernatants and its identi-

fication as cytosolic superoxide dismutase. J Cell Biol 1990; 111:1217-23.

150. Pluthero FG, Axelrad AA. Superoxide dismutase as an inhibitor of erythroid progenitor cell cycling. Ann NY Acad Sci 1991; 628:222-32.

151. Melendez JA, Baglioni C. Reduced expression of manganese superoxide dismutase in cells resistant to cytolysis by tumor necrosis factor. Free Radic Biol Med 1992; 12:151-9.

152. Klefstrom J, Vastrik I, Saksela E et al. c-Myc induces cellular susceptibility to the cytotoxic action of TNF-alpha. EMBO J 1994; 13:5442-50.

153. Fernandez A, Marin MC, McDonnell T et al. Differential sensitivity of normal and Ha-ras-transformed C3H mouse embryo fibroblasts to tumor necrosis factor: Induction of bcl-2, c-myc, and manganese superoxide dismutase in resistant cells. Oncogene 1994; 9:2009-17.

154. Lin PS, Ho KC, Sung SJ et al. Cytotoxicity and manganese superoxide dismutase induction by tumor necrosis factor-alpha and ionizing radiation in MCF-7 human breast carcinoma cells. Lymphokine Cytokine Res 1993; 12:303-8.

155. Skaper SD, Facci L, Leon A. Inflammatory mediator stimulation of astrocytes and meningeal fibroblasts induces neuronal degeneration via the nitridergic pathway. J Neurochem 1995; 64:266-76.

156. Mattey DL, Nixon N, Alldersea JE et al. Alpha, mu and pi class glutathione S- transferases in human synovium and cultured synovial fibroblasts: Effects of interleukin-1 alpha, hydrogen peroxide and inhibition of eicosanoid synthesis. Free Radic Res Commun 1993; 19:159-71.

157. Khan NA, Quemener V, Moulinoux JP. Role of protein kinase C activators and inhibitors, calmodulin antagonists and membrane sialic acids in polyamine transport in murine leukemia cells. Cell Mol Biol 1989; 35:215-24.

158. Cerutti P, Krupitza G, Larsson R et al. Physiological and pathologic effects of oxidants in mouse epidermal cells. Ann NY Acad Sci 1988; 551:75-81.

159. Stewart BW. Mechanisms of apoptosis: Integration of genetic, biochemical, and cellular indicators. J Natl Cancer Inst 1994; 86:1286-96.

160. Orrenius S, McCabe Jr MJ, Nicotera P. Ca(2+)-dependent mechanisms of cytotoxicity and programmed cell death. Toxicol Lett 1992; 64-65 Spec No:357-64.

161. Ribeiro JM, Carson DA. Ca^{2+}/Mg(2+)-dependent endonuclease from human spleen: purification, properties, and role in apoptosis. Biochem 1993; 32:9129-36.

162. Ojeda F, Guarda MI, Maldonado C et al. Protein Kinase-C-involvement in thymocyte apoptosis induced by hydrocortisone. Cellular Immunol 1990; 125:535-9.

163. McCabe Jr MJ, Jiang SA, Orrenius S. Chelation of intracellular zinc triggers apoptosis in mature thymocytes. Lab Invest 1993; 69:101-10.

164. Kluck RM, McDougall CA, Harmon BV et al. Calcium chelators induce apoptosis—evidence that raised intracellular ionised calcium is not essential for apoptosis. Biochim Biophys Acta 1994; 1223:247-54.

165. Wong GHW, Elwell JH, Oberley LW et al. Manganous superoxide dismutase is essential for cellular resistance to cytotoxicity of tumor necrosis factor. Cell 1989; 58:923-31.

166. Manchester KM, Heston WD, Donner DB. Tumour necrosis factor- induced cytotoxicity is accompanied by intracellular mitogenic signals in ME-180 human cervical carcinoma cells. Biochem J 1993; 290:185-90.

167. Taylor WG. Toxicity and hazards to successful culture: Cellular responses to damage induced by light, oxygen or heavy metals. In Vitro Monograph 1984; 5:58-70.

168. Minotti G. Metals and membrane lipid damage by oxy-radicals. Ann NY Acad Sci 1988; 551:34-46.

169. Cantoni O, Fumo M, Cattabeni F. Role of metal ions in oxidant cell injury. Biological Trace Element Res 1989; 21:277-81.

170. Halliwell B, Gutteridge JMC. Free Radicals in Biology and Medicine, second edition. Oxford: Clarendon Press, 1989.

171. Colton CA, Snell J, Chernyshev O et al. Induction of superoxide anion and nitric oxide production in cultured microglia. Ann N Y Acad Sci 1994; 738:54-63.

172. Leon P, Redmond HP, Shou J et al. Interleukin 1 and its relationship to endotoxin tolerance. Arch Surg 1992; 127:146-51.

173. Rathakrishnan C, Tiku K, Raghavan A et al. Release of oxygen radicals by articular chondrocytes: A study of luminol-dependent chemiluminescence and hydrogen peroxide secretion. J Bone Miner Res 1992; 7:1139-48.

174. Radeke HH, Meier B, Topley N et al. Interleukin 1-alpha and tumor necrosis factor-alpha induce oxygen radical production in mesangial cells. Kidney Int 1990; 37:767-75.

175. Desiderio MA, Grassilli E, Bellesia E et al. Involvement of ornithine decarboxylase and polyamines in glucocorticoid-induced apoptosis of rat thymocytes. Cell Growth Differ 1995; 6:505-13.

176. Slater AF, Nobel CS, Maellaro E et al. Nitrone spin traps and a nitroxide antioxidant inhibit a common pathway of thymocyte apoptosis. Biochem J 1995; 306:771-78.

177. Alarcon RA, Meienhofer J, Atherton E. Isophosphamide as a new acrolein-producing antineoplastic isomer of cyclophosphamide. Can Res 1972; 32:2519-23.

178. Sladek NE. Bioassay and relative cytotoxic potency of cyclophosphamide metabolites generated in vitro and in vivo. Can Res 1973; 33:1150-8.

179. Goldberg MT, Tackaberry LE, Hardy MH et al. Nuclear aberrations in hair follicle cells of patients receiving cyclophosphamide. A possible in vivo assay for human exposure to genotoxic agents. Arch Toxicol 1990; 64:116-21.

180. Davidoff AN, Mendelow BV. Cell-cycle disruptions and apoptosis induced by the cyclophosphamide derivative mafosfamide. Exp Hematol 1993; 21:922-7.

181. Meyn RE, Stephens LC, Hunter NR et al. Induction of apoptosis in murine tumors by cyclophosphamide. Cancer Chemother Pharmacol 1994; 33:410-4.

182. Chen B, Cyr DG, Hales BF. Role of apoptosis in mediating phosphoramide mustard-induced rat embryo malformations in vitro. Teratology 1994; 50:1-12.

183. de Groot CJ, Martens AC, Hagenbeek A. Aldehyde dehydrogenase involvement in a variant of the brown Norway rat acute myelocytic leukaemia (BNML) that acquired cyclophosphamide resistance in vivo. Eur J Cancer 1994; 30A:2137-43.

184. Jones RJ, Barber JP, Vala MS et al. Assessment of aldehyde dehydrogenase in viable cells. Blood 1995; 85:2742-6.

185. Bunting KD, Lindahl R, Townsend AJ. Oxazaphosphorine-specific resistance in human MCF-7 breast carcinoma cell lines expressing transfected rat class 3 aldehyde dehydrogenase. J Biol Chem 1994; 269:23197-203.

186. Andersson BS, Mroue M, Britten RA et al. The role of DNA damage in the resistance of human chronic myeloid leukemia cells to cyclophosphamide analogues. Can Res 1994; 54: 5394-400.

187. Rekha GK, Sreerama L, Sladek NE. Intrinsic cellular resistance to oxazaphosphorines exhibited by a human colon carcinoma cell line expressing relatively large amounts of a class-3 aldehyde dehydrogenase. Biochem Pharmacol 1994; 48:1943-52.

188. Maki PA, Sladek NE. Sensitivity of aldehyde dehydrogenases in murine tumor and hematopoietic progenitor cells to inhibition by chloral hydrate as determined by the ability of chloral hydrate to potentiate the cytotoxic action of mafosfamide. Biochem Pharmacol 1993; 45:231-9.

189. Chen G, Waxman DJ. Identification of glutathione S-transferase as a determinant of 4-hydroperoxycyclophosphamide resistance in human breast cancer cells. Biochem Pharmacol 1995; 49:1691-1701.

190. Saab NH, West EE, Bieszk NC et al. Synthesis and evaluation of unsymmetrically substituted polyamine analogues as modulators of human spermidine/spermine-N1-acetyltransferase (SSAT) and as potential antitumor agents. J Med Chem 1993; 36:2998-3004.

191. Ferioli ME, Scalabrino G. Persistently decreased hepatic levels of 5'-deoxy-5'-methylthioadenosine during regeneration of and chemical carcinogenesis in rat liver. J Natl Cancer Inst 1986; 76:1217-21.

192. Feo F, Garcea R, Daino L et al. Variations of S-adenosyl-L-methionine and 5'-methylthioadenosine content and liver growth. In: Perin A, Scalabrino G, Sessa A, Feriolo ME, eds. Perspectives in Polyamine Research. Italy: Wichtig Editore 1988:73-8.

193. Pegoraro L, Palumbo A, Erikson J et al. A 14;18 and an 8;14 chromosome translocation in a cell line derived from an acute B-cell leukemia. Proc Natl Acad Sci USA 1984; 81:7166-70.

194. Tsujimoto Y, Finger LR, Yunis J et al. Cloning of the chromosome breakpoint of neoplastic B cells with the t(14;18) chromosome translocation. Science 1984; 226:1097-9.

195. Hengartner MO, Horvitz HR. Activation of C. elegans cell death protein CED-9 by an amino-acid substitution in a domain conserved in Bcl-2. Nature 1994; 369:318-20.

196. Lotem J, Sachs L. Regulation of bcl-2, bcl-XL and bax in the control of apoptosis by hematopoietic cytokines and dexamethasone. Cell Growth Differ 1995; 6:647-53.

197. Reed JC. Bcl-2 and the regulation of programmed cell death. J Cell Biol 1994; 124:1-6.

198. Marthinuss J, Lawrence L, Seiberg M. Apoptosis in Pam212, an epidermal keratinocyte cell line: A possible role for bcl-2 in epidermal differentiation. Cell Growth Differ 1995; 6:239-50.

199. Dole MG, Jasty R, Cooper MJ et al. Bcl-xL is expressed in neuroblastoma cells and modulates chemotherapy-induced apoptosis. Can Res 1995; 55:2576-82.

200. Yuan J, Shaham S, Ledoux S et al. The C. elegans cell death gene ced-3 encodes a protein similar to mammalian interleukin-1 beta-converting enzyme. Cell 1993; 75:641-52.

201. Walker NP, Talanian RV, Brady KD et al. Crystal structure of the cysteine protease interleukin-1 beta-converting enzyme: A (p20/p10)2 homodimer. Cell 1994; 78:343-52.

202. Faucheu C, Diu A, Chan AW et al. A novel human protease similar to the interleukin-1 beta converting enzyme induces apoptosis in transfected cells. EMBO J 1995; 14:1914-22.

203. Fernandes-Alnemri T, Litwack G, Alnemri ES. CPP32, a novel human apoptotic protein with homology to Caenorhabditis elegans cell death protein Ced-3 and mammalian interleukin-1 beta-converting enzyme. J Biol Chem 1994; 269:30761-4.

204. Fernandes-Alnemri T, Litwack G, Alnemri ES. Mch2, a new member of the apoptotic Ced-3/Ice cysteine protease gene family. Can Res 1995; 55:2737-42.

205. Kuma S, Kinoshita M, Noda M et al. Induction of apoptosis by the mouse Nedd2 gene, which encodes a protein similar to the product of the Caenorhabditis elegans cell death gene ced-3 and the mammalian IL-1 beta-converting enzyme. Genes Dev 1994; 8:1613-26.

206. Schwartz LM, Osborne BA. Ced-3/ICE: Evolutionarily conserved regulation of cell death. Bioessays 1994; 16:387-9.

207. Kuida K, Lippke JA, Ku G et al. Altered cytokine export and apoptosis in mice deficient in interleukin-1 beta converting enzyme. Science 1995; 267:2000-3.

208. Kumar S. ICE-like proteases in apoptosis. Trends Biochem Sci 1995; 20:198-202.

209. Tewari M, Quan LT, O'Rourke K et al. Yama/CPP32 beta, a mammalian homolog of CED-3, is a CrmA-inhibitable protease that cleaves the death substrate poly(ADP-ribose) polymerase. Cell 1995; 81:801-9.

210. Wang L, Miura M, Bergeron L et al. Ich-1, an Ice/ ced-3-related gene, encodes both positive and negative regulators of programmed cell death. Cell 1994; 78:739-50.

211. Tewari M, Dixit VM. Fas- and tumor necrosis factor-induced apoptosis is inhibited by the poxvirus crmA gene product. J Biol Chem 1995; 270:3255-60.

212. Lazebnik YA, Kaufmann SH, Desnoyers S et al. Cleavage of poly(ADP-ribose) polymerase by a proteinase with properties like ICE. Nature 1994; 371:346-7.

213. Irmler M, Hertig S, MacDonald HR et al. Granzyme A is an interleukin 1 beta-converting enzyme. J Exp Med 1995; 181:1917-22.

214. Thornberry NA, Molineaux SM. Interleukin-1 beta converting enzyme: A novel cysteine protease required for IL-1 beta production and implicated in programmed cell death. Protein Sci 1995; 4:3-12.

215. Li P, Allen H, Banerjee S et al. Mice deficient in IL-1 beta-converting enzyme are defective in production of mature IL-1 beta and resistant to endotoxic shock. Cell 1995; 80:401-11.

216. Xue D, Horvitz HR. Inhibition of the Caenorhabditis elegans cell-death protease CED-3 by a CED-3 cleavage site in baculovirus p35 protein. Nature 1995; 377:248-51.

217. Kleppe K, Osland A, Fosse V et al. Effect of polyamines on enzymes involved in DNA repair. Med Biol 1981; 59:374-80.

218. Rowlatt C, Smith GJ. Ultrastructural studies on chromatin digestion by micrococcal nuclease in the presence of polyamines. J Cell Sci 1981; 48:171-9.

219. Brune B, Hartzell P, Nicotera P et al. Spermine prevents endonuclease activation and apoptosis in thymocytes. Exp Cell Res 1991; 195:323-9.

220. Aller P, Baserga R. Selective increase of c-myc mRNA levels by methylglyoxal-bis (guanylhydrazone) and novobiocin in serum-stimulated fibroblasts. J Cell Physiol 1986; 128:362-6.

221. Celano P, Baylin SB, Giardiello FM et al. Effect of polyamine depletion on c-myc expression in human colon carcinoma cells. J Biol Chem 1988; 263:5491-4.

222. Celano P, Baylin SB, Casero Jr RA. Polyamines differentially modulate the transcription of growth-associated genes in human colon carcinoma cells. J Biol Chem 1989; 264:8922-7.

223. Celano P, Berchtold CM, Giardiello FM et al. Modulation of growth gene expression by selective alteration of polyamines in human colon carcinoma cells. Biochem Biophys Res Commun 1989; 165:384-90.

224. Davidoff AN, Mendelow BV. C-myc expression is down-regulated in mafosfamide-treated HL-60 cells undergoing apoptosis. Anticancer Res 1993; 13:1167-70.

225. Oren M. The involvement of oncogenes and tumor suppressor genes in the control of apoptosis. Cancer Metastasis Rev 1992; 11:141-8.

226. Klinken SP, Holmes KL, Morse HC et al. Transcriptional and post-transcriptional regulation of c-myc, c-myb, and p53 during proliferation and differentiation of murine erythroleukemia cells treated with DFMO and DMSO. Exp Cell Res 1988; 178:185-98.

227. Packham G, Cleveland JL. The role of ornithine decarboxylase in c-Myc-induced apoptosis. Curr Top Microbiol Immunol 1995; 194:283-90.

228. Charollais RH, Mester J. Resumption of cell cycle in BALB/c-3T3 fibroblasts arrested by polyamine depletion: relation with competence gene expression. J Cell Physiol 1988; 137:559-64.

229. Watanabe T, Sherman M, Shafman T et al. Effects of ornithine decarboxylase inhibition on c-myc expression during murine erythroleukemia cell proliferation and differentiation. J Cell Physiol 1986; 127:480-4.

230. Luk GD, Canellakis ZN. Diacetylputrescine and its analog suppress c-myc expression and activation of human B-lymphocytes. Biochem Intl 1990; 20:169-76.

231. Wang JY, McCormack SA, Viar MJ et al. Decreased expression of protooncogenes c-fos, c-myc, and c-jun following polyamine depletion in IEC-6 cells. Am J Physiol 1993; 265:G331-8.

232. Kane DJ, Sarafian TA, Anton R et al. Bcl-2 inhibition of neural death: decreased generation of reactive oxygen species. Science 1993; 262:1274-7.

233. Bullock G, Tang C, Tourkina E et al. Effect of combined treatment with interleukin-3 and interleukin-6 on 4-hydroperoxycyclophosphamide-induced programmed cell death or apoptosis in human myeloid leukemia cells. Exp Hematol 1993; 21:1640-7.

234. Leger JG, Montpetit ML, Tenniswood MP. Characterization and cloning of androgen-repressed mRNAs from rat ventral prostate. Biochem Biophys Res Comm 1987; 147:196-203.

235. Buttyan R, Olsson CA, Pintar J et al. Induction of the TRPM-2 gene in cells undergoing programmed cell death. Molec Cell Biol 1989; 9:3473-81.

236. Schwartz LM, Kosz L, Kay BK. Gene activation is required for developmentally programmed cell death. Proc Natl Acad Sci USA 1990; 87:6594-8.

237. Gabig TG, Mantel PL, Rosli R et al. Requiem: A novel zinc finger gene essential for apoptosis in myeloid cells. J Biol Chem 1994; 269:29515-9.

238. Cruz-Reyes J, Tata JR. Cloning, characterization and expression of two Xenopus bcl-2-like cell-survival genes. Gene 1995; 158:171-9.

239. Kawakami T, Furukawa Y, Sudo K et al. Isolation and mapping of a human gene (PDCD2) that is highly homologous to Rp8, a rat gene associated with programmed cell death. Cytogenet Cell Genet 1995; 71:41-3.

240. Naora H, Nishida T, Shindo Y et al. Association of nbl gene expression and glucocorticoid-induced apoptosis in mouse thymus in vivo. Immunol 1995; 85:63-8.

241. Sun D, Ziegler R, Milligan CE et al. Apolipophorin III is dramatically up-regulated during the programmed death of insect skeletal muscle and neurons. J Neurobiol 1995; 26:119-29.

242. Vaux DL, Hacker G. Cloning of mouse RP-8 cDNA and its expression during apoptosis of lymphoid and myeloid cells. DNA Cell Biol 1995; 14:189-93.

243. Hamburger V, Brunso-Bechtold JK, Yip JW. Neuronal death in the spinal ganglia of the chick embryo and its reduction by nerve growth factor, J Neurosci 1981; 1:60-71.

244. Koury MJ, Bondurant MC. Erythropoietin retards DNA breakdown and prevents programmed death in erythroid progenitor cells. Science 1990; 248:378-81.

245. Crompton T. Il-3-dependent cells die by apoptosis on removal of their growth factor. Growth Factors 1991; 4:109-16.

246. Treves S, Trentini PL, Ascanelli M et al. Apoptosis is dependent on intracellular zinc and independent of intracellular calcium in lymphocytes. Exp Cell Res 1994; 211:339-43.

247. Rabacchi SA, Ensini M, Bonfanti L et al. Nerve growth factor reduces apoptosis of axotomized retinal ganglion cells in the neonatal rat. Neuroscience 1994; 63:969-73.

248. Stimac E, Morris DR. Messenger RNAs coding for enzymes of polyamine biosynthesis are induced during the G0-G1 transition but not during traverse of the normal G1 phase. J Cell Physiol 1987; 133:590-4.

249. Packham G, Cleveland JL. c-Myc and apoptosis. Biochim Biophys Acta 1995; 1242:11-28.

250. Packham G, Cleveland JL. Ornithine decarboxylase is a mediator of c-Myc-induced apoptosis. Mol Cell Biol 1994; 14:5741-7.

251. Wagner AJ, Meyers C, Laimins LA et al. c-Myc induces the expression and activity of ornithine decarboxylase. Cell Growth Differ 1993; 4:879-83.

252. Green DR, Mahboubi A, Nishioka W et al. Promotion and inhibition of activation-induced apoptosis in T-cell hybridomas by oncogenes and related signals. Immunol Rev 1994; 142:321-42.

253. Grassilli E, Bettuzzi S, Monti D et al. Studies on the relationship between cell proliferation and cell death: opposite patterns of SGP-2 and ornithine decarboxylase mRNA accumulation in PHA-stimulated human lymphocytes. Biochem Biophys Res Commun 1991; 180:59-63.

254. Askew DS, Ashmun RA, Simmons BC et al. Constitutive c-myc expression in an IL-3-dependent myeloid cell line suppresses cell cycle arrest and accelerates apoptosis. Oncogene 1991; 6:1915-22.

255. Coffino P, Poznanski A. Killer polyamines? J Cell Biochem 1991; 45:54-8.

256. Demarcq C, Bunch RT, Creswell D et al. The role of cell cycle progression in cisplatin-induced apoptosis in Chinese hamster ovary cells. Cell Growth Differ 1994; 5:983-93.

257. Houghton JA, Harwood FG, Houghton PJ. Cell cycle control processes determine cytostasis or cytotoxicity in thymineless death of colon cancer cells. Cancer Res 1994; 54:4967-73.

258. Donaldson KL, Goolsby GL, Kiener PA et al. Activation of p34cdc2 coincident with taxol-induced apoptosis. Cell Growth Differ 1994; 5:1041-50.

259. Dubrez L, Goldwasser F, Genne P et al. The role of cell cycle regulation and apoptosis triggering in determining the sensitivity of leukemic cells to topoisomerase I and II inhibitors. Leukemia 1995; 9:1013-24.

260. Fotedar R, Flatt J, Gupta S et al. Activation-induced T-cell death is cell cycle dependent and regulated by cyclin B. Mol Cell Biol 1995; 15:932-42.

261. Penninger JM, Mak TW. Signal transduction, mitotic catastrophes, and death in T-cell development. Immunol Rev 1994; 142:231-72.

262. Shimizu T, O'Connor PM, Kohn KW et al. Unscheduled activation of cyclin B1/Cdc2 kinase in human promyelocytic leukemia

cell line HL60 cells undergoing apoptosis induced by DNA damage. Can Res 1995; 55:228-31.

263. LaVoie HA, Witorsch RJ. Investigation of intracellular signals mediating the anti-apoptotic action of prolactin in Nb2 lymphoma cells. Proc Soc Exp Biol Med 1995; 209:257-69.

264. Hernandez-Caselles T, Stutman O. Immune functions of tumor necrosis factor. 1. Tumor necrosis factor induces apoptosis of mouse thymocytes and can also stimulate or inhibit IL-6-induced proliferation depending on the concentration of mitogenic costimulation. J Immunol 1993; 151:3999-4012.

265. Chung DH, Evers BM, Townsend Jr CM et al. Cytokine regulation of gut ornithine decarboxylase gene expression and enzyme activity. Surgery 1992; 112:364-9.

266. Donato NJ, Rotbein J, Rosenblum MG. Tumor necrosis factor stimulates ornithine decarboxylase activity in human fibroblasts and tumor target cells. J Cell Biochem 1991; 46:69-77.

267. Endo Y, Matsushima K, Onozaki K et al. Role of ornithine decarboxylase in the regulation of cell growth by IL-1 and tumor necrosis factor. J Immunol 1988; 141:2342-8.

268. Endo Y. Induction of histidine and ornithine decarboxylase activities in mouse tissues by recombinant interleukin-1 and tumor necrosis factor. Biochem Pharmacol 1989; 38:1287-92.

269. Grzelkowska K, Motyl T, Malicka E et al. Effect of orotic acid on TGF-beta 1-induced growth inhibition of L1210 leukemic cells. Int J Hematol 1995; 61:23-33.

270. Motyl T, Kasterka M, Grzelkowska K et al. TGF-beta 1 inhibits polyamine biosynthesis in K 562 leukemic cells. Ann Hematol 1993; 67:285-8.

271. Pierce GB, Lewellyn AL. H2O2 mediated cell death and division in cleaving mouse embryos. Serono Symp Publ Raven Press 1991;82:17-22.

272. Juntti-Berggren L, Larsson O, Rorsman P et al. Increased activity of L-type Ca^{2+} channels exposed to serum from patients with type I diabetes. Science 1993; 261:86-90.

273. Freund WD, Reddig S. AMPA/Zn(2+)-induced neurotoxicity in rat primary cortical cultures: Involvement of L-type calcium channels. Brain Res 1994; 654:257-64.

274. Herman MD, Reuveny E, Narahashi T. The effect of polyamines on voltage-activated calcium channels in mouse neuroblastoma cells. J Physiol (Lond) 1993; 462:645-60.

275. McBurney RN, Daly D, Fischer JB et al. New CNS-specific calcium antagonists. J Neurotrauma 1992; 9 Suppl 2:S531-43.

276. Jiang S, Chow SC, McCabe Jr MJ et al. Lack of Ca^{2+} involvement in thymocyte apoptosis induced by chelation of intracellular Zn^{2+}. Lab Invest 1995; 73:111-7.

277. Zalewski PD, Forbes IJ, Giannakis C. Physiological role for zinc in prevention of apoptosis (gene-directed death). Biochem Int 1991; 24:1093-101.

278. Zalewski PD, Forbes IJ, Betts WH. Correlation of apoptosis with change in intracellular labile Zn(II) using zinquin [(2-methyl-8-p-toluenesulphonamido-6-quinolyloxy)acetic acid], a new specific fluorescent probe for Zn(II). Biochem J 1993; 296:403-8.

279. Trout JJ, Koenig H, Goldstone AD et al. N-methyl-D-aspartate receptor excitotoxicity involves activation of polyamine synthesis: Protection by alpha-difluoromethylornithine. J Neurochem 1993; 60:352-5.

280. Reynolds IJ. Arcaine uncovers dual interactions of polyamines with the N-methyl-D-aspartate receptor. J Pharmacol Exp Ther 1990; 255:1001-7.

281. Sacaan AI, Johnson KM. Competitive inhibition of magnesium-induced [3H]N-(1-[thienyl] cyclohexyl)piperidine binding by arcaine: Evidence for a shared spermidine-magnesium binding site. Mol Pharmacol 1990; 38:705-10.

282. Sacaan AI, Johnson KM. Spermidine reverses arcaine's inhibition of N-methyl-D-aspartate-induced hippocampal [3H]norepinephrine release. J Pharmacol Exp Ther 1990; 255:1060-3.

283. Ogita K, Yoneda Y. Solubilization of spermidine-sensitive (+)-[3H]5-methyl-10,11-dihydro-5H-dibenzo[a,d]cyclohepten-5,10- imine ([3H]MK-801) binding activity from rat brain. J Neurochem 1990; 55:1515-20.

284. Yoneda Y, Ogita K, Enomoto R. Characterization of spermidine-dependent [3H](+)-5-methyl-10,11-dihydro-5H-dibenzo[a, d]cyclo-hepten-5,10-imine (MK-801) binding in brain synaptic membranes treated with Triton X-100. J Pharmacol Exp Ther 1991; 256: 1161-72.

285. Yoneda Y, Ogita K, Enomoto R et al. Identification and characterization of specific binding sites of [3H]spermidine in synaptic membranes of rat brain. Brain Res 1991; 563:17-27.

286. Williams K, Romano C, Dichter MA et al. Modulation of the NMDA receptor by polyamines. Life Sci 1991; 48:469-98.

287. Bakker MH, McKernan RM, Wong EH et al. [3H]MK-801 binding to N-methyl-D-aspartate receptors solubilized from rat brain: effects of glycine site ligands, polyamines, ifenprodil, and desipramine. J Neurochem 1991; 57:39-45.

288. Nussenzveig IZ, Sircar R, Wong ML et al. Polyamine effects upon N-methyl-D-aspartate receptor functioning: Differential alteration by glutamate and glycine site antagonists. Brain Res 1991; 561:285-91.

289. Lehmann J, Colpaert F, Canton H. Glutamate and glycine co-activate while polyamines merely modulate the NMDA receptor complex. Prog Neuropsychopharmacol Biol Psychiatry 1991; 15:183-90.

290. Romano C, Williams K, DePriest S et al. Effects of mono-, di-, and triamines on the N-methyl-D-aspartate receptor complex: A model of the polyamine recognition site. Mol Pharmacol 1992; 41:785-92.

291. Rock DM, MacDonald RL. Spermine and related polyamines produce a voltage-dependent reduction of N-methyl-D-aspartate receptor single-channel conductance. Mol Pharmacol 1992; 42:157-64.

292. Marvizon JC, Baudry M. NMDA receptor activation by spermine requires glutamate but not glycine. Eur J Pharmacol 1993; 244:103-4.

293. Enomoto R, Ogita K, Han D et al. Differential potentiation by spermidine of abilities of a variety of displacers for [3H]MK-801 binding in hippocampal synaptic membranes. Neurosci Res 1993; 16:217-24.

294. Reynolds IJ. [3H]CGP 39653 binding to the agonist site of the N-methyl-D-aspartate receptor is modulated by Mg^{2+} and polyamines independently of the arcaine-sensitive polyamine site. J Neurochem 1994; 62:54-62.

295. Mishra OP, Delivoria-Papadopoulos M. Modification of modulatory sites of NMDA receptor in the fetal guinea pig brain during development. Neurochem Res 1992; 17:1223-8.

296. Bowe MA, Nadler JV. Polyamines antagonize N-methyl-D-aspartate-evoked depolarizations, but reduce Mg^{2+} block. Eur J Pharmacol 1995; 278:55-65.

297. Reynolds IJ. Interactions between zinc and spermidine on the N-methyl-D-aspartate receptor complex: Clues to the mechanism of action of 1,10-bis(guanidino)decane and pentamidine. J Pharmacol Exp Ther 1992; 263:632-8.

298. Reynolds IJ. 1,5-(Diethylamino)piperidine, a novel spermidine analogue that more specifically activates the N-methyl-D-aspartate receptor-associated polyamine site. Mol Pharmacol 1992; 41:989-92.

299. Marvizon JC, Baudry M. [3H]dizocilpine association kinetics distinguish stimulatory and inhibitory polyamine sites of N-methyl-D-aspartate receptors. J Neurochem 1994; 63:963-71.

300. Marvizon JC, Baudry M. Allosteric interactions and modulator requirement for NMDA receptor function. Eur J Pharmacol 1994; 269:165-75.

301. Bergeron RJ, Weimar WR, Wu Q et al. Impact of polyamine analogues on the NMDA receptor. J Med Chem 1995; 38:425-8.

302. Rock DM, Macdonald RL. The polyamine spermine has multiple actions on N-methyl-D-aspartate receptor single-channel currents in cultured cortical neurons. Mol Pharmacol 1992; 41:83-8.

303. Lombardi G, Szekely AM, Bristol LA et al. Induction of ornithine decarboxylase by N-methyl-D-aspartate receptor activation is unrelated to potentiation of glutamate excitotoxicity by polyamines in cerebellar granule neurons. J Neurochem 1993; 60:1317-24.

304. Williams K, Pullan LM, Romano C et al. An antagonist/partial agonist at the polyamine recognition site of the N-methyl-D-aspartate receptor that alters the properties of the glutamate recognition site. J Pharmacol Exp Ther 1992; 262:539-44.

305. Oblin A, Schoemaker H. Complex allosteric modulation of the binding of the NMDA receptor antagonist [3H]CGP39653. Eur J Pharmacol 1994; 266:103-6.

306. Levy DI, Sucher NJ, Lipton SA. Glutathione prevents N-methyl-D-aspartate receptor-mediated neurotoxicity. NeuroReports 1991; 2:345-7.

307. Murphy TH, Miyamoto M, Sastre A et al. Glutamate toxicity in a neuronal cell line involves inhibition of cystine transport leading to oxidative stress. Neuron 1989; 2:1547-58.

308. Murphy TH, Schnaar RL, Coyle JT. Immature cortical neurons are uniquely sensitive to glutamate toxicity by inhibition of cystine uptake. FASEB J 1990; 4:1624-33.

309. Markwell MAK, Berger SP, Paul SM. The polyamine synthesis inhibitor α-difluoromethylornithine blocks NMDA-induced neurotoxicity. Eur J Pharmacol 1990; 182:607-9.

310. Erdö SL, Michler A, Wolff JR et al. Lack of excitotoxic cell death in serum-free cultures of rat cerebral cortex. Brain Res 1990; 526:328-32.

311. Murphy TH, Baraban JM. Glutamate toxicity in immature cortical neurons precedes development of glutamate receptor currents. Develop Brain Res 1990; 57:146-50.

312. Kato K, Puttfarcken PS, Lyons WE et al. Developmental time course and ionic dependence of kainate-mediated toxicity in rat cerebellar granule cell cultures. J Pharm Exptl Therapeut 1991; 256:402-11.

313. Kure S, Tominaga T, Yoshimoto T et al. Glutamate triggers internucleosomal DNA cleavage in neuronal cells. Biochem Biophys Research Comm 1991; 179:39-45.

314. Puttfarcken PS, Lyons WE, Coyle JT. Dissociation of nitric oxide generation and kainate-mediated neuronal degeneration in primary cultures of rat cerebellar granule cells. Neuropharmacol 1992; 31:565-75.

315. Khan NA, Masson I, Quemener V et al. Polyamine binding sites in the rat brain hippocampus plasma membranes: MK 801 does not influence the binding process. Membr Biochem 1990; 9:163-9.

316. Baudry M, Najm I. Kainate-induced seizure activity stimulates the polyamine interconversion pathway in rat brain. Neurosci Lett 1994; 171:151-4.

317. Najm I, el-Skaf G, Tocco G et al. Seizure activity-induced changes in polyamine metabolism and neuronal pathology during the postnatal period in rat brain. Brain Res Dev Brain Res 1992; 69:11-21.

318. Najm I, el-Skaf G, Massicotte G et al. Changes in polyamine levels and spectrin degradation following kainate-induced seizure activity: Effect of difluoromethylornithine. Exp Neurol 1992; 116:345-54.

319. Beninati S, Piacentini M, Cocuzzi ET et al. Covalent incorporation of polyamines as gamma-glutamyl derivatives into CHO cell protein. Biochim Biophys Acta 1988; 952:325-33.

320. Beninati S, Abbruzzese A, Cardinali M. Differences in the post-translational modification of proteins by polyamines between weakly and highly metastatic B16 melanoma cells. Int J Cancer 1993; 53:792-7.

321. Davies PJ, Chiocca EA, Basilion JP et al. Transglutaminases and their regulation: Implications for polyamine metabolism. Adv Exp Med Biol 1988; 250:391-401.

322. McCormack SA, Wang JY, Viar MJ et al. Polyamines influence transglutaminase activity and cell migration in two cell lines. Am J Physiol 1994; 267:C706-14.

323. M'Rabet-Touil H, Blachier F, Hellio N et al. Transglutaminase activity in enterocytes isolated from pig jejunum. Mol Cell Biochem 1995; 146:49-54.

324. Piacentini M, Fesus L, Sartori C et al. Retinoic acid-induced modulation of rat liver transglutaminase and total polyamines in vivo. Biochem J 1988; 253:33-8.

325. Melino G, Farrace MG, Ceru MP et al. Correlation between transglutaminase activity and polyamine levels in human neuroblastoma cells. Effect of retinoic acid and alpha- difluoromethylornithine. Exp Cell Res 1988; 179:429-45.

326. Shin DM, Gimenez IB, Lee JS et al. Expression of epidermal growth factor receptor, polyamine levels, ornithine decarboxylase activity, micronuclei, and transglutaminase I in a 7,12-dimethylbenz(a)anthracene-induced hamster buccal pouch carcinogenesis model. Can Res 1990; 50:2505-10.

327. Wang JY, Viar MJ, Johnson LR. Regulation of transglutaminase activity by polyamines in the gastrointestinal mucosa of rats. Proc Soc Exp Biol Med 1994; 205:20-8.

328. Hand D, Elliott BM, Griffin M. Correlation of changes in transglutaminase activity and polyamine content of neoplastic tissue during the metastatic process. [published erratum appears in Biochim Biophys Acta 1987; 931:385]. Biochim Biophys Acta 1987; 930:432-7.

329. Romijn JC. Polyamines and transglutaminase actions. Andrologia 1990; 22 Suppl 1:83-91.

330. Piacentini M, Sartori C, Beninati S et al. Ornithine decarboxylase, transglutaminase, diamine oxidase and total diamines and poly-amines in maternal liver and kidney throughout rat pregnancy. Biochem J 1986; 234:435-40.

331. Piacentini M, Fesus L, Farrace MG et al. The expression of tissue transglutaminase in two human cancer cell lines is related with the programmed cell death (apoptosis). Eur J Cell Biol 1991; 54:246-54.

332. Kvedar JC, Pion IA, Bilodeau EB et al. Detection of substrates of keratinocyte transglutaminase in vitro and in vivo using a mono-clonal antibody to dansylcadaverine. Biochemistry 1992; 31:49-56.

333. Porta R, Metafora S, Esposito C et al. Biological activities of a major protein secreted from the rat seminal vesicles after structural modification catalyzed by transglutaminase in vitro. Immuno-pharmacology 1993; 25:179-88.

334. Ientile R, Merendino RA, Fabiano C et al. Polyamines are involved in retinoic acid-mediated induction of tissue transglutaminase in human peripheral blood monocytes. Res Commun Chem Pathol Pharmacol 1992; 77:313-26.

335. Johnson LR, Tseng CC, Tipnis UR et al. Gastric mucosal orni-thine decarboxylase: Localization and stimulation by gastrin. Am J Physiol 1988; 255:G304-12.

336. Donato NJ, Ware CF, Byus CV. A rat monoclonal antibody which interacts with mammalian ornithine decarboxylase at an epitope involved in phosphorylation. Biochim Biophys Acta 1986; 884:370-82.

337. Gilmour SK, Aglow E, O'Brien TG. Heterogeneity of ornithine decarboxylase expression in 12-O-tetradecanoylphorbol-13-acetate-treated mouse skin and in epidermal tumors. Carcinogenesis 1986; 7:943-47.

338. Hietala O, Dzubow L, Dlugosz AA et al. Activation of human squa-mous cell carcinoma ornithine decarboxylase activity by guanosine triphosphate. Cancer Res 1988; 48:1252-7.

339. Greenfield ARL, Taffet SM, Haddox MK. Immunocytochemical localization of ornithine decarboxylase in cultured murine cells. Cell Tissue Res 1986; 243:33-40.

340. Verrando P, Juhlin L, Lacour JP et al. Immunohistochemical lo-calization of ornithine decarboxylase in human skin. J Dermatol 1987; 14:112-7.

341. Delcros JG, Clement S, Thomas V et al. Differential recognition of free and covalently bound polyamines by the monoclonal anti-spermine antibody SPM8-2. J Immunol Methods 1995; 185:191-8.

342. Fujiwara K, Furukawa K, Nakayama E et al. Production and char-acterization of monoclonal antibodies against the polyamine, spermine: Immunocytochemical localization in rat tissues. Histo chem 1994; 102:397-404.

343. Fujiwara K, Araki M, Kitagawa T et al. A new enzyme-linked immunosorbent assay (ELISA) for studying immunocytochemical procedures using an antiserum produced against spermidine as a model. Histochemistry 1993; 99:477-83.

344. Schipper RG, Jonis JA, Rutten RG et al. Preparation and characterization of polyclonal and monoclonal antibodies to polyamines. J Immunol Methods 1991; 136: 23-30.

345. Fukuda M, Kono T, Ishii M et al. Increased expression of the ornithine decarboxylase gene in mouse skin by ultraviolet light: Detection by in situ hybridization technique. Arch Dermatol Res 1990; 282:487-9.

346. Kono T, Fukuda M, Ishii M et al. Detection of ornithine decarboxylase gene expression in 12-O-tetradecanoylphorbol-13-acetate-treated mouse skin using in situ hybridization. Acta Derm Venereol 1991; 71:104-7.

347. Halbhuber KJ, Linss W. Possibilities for the use of cerium for the ultrahistochemical demonstration of enzymes]. Acta Histochem Suppl 1984; 30:313-7.

348. Angermuller S, Fahimi HD. Light microscopic visualization of the reaction product of cerium used for localization of peroxisomal oxidases. J Histochem Cytochem 1988; 36:23-8.

349. Gossrau R, van Noorden CJ, Frederiks WM. Enhanced light microscopic visualization of oxidase activity with the cerium capture method. Histochem 1989; 92:349-53.

350. Seitz J, Keppler C, Fahimi HD et al. A new staining method for the detection of activities of H2O2-producing oxidases on gels and blots using cerium and 3,3'-diaminobenzidine. Electrophoresis 1991; 12:1051-5.

351. van Noorden CJ, Frederiks WM. Cerium methods for light and electron microscopical histochemistry. J Microsc 1993; 171:3-16.

352. Frederiks WM, Bosch KS. Quantitative aspects of enzyme histochemistry on sections of freeze-substituted glycol methacrylate-embedded rat liver. Histochem 1993; 100:297-302.

353. Halbhuber KJ, Hulstaert CE, Feuerstein H et al. Cerium as capturing agent in phosphatase and oxidase histochemistry. Theoretical background and applications. Prog Histochem Cytochem 1994; 28:1-120.

354. Karnovsky MJ. Cytochemistry and reactive oxygen species: A retrospective. Histochem 1994; 102:15-27.

355. Nakos G, Gossrau R. Light microscopic visualization of semicarbazide-sensitive amine oxidase (benzylamine oxidase) using a cerium method. Folia Histochem Cytobiol 1994; 32:3-10.

356. Beard ME, Baker R, Conomos P et al. Oxidation of oxalate and polyamines by rat peroxisomes. J Histochem Cytochem 1985; 33:460-64.

357. Van den Munckhof RJ, Denyn M, Tigchelaar-Gutter W et al. In situ substrate specificity and ultrastructural localization of polyamine oxidase activity in unfixed rat tissues. J Histochem Cytochem 1995; 43:1155-62.

358. Nakos G, Gossrau R. Visualization of hydrogen peroxide (H_2O_2)-production from histamine. Anat Anz 1995; 177:431-8.

359. Nakos G, Gossrau R. Light microscopic visualization of diamine oxidase using a cerium method. Eur J Histochem 1994; 38:13-22.

360. Fujimoto T, Inomata K, Ogawa K. A cerium method for the ultracytochemical localization of monoamine oxidase activity. Histochem J 1982; 14:87-98.

361. Gossrau R, Frederiks WM, van Noorden CJ. Histochemistry of reactive oxygen-species (ROS)-generating oxidases in cutaneous and mucous epithelia of laboratory rodents with special reference to xanthine oxidase. Histochem 1990; 94:539-44.

362. Gossrau R, Frederiks WM, van Noorden CJ et al. Light microscopical detection of H2O2-generating oxidases using cerium ions and aqueous incubation media. Acta Histochem 1991; 90:27-37.

363. Nakos G, Gossrau R. Light microscopic visualization of monoamine oxidase using a cerium method. Acta Histochem 1993; 95:203-19.

364. Nakos G, Gossrau R. Hydrogen peroxide (H_2O_2) production by monoamine oxidase in rat tissues using endogenous catecholamines as substrates. A comparison of catalytic monoamine oxidase histochemistry and recently published catechol-O-methyltransferase immunohistochemistry. Acta Histochem 1995; 97:121-7.

365. El Baze P, Milano G, Verrando P et al. Distribution of polyamines in human epidermis. J Dermatol 1985; 112:393-6.

366. McCormack SA, Johnson LR. Role of polyamines in gastrointestinal mucosal growth. Am J Physiol 1991; 260:G795-806.

367. Johnson LR, Tseng CC, Wang P et al. Mucosal ornithine decarboxylase in the small intestine: Localization and stimulation. Am J Physiol 1989; 256:G624-30.

368. Gossrau R, van Noorden CJ, Frederiks WM. Pitfalls in the light microscopical detection of NADH oxidase. Histochem J 1990; 22:155-61.

369. Halbhuber KJ, Feuerstein H, Zimmermann N et al. Improved light microscopic demonstration of D-amino acid oxidase activity in cryotome sections using cerium ions as capturing and amplifying agent—the Ce/Ce-H_2O_2-DAB procedure. Cell Mol Biol 1991; 37:279-94.

370. Frederiks WM, Marx F. A histochemical procedure for light microscopic demonstration of xanthine oxidase activity in unfixed cryostat sections using cerium ions and a semipermeable membrane technique. J Histochem Cytochem 1993; 41:667-70.

371. Johnson LR, Wang P, Haddox K. Ornithine decarboxylase in large bowel mucosa: Regulation by gastrin, secretin and EGF. J Physiol Pharmacol 1992; 43:33-41.

372. Bloom W, Fawcett DW. The Esophagus and Stomach. In: A Textbook of Histology. Tenth Edition. Philadelphia: WB Saunders, 1975:639-57.

373. Shinki T, Kadofuku T, Sato T et al. Spermidine N1-acetyltransferase has a larger role than ornithine decarboxylase in 1 alpha,25-dihydroxyvitamin D3-induced putrescine synthesis. J Biol Chem 1986; 261:11712-6.

374. Smirnov IV, Feuerstein BG, Pellarin M et al. Pretreatment with the polyamine analog 1,19-bis- (ethylamino)-5,10,15-triazanonadecane (BE-4444) inhibits etoposide cytotoxicity in U-251 MG (NCI) human brain tumor cells. Cell Mol Biol (Noisy-le-grand) 1994; 40:975-80.

375. McCloskey DE, Casero Jr RA, Woster PM et al. Induction of programmed cell death in human breast cancer cells by an unsymmetrically alkylated polyamine analogue. Cancer Res 1995; 55:3233-6.

376. Szabo C, Southan GJ, Thiemermann C et al. The mechanism of the inhibitory effect of polyamines on the induction of nitric oxide synthase: Role of aldehyde metabolites. Br J Pharmacol 1994; 113:757-66.

=== CHAPTER 7 ===

POLYAMINE INHIBITORS AND ANALOGS

Debora L. Kramer

I. INTRODUCTION

Perhaps more than in most other research areas, biosynthetic inhibitors have historically played a critical and determining role in the progression of polyamine research. Although now confirmed with auxotrophic mutants deficient in polyamine biosynthesis, the critical dependence of cell growth on polyamine biosynthesis was first established with polyamine inhibitors. The potent inhibitor of the polyamine enzyme S-adenosylmethionine decarboxylase (AdoMetDC, also abbreviated as SAMDC), methylglyoxal bis(guanylhydrazone) (MGBG),[1,2] was among the first inhibitors used to strongly suggest that cell growth was dependent on sustained polyamine biosynthesis. Interpretation of MGBG findings remained problematic due to nonspecific effects of the drug and its shared uptake with polyamines, a property which rendered critical reversal experiments with exogenous polyamines untenable. These complications were eliminated when the mechanism-based irreversible and specific inhibitor of ornithine decarboxylase (ODC), DL-α-difluoromethylornithine (DFMO)[3] was introduced in 1978 and used to unequivocally demonstrate that polyamine depletion led to growth inhibition and that the well known induction of

Polyamines in Cancer: Basic Mechanisms and Clinical Approaches, edited by Kenji Nishioka. © 1996 R.G. Landes Company.

ODC was critical to the initiation of cell growth. Since these inhibitors, a wide variety of potent and highly specific inhibitors have been developed for almost all of the polyamine biosynthetic enzymes as well as those associated with polyamine catabolism (Fig. 7.1). Such compounds have been widely used in a variety of prokaryotic and eukaryotic systems to (a) confirm the association of polyamine biosynthesis with cell proliferation and other functions of cell physiology; (b) probe the possible role of polyamines in supporting cell proliferation; (c) examine the complicated regulatory mechanisms underlying polyamine biosynthesis and metabolism and (d) determine the potential of polyamine biosynthesis as a target site for antiproliferative therapeutic applications ranging from parasitic diseases to cancer. Interestingly, both MGBG and DFMO continue to have utility in all four areas including the last where they are currently undergoing clinical trial (Fig. 7.2).

Though not as widely utilized as inhibitors, polyamine analogs have also found application in polyamine research and therapeutics. In 1964, Israel and colleagues were among the first to design and synthesize spermine analogs as potential anticancer agents.[4,5] Morris and colleagues were the first to recognize the potential of analogs as research tools.[6] They synthesized a series of aliphatic homologs of spermidine which were designed to delineate various structure-function relationships relative to the role of spermidine in prokaryotic cell growth. Porter and Bergeron[7] used these compounds in this manner to define the structural tolerance of spermidine in eukaryotic cell growth. Aside from putrescine analogs designed as inhibitors of ODC, the earliest sustained program in polyamine analogs involved the combined efforts of Bergeron, Porter and collaborators. Beginning in 1982 with biological studies of spermidine analogs,[8] originally designed as intermediates in the synthesis of microbial siderophores,[9] these investigators introduced specifically designed spermidine analogs[10-16] followed by a much larger array of spermine analogs.[17-22] Their efforts have been joined by several other groups so that the area of polyamine analogs has evolved into one of considerable size and application within the field. Although originally intended as potential anticancer agents,[23-26] these analogs are finding increasing usefulness in other therapeutic areas[27] and also in studying regulatory responses asso-

---

Primary Enzymes

Ornithine Decarboxylase (ODC)
    DFMO (MDL-71782) and MFMO (Bey, Merrell-Dow)
    RRMAP (MDL-72175) (Mamont, Merrell-Dow)
    APA (Khomutov, Moscow Academy of Sciences)
    AFPA (Stanek, Ciba-Geigy)

S-Adenosylmethionine Decarboxylase (AdoMetDC)
    AMA (Khomutov, Moscow)
    AbeAdo (MDL-73811) (Seiler, Merrell-Dow)
    MAOEA, MHZPA (Secrist, Southern Research Institute)
    CGP-48664 (Stanek, Ciba-Geigy)

Spermidine Synthase
    AdoDATO (Coward, University of Michigan)
    MCHA (Shirahata, Japan Joshai University)

Spermine Synthase
    AdoDATAD (Coward, Michigan)
    BDAP (Mamont, Merrell-Dow)
    APCHA (Shirahata, Japan)
    DMTA (Coward, Michigan)

Spermidine/Spermine N^1-Acetyltransferase (SSAT)
    None for cultured cells

Polyamine Oxidase (PAO)
    MDL-72527 (Seiler, Merrell-Dow)

Related Enzymes

S-Adenosylmethionine Synthase
    L-cisAMB (Sufrin, Roswell Park Cancer Institute)

N^8-Acetyl Spermidine Deacetylase
    APAHHA (Blankenship and Fries, University of the Pacific)

Fig. 7.1. The most selective and effective inhibitors of each of the polyamine metabolic enzymes The structures for each of these inhibitors are represented in Figure 7.3.

ciated with polyamine pool maintenance,[10,28] and more recently in probing polyamine function. Rather than introducing the multitude of polyamine derivatives synthesized to study polyamine metabolism or function, this chapter will only include those analogs developed as potential therapeutic agents.

Polyamine inhibitors and analogs have been frequently reviewed[10,21,24,25,29,30-32] particularly in their role as potential anticancer agents. Although at present, there are at least six such agents entering or undergoing phase I clinical trial (Fig. 7.2), it is not the purpose of this chapter to further survey the therapeutic potential of such compounds. Rather, it will briefly review current

Current Polyamine Clinical Studies	
Inhibitor/Analog	**Indication/Status**
DFMO	chemoprevention trial anti-trypanosomal therapy brain tumors cervical dysplasia
MGBG	non-Hodgkins lymphoma
DENSPM (DE-333)	melanoma, lung cancer, etc Phase I underway Phase II imminent
DEHSPM (DE-444)	AIDS-related diarrhea Phase I underway
DE-373 (BEPH)	solid tumors Phase I discontinued
CGP-48664	melanoma, lung cancer, etc Phase I underway
DE-4444	solid tumors Phase I pending

Fig. 7.2. Current clinical trials with polyamine biosynthetic inhibitors and polyamine analogs. The sponsor or company supporting these efforts are as follows: DFMO, National Cancer Institute and World Health Organization; DENSPM, SunPharm and Parke Davis; DEHSPM, SunPharm; DE-373, Marion Merrell-Dow; CGP-48664, Ciba-Geigy; DE-4444, National Cancer Institute.

inhibitors and analogs, describe the recently elucidated polyamine regulatory responses which confront such molecules in cells, and then focus on the relationship between polyamine pool changes achieved with inhibitors and inhibitor combinations in the process of cell proliferation.

II. POLYAMINE INHIBITORS

A. ODC INHIBITORS

The first rationally designed inhibitors of ODC were produced by Bey and his colleagues at Merrell-Dow.[33,34] These investigators chemically altered either the substrate, ornithine, or the product, putrescine, to produce a series of competitive or enzyme-activated irreversible inhibitors of ODC. In general, competitive inhibitors bind reversibly, stabilize the enzyme and lead to an accumulation of the ODC protein. This feature facilitates a rapid recovery of polyamine biosynthesis upon drug removal. As a rule, reversible inhibitors are not as effective as irreversible (enzyme-activated) inhibitors in achieving polyamine depletion. The most potent of the competitive series are the aminooxy derivatives of putrescine that act at the pyridoxal phosphate (PLP) cofactor binding site and inhibit ODC at 100-fold lower levels (in the nM range) when compared to other ornithine derivatives. One of the inhibitors of this series warrants consideration. First developed by the Khomutov's in 1985,[35,36] the putrescine analog, 1-aminooxy-3-aminopropane (APA, shown in Fig. 7.3), potently inhibits ODC (Ki = 3.2 nM) and decreases polyamine pools and cell growth in the low micromolar range. Although it affects other polyamine biosynthetic enzymes,[35] APA is relatively selective for ODC at low concentrations. In fact, L1210 cells which overproduce ODC are resistant to the growth inhibitory effects of APA, and concurrent treatment with putrescine abrogates APA mediated growth inhibition in other cell lines.[37] Traditionally, prevention of growth inhibition by concurrent treatment with exogenous polyamines is indicative of an inhibitor's specificity for the polyamine pathway. These data are meaningful as long as the inhibitor does not rely on the polyamine transporter for uptake, otherwise, polyamines prevent its intracellular accumulation. APA (unlike MGBG) does

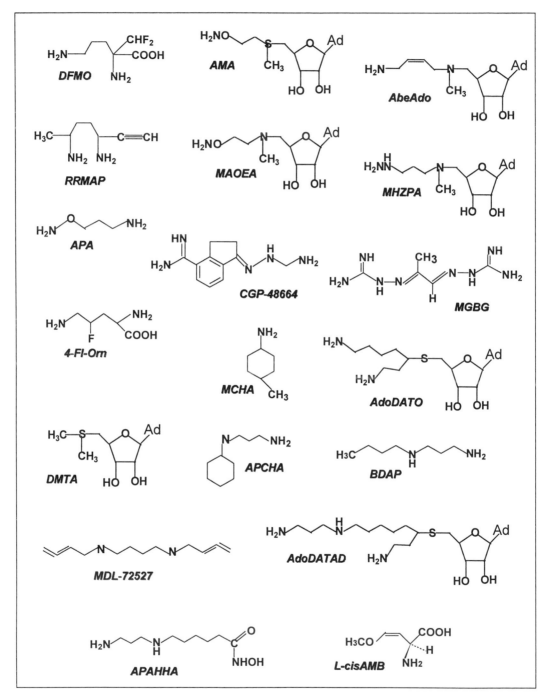

Fig. 7.3. Structures of the biosynthetic inhibitors and the alternative substrate for ODC, 4-Fl-Orn. The complete chemical names are included in the text. Ad = Adenosine.

not rely on the polyamine transporter for cellular uptake.[38] Chemists at Ciba-Geigy synthesized a series of analogs designed to take advantage of the potent enzyme and growth inhibitory features of APA and to further evaluate the therapeutic potential of this novel structure. The analog, 3-aminooxy-2-fluoro-1-propanamine (AFPA), was more selective and potent than APA and acted as an irreversible inhibitor of ODC.[39] When compared with DFMO, AFPA demonstrated much greater antitumor activity against the human T24 bladder carcinoma[39,40] and is currently being considered for clinical development.

The design of irreversible inhibitors for ODC was based on the success of earlier enzyme-activated inhibitors to other PLP-dependent enzymes. Thus, mechanism-based derivatives of ornithine serve as alternative substrates, are decarboxylated by ODC, and generate a reactive species that covalently binds to the active site.[41] A detailed mechanistic and structure/function analysis describing their development is available.[33] The best derivatives are the α-fluoromethylornithine series,[3,42] that irreversibly bind ODC and inactivate the enzyme. Although more potent irreversible inhibitors of the enzyme were identified,[43] DFMO (Figs. 7.1 and 7.3) was the first to be developed for clinical testing (Fig. 7.2). In the mid 1980s, DFMO underwent a limited clinical evaluation against solid tumors and failed due to a lack of potency. The latter can be largely attributed to the inability of DFMO to penetrate cells effectively—typically millimolar concentrations are required to achieve in vitro growth inhibition. Owing to its long time availability from Merrell-Dow and its extreme reliability as a specific ODC inhibitor, DFMO has achieved the most widespread use of any polyamine inhibitor.[32] As is now known to be typical of most ODC inhibitors, DFMO depletes intracellular putrescine and spermidine pools with only minimal changes in spermine pools. The data are consistent with a critical role for spermidine in cell growth. Thus, when growth halts due to spermidine depletion, spermine pools remain constant since they can no longer be diluted by cell division, the major mechanism for intracellular polyamine reduction. The potential for spermine to substitute for spermidine in cell growth will be discussed later.

Other second generation irreversible inhibitors modeled after DFMO were methyl esterified (E)-α-fluoromethyldehydro-ornithine (MFMO)[42] and the putrescine analog, (2R,5R)-6-heptyne-2,5-diamine (MDL-72175, also known as RRMAP, shown in Fig. 7.3),[43-46] and found to be 10 to 100 times more potent than DFMO because they were able to penetrate cells more effectively. Under certain conditions RRMAP depleted spermine pools more effectively than DFMO,[44,47] but no additional effects on growth inhibition were detected. This is somewhat unexpected since as will be discussed later, inhibitor combinations which bring about depletion of all three polyamines are more effective than single enzyme inhibitors which invariably leave one of the polyamines.

B. AdoMetDC Inhibitors

An appealing biological feature of AdoMetDC inhibitors is that while they increase putrescine pools, they concomitantly deplete both spermidine and spermine pools. Rationally designed inhibitors with the ability to achieve selective and sustained inhibition of the enzyme in cell culture have been classified as either substrate (AdoMet) or product (dcAdoMet) based derivatives. The only effective alternative structure to these nucleoside inhibitors is MGBG. Several reviews describing the mechanism of AdoMetDC inhibition for each type of inhibitor are available.[29,30] Foremost among the specific AdoMetDC inhibitors are the irreversible nucleoside derivatives which bind covalently to the pyruvate moiety of the AdoMetDC active site. These include S-(5'-deoxy-5'-adenosyl)methylthioethylhydroxylamine (AMA),[48] 5'-deoxy-5'-[N-methyl-N-(3-hydrazinopropyl)]aminoadenosine (MHZPA),[49] and 5'-deoxy-5'-{N-methyl-N-[2-(amino-oxy)ethyl]}aminoadenosine (MAOEA) (structures in Fig. 7.3).[49] Although these inhibitors have served as useful tools for studying the regulation of AdoMetDC and the cellular consequences of spermidine and spermine depletion,[49-51] their susceptibility to degradation have limited their utility as experimental antitumor agents. Based on the successful design of DFMO, the enzyme-activated irreversible inhibitor, 5'-{[(Z)-4-amino-2-butenyl]methylamino}-5'-deoxy-adenosine (MDL-73811, also known as AbeAdo, shown in Fig. 7.3) was designed for AdoMetDC.[52] Unlike other nucleoside inhibitors, this inhibitor was stable in animals,[53] demonstrated sustained inactivation of AdoMetDC[51,53] and markedly reduced tumor growth sufficient to warrant therapeutic applications.[53] Unfortunately, this inhibitor has not been developed for clinical trial but remains an excellent tool for biochemical studies. For example, chronic treatment of L1210 cells with AbeAdo led to the first demonstration that cell growth was dependent on spermidine for the synthesis of hypusinated eIF-5A translation factor[54,55] (discussed later). At present, two synthetic programs are continuing to study new derivatives of AdoMet and AbeAdo. Woster and colleagues have evaluated the potential for irreversible inhibition of AdoMetDC by certain diastereomeric forms of AdoMet derivatives that can distinguish between the human, *Escherichia coli* and *Trypanosoma brucei brucei* enzymes.[56-59] Sufrin's group is designing new derivatives of AbeAdo[60] to improve on the anti-trypanosomal effects already observed by Bitonti.[52] These studies may lead to the basis for the selective treatment of certain parasitic as well as other disease states.

MGBG (Figs. 7.1, 7.3 and 7.4) achieved clinical utility as an experimental antitumor agent prior to an understanding of its multiple biochemical effects. The discovery that it inhibited AdoMetDC and polyamine biosynthesis was among the earliest indications that polyamines are required for cell growth.[2] Its initial clinical failure due to host toxicity is attributable in part to a lack of understanding of its pharmacokinetics—unaltered drug persisted in tissues for weeks. Because pure polyamine inhibitors such as DFMO are by comparison relatively nontoxic, it is now believed that the severe host toxicities of MGBG are probably related to nonspecific effects such as interference with mitochondrial structure and function.[1,2] Several attempts to revive MGBG clinically including combination studies with DFMO could not effectively offset eventual toxicity with sufficient antitumor activity.[23] It may have found a niche in the treatment of non-Hodgkin's lymphoma in AIDS patients and is currently undergoing a multi-institutional evaluation (Fig. 7.2).

Despite its clinical limitations, its potency as a non-nucleoside analog inhibitor of AdoMetDC and its ability to utilize polyamine transport to gain entry and concentrate in cells render it a novel and interesting polyamine antagonist. In 1979, Paul et al[61] proposed that the structural similarities between MGBG and the substrate AdoMet (Fig. 7.4) may serve as determinants in the ability of MGBG to inhibit AdoMetDC. In recognition of the unique biological properties of MGBG and of its importance as the only

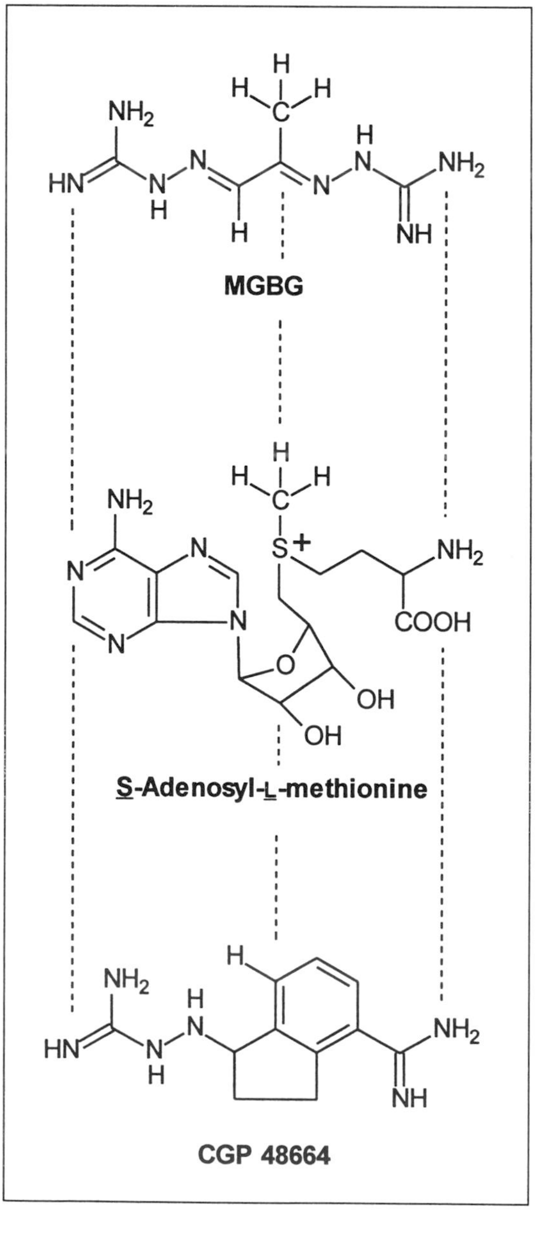

Fig. 7.4. Structural correlation of MGBG and CGP-48664 to AdoMet. A recent update by Dr. B. Paul, B. Mayer, and C.W. Porter to the original publication[61] describing the structural similarities between MGBG and AdoMet.

alternative structure to nucleoside inhibitors of AdoMetDC, Ciba-Geigy initiated a synthetic program to develop structural derivatives of MGBG.[62] Those showing increased potency as inhibitors of AdoMetDC, remaining metabolically stable and at the same time displaying minimized nonspecific effects, were chosen. The bicyclic analog of MGBG, 4-(aminoiminomethyl)-2,3-dihydro-1H-inden-1-one-diaminomethylenehydrazone (CGP-48664, shown in Figs. 7.3 and 7.4)[63] not only fulfilled these criteria but represents the candidate with sufficient broad and potent antitumor activity[64] to warrant clinical trial. Interestingly, by rendering the compound more specific for polyamine biosynthesis, the investigators eliminated most of the severe toxicities associated with the parent compound. Thus, CGP-48664 has a much broader therapeutic window than MGBG.

The mechanistic basis for the antiproliferative activity of CGP-48664 has been extensively evaluated in cell culture systems. The reader is cautioned that before in vitro results can be extended to in vivo systems considerably more animal studies need to be completed. CGP-48664 acts as a tight binding competitive inhibitor of AdoMetDC (Dr. Helmut Mett, personal communication), and has a Ki (4.7 nM) which is ~200 and 50 times more potent than that of MGBG or AMA, respectively.[64] Thus, AdoMetDC activity in many cell types treated with CGP-48664 decreases similar to other irreversible inhibitors of AdoMetDC. This is in contrast to treatment with MGBG where, as a result of enzyme stabilization, enzyme activity increases several-fold. Despite its increased affinity towards the enzyme, the antiproliferative activity of CGP-48664 against a panel of tumor cell lines ranges similar to that of MGBG, in the low micromolar range.[64] This appears to be due to the fact that unlike MGBG which utilizes the polyamine transporter and is effectively concentrated in cells in this manner, CGP-48664 does not share the same uptake mechanism. Mutant cell lines lacking polyamine transport are resistant to MGBG, but they remain sensitive to CGP-48664.[64] Thus, in addition to having attenuated mitochondrial effects, CGP-48664 differs from MGBG by utilizing an alternative transport mechanism. The specificity of CGP-48664 for AdoMetDC is strongly supported by intracellular polyamine perturbations that appear similar to highly specific nucleoside inhibitors. These include a rapid depletion of spermidine and spermine pools, while putrescine pools accumulate remarkably due to compensatory increases in ODC activity and blockade of synthesis beyond putrescine. Without competition for uptake (not the case with MGBG), prevention and/or reversal studies demonstrate that growth inhibition in L1210 cells was completely prevented by spermidine treatment.

Perhaps the specificity of CGP-48664 is best indicated by CHO cells made resistant to the drug (CHO/664 cells) by long-term exposure and clonal selection. Resistance of >1000-fold to CGP-48664 was accompanied by amplification of the AdoMetDC gene, an increase in AdoMetDC mRNA and an increase in AdoMetDC activity.[65] The CHO/664 cells represent the first example of cells which overexpress this gene due to stable gene amplification. These cells have usefulness for determining the consequences of this phenotype on cellular behavior, studying the regulation of this enzyme and its relationship to intracellular polyamine pools and/or transport, and for evaluating the specificity of other potential inhibitors to AdoMetDC. In this regard, CHO/664 cells were found to be cross resistant to the nucleoside inhibitors, AMA and MDL-73811.[65]

C. SPERMIDINE SYNTHASE INHIBITORS

Growth inhibition was attainable using inhibitors of ODC or AdoMetDC provided they penetrated cells and were reasonably potent as enzyme inhibitors. Since the former leave residual spermine pools and the latter, putrescine pools, the two inhibitor types have spermidine depletion in common. Since this suggests that spermidine may actually be the critical polyamine for cell growth, it was speculated that an effective depletion of this pool might be accomplished by direct inhibition of spermidine synthase.[66-68] The transition state analog, S-adenosyl-3-thio-1,8-diaminooctane (AdoDATO, shown in Fig. 7.3) designed and synthesized by Coward's group was found to specifically and potently inhibit spermidine synthase and effectively deplete spermidine pools.[69-71] This depletion of spermidine resulted in growth inhibition in several cell lines[67] and inhibition of MEL cell differentiation.[72] The consequences of AdoDATO treatment differed from those of ODC and AdoMetDC inhibitors in that, in addition to depleting spermidine pools, there was an increase in intracellular putrescine and spermine pools resulting in no change in the total polyamine content of the cells.[67,69,70] As shown by inhibitor combination studies (to be discussed later), this almost certainly compromised the growth inhibitory potential of AdoDATO.

Several competitive inhibitors to the putrescine binding site of spermidine synthase include methylthiopropylamine (MTPA),[73] dicyclohexylamine (DCHA),[74] and trans-4-methylcyclohexylamine (MCHA, shown in Fig. 7.3).[66,68] Overall, these inhibitors have been most useful for studying the regulatory responses of the polyamine pathway to spermidine depletion. Although they are capable of inhibiting growth of cultured cells, the specificity of these compounds for therapeutic use remains in doubt.

D. Spermine Synthase Inhibitors

Selective spermine synthase inhibitors (shown in Fig. 7.3) include the multisubstrate adduct analog *S*-adenosyl-1,12-diamino-3-thio-9-azadodecane (AdoDATAD),[75] *N*-(*n*-butyl)-1,3-diaminopropane (BDAP),[76,77] *N*-(3-aminopropyl)cyclohexylamine (APCHA),[68] and *S*-methyl-5'-methylthioadenosine (DMTA).[78] Of these, AdoDATAD which like AdoDATO was also synthesized by Coward's group is regarded as the most specific for the enzyme.[75] Typically, these inhibitors effectively deplete spermine pools to less than 10% of control levels in cultured cells, but due to a compensatory rise in AdoMetDC, spermidine pools actually increase.[79,80] Total intracellular polyamine levels are not reduced, and growth is not inhibited[81] most likely because spermidine pools are unaffected. The regulatory response of AdoMetDC has also compromised the use of these inhibitors in combination studies.[79] For example, AdoDATO plus DMTA or AdoDATAD treatment did not deplete spermidine and spermine pools, but rather resulted in cells containing a normal polyamine profile.[67,78,82] When either AdoDATAD or DMTA was combined with DFMO, the cells displayed a polyamine profile similar to DFMO treatment alone.[78] Although their obvious therapeutic potential is not apparent, inhibitors of spermine synthase have been useful in studying the regulatory consequences of spermine versus spermidine depletion. The fact that repression of AdoMetDC translation was greater for spermine[80] than spermidine became important in the development of polyamine analogs (discussed below). In general, the fact that cell growth was not affected by spermine pool depletion,[81] except in one case with prolonged BDAP treatment,[76] supports the possibility that spermine may not be essential for cell growth.

E. SSAT INHIBITORS

There are at least two enzymes known to be involved in the acetylation of spermidine and spermine.[83] One is the cytoplasmic spermidine/spermine N^1-acetyltransferase (SSAT) which specifically acetylates the aminopropyl moiety at both ends of the spermine molecule and at one end of the spermidine molecule. It is rate-limiting in the pathway which back-converts spermine to spermidine and the latter to putrescine via polyamine oxidase.[84,85] The other is the nuclear N^8-spermidine acetyltransferase (SAT) which specifically acetylates the aminobutyl moiety at one end of the spermidine molecule.[86] At present, no specific inhibitors of either acetylase enzymes are available to study the cellular consequences. An acetylCoA transition state analog has been synthesized to inhibit isolated extracts of SSAT, but since it is charged, it is not transported into cells.[87] Interest in this enzyme has been rejuvenated by the discovery that certain analogs of spermidine and spermine are capable of inducing SSAT up to 10,000 times basal levels.[18,88-92] The mechanism(s) involved in this induction are at least partially due to enzyme inhibition and will be discussed with polyamine analogs. The contribution of analog mediated SSAT induction to polyamine depletion and inhibition of cell growth, cytotoxicity, or apoptosis has been established on the basis of correlation's which although compelling, are not definitive. For example, unsymmetrically alkylated analogs of spermine with one terminal ethylation were recently shown to inhibit isolated SSAT and induce SSAT following cell treatment similar to the more extensively studied bisethylated analogs.[84,93] More recently these same two analogs not only elicited a cytotoxic response in human lung cell lines,[93] but induced apoptosis in human breast cancer cells.[94] This is the first example of induction of the apoptotic process by polyamine analogs. Establishing a better understanding of the structure-activity relationships involved in analog induction of SSAT may help design specific SSAT inhibitors that would be extremely useful in evaluating its involvement in some of these issues.

The interaction of spermidine and spermine with DNA has been frequently modeled and convincingly demonstrated to occur in acellular systems.[30] In the case of spermidine, the acetylation by the nuclear enzyme (SAT) at the N^8 position reduces the positive charge by one, and presumably decreases its ability to interact with DNA and destabilizes chromosomal structure. It is proposed that once nuclear spermidine is acetylated, it can be readily transported to the cytoplasm and further acted on by N^8-acetylspermidine deacetylase to regenerate spermidine thus giving rise to a possible regulatory cycle. Although no specific inhibitor for SAT has been identified to date, a series of inhibitors of the deactylase enzyme have been synthesized, the most potent being 6-[(3-amino-propyl)amino]-*N*-hydroxyhexanamide (APAHHA, shown in Fig. 7.3).[86] It may prove useful in resolving the importance of these enzymes in spermidine pool maintenance and its role in DNA stabilization, chromatin condensation and ultimately cell growth.

F. POLYAMINE OXIDASE INHIBITORS

The back conversion of spermine to spermidine and of spermidine to putrescine is mediated by the consecutive actions of N^1-acetylation (SSAT)[84,85] followed by oxidative removal of acetamidopropanal by polyamine oxidase (PAO).[71] By allowing for interconversion of the various polyamine species, the pathway affords the cell greater latitude in maintaining the proper balance of pools to ensure continued cell growth when the biosynthetic pathway is compromised or perturbed.[71,95] Although no inhibitors have been designed to specifically inactivate SSAT, a series of compounds have been designed by Seiler and colleagues[96,97] which very potently and efficiently inhibit PAO. The most widely used of this series is the polyamine analog, N^1,N^2-bis(2,3-butadienyl)-1,4-butanediamine (MDL-72527, shown in Fig. 7.3). Cells treated with this inhibitor alone are not growth inhibited, indicating that the back conversion pathway is not critical for cell growth under normal conditions. However, this inhibitor has been used to augment the effects of biosynthetic inhibitors and to achieve greater depletion of the polyamine pools and growth inhibition.[98,99] Several examples of these combinations will follow to demonstrate the importance and recruitment of the back conversion enzymes to circumvent polyamine depletion strategies. In another instance, MDL-72527 was effectively used in combination with the polyamine analog N,N^1-bis-[3-(ethylamino)-propyl]-1-7-heptane-diamine (BE-373) in order to prevent its metabolism by PAO and thereby enhance this analog's antiproliferative activity.[100]

G. AdoMet Synthase

Perhaps because AdoMet is the substrate for transmethylation reactions, the enzyme AdoMet synthase is generally not considered an important component of polyamine biosynthesis. Yet AdoMet is solely responsible for the production of dcAdoMet, the metabolite which contributes the aminopropyl moieties to form spermidine and spermine via the spermidine and spermine synthase reactions, respectively. The by-product of these reactions 5'-methylthioadenosine (MTA) will be considered below. Despite the potential duality of consequences, several groups have pursued the development of inhibitors of AdoMet synthase and considered their potential as chemotherapeutic agents.[24,101] The most effective inhibitor is L-2-amino-4-methoxy-cis-but-3-enoic acid (L-cisAMB, shown in Fig. 7.3) synthesized by Sufrin and coworkers.[102] Among other studies, the inhibitor has been used to examine the relationship between AdoMet pools and polyamine biosynthesis and to evaluate various regulatory responses.[103,104] From these and other studies such as those with CHO cells overexpressing AdoMetDC,[65] it seems apparent that AdoMet pools are remarkably well maintained and difficult to deplete under most circumstances. The implication that AdoMet synthase is sensitively regulated, and exists in multiple forms[105] warrants investigation especially since the cDNA has recently been cloned.[106]

H. MTA Phosphorylase

Portions of the by-product of polyamine biosynthesis, methylthioadenosine (MTA), are recycled back to adenine and to methionine for continued use in AdoMet biosynthesis.[107] The first step in that recycling pathway is mediated by MTA phosphorylase catalyzing the removal of the 3' phosphate group. Interest in this enzyme derives from the original finding by Toohey et al[108] that MTA phosphorylase is deficient in various tumor cell types. This lead has been actively pursued for some time by Carson and coworkers[109] who recently made the important discovery that MTA phosphorylase deficiency is associated with the loss of a specific tumor suppressor gene.[110] Since MTA is known to be toxic to cells,[111] those which are deficient in MTA phosphorylase have developed the means to actively export the metabolite. The rationale for inhibiting the enzyme is 2-fold: accumulation of MTA may be toxic to cells which have not yet acquired an export mechanism and/or certain tumor cell types such as those which are methionine-dependent[112] may be susceptible to interference with the recycling pathway. Analogs of MTA could potentially inhibit the enzyme, serve as substrates producing a toxic product, or act as more potent inhibitors of cell growth compared to MTA. Using these rationale, Sufrin and colleagues synthesized a panel of halogen-substituted MTA analogs.[110] One, 5'-hydroxyethylthioadenosine (HETA), has particular therapeutic potential in the treatment of the parasitic disease trypanosomiasis, commonly known as sleeping sickness. Although it is nontoxic to mammalian cells, its activity against the parasite both in vitro and in vivo involves interference with the recycling pathway.[113] The finding represents an important new lead in the treatment of this disease. The fluoro-analog, 5'-deoxy-5'-[(2-monofluoroethyl)thio]adenosine (MFETA), of this series was the most effective inhibitor as well as substrate towards the mammalian MTA phosphorylase and was the most potent inhibitor of cell growth.[114]

I. INHIBITOR COMBINATIONS

The combination of specific polyamine enzyme inhibitors offers the potential (a) to examine the consequences of maximal depletion of all three polyamine pools, (b) to evaluate the relative abilities of individual polyamines to support growth and viability, and (c) to more clearly understand pathway regulatory mechanisms. The combination is especially useful in the case of ODC and AdoMetDC inhibitors since the two enzymes are coregulated by intracellular polyamine pools so that inhibition of one results in a compensatory increase in the other. Although it has been shown that an ODC or AdoMetDC inhibitor can effectively shut down polyamine biosynthesis, their combined use provides a near total depletion of all three polyamine pools and a correspondingly greater effect on cell growth and colony formation.[48,53] Since the combination metabolically immobilizes the entire pathway, individual polyamine pools can be restored exogenously without their subsequent conversion to higher polyamines. Experiments of this nature were used to show that in L1210 cells, only spermidine was able to maintain cell growth and colony formation similar to untreated cells.[48] Although putrescine and spermine were capable of supporting growth during short-term incubations, they were far less effective than spermidine during extended incubations. Subsequent studies by Pegg's group suggest that this finding is related to the incorporation of spermidine into hypusine and the protein synthesis initiation factor eIF-5A.[54,115,116] Following prolonged exposure to the AdoMetDC inhibitor AbeAdo (8-12 cell doubling periods), growth was cytotoxically affected, and this was correlated to the loss of hypusinated eIF-5A. Clearly, spermine could not substitute for spermidine in this particular cellular function. However, since growth is cytostatically affected within one or two cell divisions, there must be other undefined functions which are supported by spermidine during the earlier phases of growth inhibition.

Numerous findings such as those reviewed above with biosynthetic inhibitors strongly suggest that spermidine is the preferred polyamine for cell growth. They do not, however, discount the possibility that putrescine and spermine at least partially substitute for spermidine in these functions. While this may not be the case under conditions of sustained growth inhibition, it is clearly true during the cytostatic phases of growth inhibition. The residual pool of spermine with ODC inhibitors and the increased putrescine pool with AdoMetDC inhibitors are capable of at least partially supporting growth of L1210 cells particularly during short-term incubations.[48] The inference that growth inhibition is indirectly related to intracellular polyamine content has had important implications in antiproliferative strategies, and total polyamine depletion is now recognized as an important goal.

To better understand the possible role of spermine in cell growth, a panel of human cell lines was compared with murine L1210 cells where exogenous spermine was observed to be unable to maintain extended cell growth (Table 7.1). Cells were incubated in the presence of DFMO and spermine. In contrast to murine L1210 cells, all of these cells were able to maintain growth between 60-95% of control in the presence of DFMO and exogenous spermine for at least 20 cell doubling times. However, by HPLC analysis, the polyamine profile showed that the large pool of spermine (about 125% of control values for each condition) was always accompanied by a small pool of spermidine (about 15-30% of control spermidine values. shown in Table 7.1). Under

Table 7.1. Dependence on back synthesis for exogenous spermine to support growth in various cell lines

Cell Lines*	L1210	LA4	K562	LOX	SH1	MALME-3M
Treatment**	Intracellular Spermidine Pools*** and Cell Growth****					
Untreated	1.61	3.2	1.64	2.20	0.56	2.62
	(0.23)	(0.62)	(0.30)	(0.54)	(0.12)	(0.28)
DFMO + SPM	<0.02	0.51	0.25	0.56	0.23	0.38
	(0.31)	(0.05)	(0.44)	(0.06)	(0.06)	
% Control Growth	4	80	73	59	95	85
DFMO + SPM + MDL-72527	<0.02	<0.02	<0.02	<0.02	<0.02	<0.02
% Control Growth	5	2	2	5	3	12

* The cell lines used are the mouse L1210 leukemia cells, human K562 leukemia cells, mouse LA4 melanoma cells, and the human LOX, SH-1, and MALME-3M melanoma cells.
** Each cell line was treated with 1mM DFMO plus 2 µM SPM and grown for at least 20 cell doubling times. When this treatment was combined with 45 µM MDL-72527, cell growth was monitored for at least six control cell doubling times. Samples were taken to determine polyamine pools and growth at 4, 8, 12 and 16 control cell doubling times for cells treated with DFMO + SPM, and at times equivalent to 4 and 6 control cell doubling times for cells treated with DFMO + SPM + MDL-72527.
*** Expressed as nmol/10^6 cells, spermidine pools represent an average of at least eight separate determinations by HPLC analysis, duplicate samples taken at each time point with standard deviations in parenthesis.
****Growth, represented as percent control growth, was determined by electronic particle counting and each number represents an average of eight values, duplicate samples taken at four separate time points, with standard deviations of <5%.

similar conditions, this same pool of spermidine did not appear in L1210 cells where growth was halted after six cell doubling times. Augmenting the DFMO and spermine treatment with the PAO inhibitor, MDL-72527, to inhibit the back conversion of spermine to spermidine, resulted in complete cessation of growth and the loss of the small spermidine pool in every cell line within four cell doubling times. At any point after growth was halted, the addition of exogenous spermidine was able to resume growth. This is illustrated in the SH-1 cells (Fig. 7.5). These data demonstrate that certain cell types are able to supplement forward synthesis of spermidine with the back conversion of spermine to spermidine in order to fulfill the absolute spermidine requirements for growth. Thus, what appeared initially to be the substitution of spermine for spermidine in supporting cell growth was in reality, supplementation of spermidine pools. Additionally, the data unequivocally demonstrate an absolute requirement of spermidine pools for cell growth functions that cannot be fulfilled by spermine. The role for spermidine is evidenced by complete cytostasis once forward and back biosynthesis is inhibited and spermidine pools reach nondetectable levels. This cytostasis occurs within four cell doubling times and is most likely unassociated with limitations in hypusine formation requiring 8-12 cell doubling times. The finding may have applied significance in treating certain tumors such as mouse leukemia L1210 which appears unable to interconvert polyamine pools and may therefore be more susceptible to inhibitors than normal tissues. It also supports the idea that the purpose of spermine in mammalian systems (spermine is not found in prokaryotes) is to serve as a reservoir to buffer the needs of the cell for spermidine.

J. FURTHER EVALUATION OF POLYAMINE BIOSYNTHETIC INHIBITORS

The measurement of polyamine pools following treatment with biosynthetic inhibitors represents a static consequence rather than a true indication of the status of metabolic flux. Our laboratory in collaboration with Ciba-Geigy recently designed a monofluoro derivative of ornithine, 4-fluoro-L-ornithine (4-Fl-Orn, structure in Fig. 7.3), to be used in measuring metabolic flux through

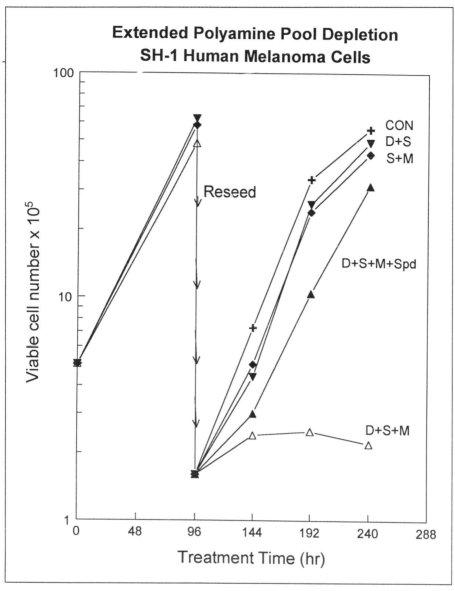

Fig. 7.5. *The effects of extended treatment with polyamine inhibitors in the human melanoma cell line, SH-1, to determine the ability of spermine to support cell growth. The SH-1 cells were grown for the initial 96 hr (3-4 cell doubling times) in the absence (CON, - + -) or presence of 1 mM DFMO plus 2 μM Spm (D+S, - ▼ -); 2 μM Spm plus 45 μM MDL-72527 (S+M, - ◆ -); and 1 mM DFMO plus 2 μM Spm plus 45μM MDL-72527 (D+S+M; - △ -). At 96 hr, these cells were reseeded and treatment was continued for an additional 144 hr. A portion of the D+S+M-treated cells were also treated at reseed with 1 μM Spd (D+S+M+Spd; - ▲ -). Cell growth was monitored by electronic particle counting and the total cell number per flask was plotted with time for each condition. Not shown were cells treated with DFMO+MDL-72527 whose growth was inhibited within the first 96 hr period. These curves are representative of at least five separate determinations and standard deviations were less than 10%.*

polyamine pools and the effects of inhibitors on this pathway.[117] Fl-Orn is recognized by ODC as an alternative substrate leading to the formation of Fl-putrescine and its subsequent conversion to Fl-spermidine and Fl-spermine. These fluorinated derivatives appeared as distinct peaks by HPLC and accumulated in a time-dependent manner with the same apparent efficiency as the natural polyamines. Substitution of the natural polyamines with the fluoro-analogs was well-tolerated by the cells for up to 72 hours.[117] These data indicate that Fl-Orn treatment could be used to monitor the rate of metabolic flux through the intracellular polyamine pools, since the static measurements of polyamine pool sizes following treatment with the enzyme inhibitors does not resolve this issue.

K. SUMMARY OF INHIBITORS

There now exists an extensive array of compounds capable of inhibiting nearly every enzyme of the polyamine biosynthetic/catabolic pathway. Treatment with the most potent and selective inhibitors alone or in combination yield a near total depletion of polyamine pools in cultured cells. This has aided our understanding of the role of the individual polyamines in cell growth and the association of the polyamines to certain cellular functions. For example, using DFMO, spermine and MDL-72527, an absolute requirement for spermidine in cell growth functions was demonstrated, and the rapid response to treatment suggested the involvement of sites other than limitations in hypusine formation. Unfortunately, even with an effective and immediate blockade of polyamine biosynthesis, a treatment time of at least four cell doubling times is required to deplete the total polyamine pool. This is because the existing polyamines which are in excess are depleted only after dilution by subsequent cell divisions. Also, the compensatory increases in uninhibited enzymes and up-regulation of polyamine transport have probably contributed to limited use of these inhibitors in vivo. For example, our dietary consumption of polyamines would potentially compromise therapy. Further, depletion of polyamine pools usually results in a state of cytostasis, and following cessation of inhibitor treatment, cell or tumor growth resumes. The systems in which inhibitors have been effective will be discussed in other chapters.

III. POLYAMINE ANALOGS

Polyamine analogs were initiated by Porter, Bergeron and colleagues[10] as an alternative approach to interference with polyamine biosynthesis. The strategy proposed to exploit inherent regulatory responses of the polyamine biosynthetic pathway—the same responses that, in fact, were responsible for at least partially compromising the effectiveness of polyamine enzyme inhibitors. In particular, these involved the regulatory responses which lead to up-regulation of ODC and AdoMetDC by polyamine pool depletion and their down-regulation by intracellular polyamine (or polyamine analog) excess.[28] This regulatory approach[10,28] proposed to identify structural analogs of spermidine and spermine which would penetrate the cells effectively, down-regulate one or both of the key biosynthetic enzymes, deplete intracellular polyamine pools, and inhibit cell growth by failing to substitute for the growth-related functions of the polyamines. This synthetic and biochemical screening effort determined that the structural modification of polyamines best meeting these criteria was alkylation (rather than acetylation in order to retain charge) of both terminal amines (rather that the central amine) with ethyl (rather that methyl or propyl) groups.[24] These N-terminally bis-ethylated-polyamine analogs accumulated intracellularly by the polyamine transport system to concentrations comparable to the natural polyamines themselves.[118] As revealed by growth inhibition prevention studies with DFMO, they were unable to support growth. A biological comparative study[119] of bis-ethyl analogs of putrescine, spermidine and spermine showed that bis(ethyl)putrescine (BEPut) was least effective at down regulating either enzyme, bis(ethyl)spermidine (BESpd) down-regulated only ODC, and bis(ethyl)spermine (BESpm), at a one log lower concentration than BESpd, down-regulated both ODC and AdoMetDC and achieved the most total depletion of all three polyamines as a single agent. The loss in enzyme activity was purely a regulatory response and, in similarity to the natural polyamines, this occurred at the level of enzyme protein synthesis specifically during translation.[120] Therefore, BESpm (also known as DESPM) became the lead compound for the regulatory strategy and has been widely used in mechanistic studies and in evaluating cell line sensitivity to this class of compounds. (The nomenclature is mixed in the literature designating the same analog as either DE or BE.)

In addition to the ability to down-regulate ODC and AdoMetDC, BESpm was also found to potently suppress polyamine uptake. Recent studies[121] have shown within 1 hour, 10 μM BESpm can effectively decrease spermidine transport by >80%. A potential chemotherapeutic benefit of this particular response would be to minimize salvage of exogenous polyamines by tumor tissues in animals since several groups have clearly demonstrated the importance of this mechanism in obviating the antitumor activity of polyamine inhibitors.[99,122] A further metabolic response of these analogs with potential significance of its own, was the very potent induction of SSAT activity. Whereas prior to these studies, SSAT was known to be inducible by up to 3-fold by toxic agents such as MGBG, BESpm was found to induce the enzyme by several hundred-fold.[17] Although unintended by analog design, this potent induction of SSAT was recognized to have the potential to contribute to polyamine depletion and hence to growth inhibition since acetylation of polyamines is known to facilitate their catabolism and/or excretion out of the cell.[85,89,92] Indeed it was first noted by Casero et al[91] that induction of SSAT correlated with cytotoxic growth inhibition. This was also confirmed in our own laboratory in the LOX and MALME-3M melanoma cell lines that displayed strikingly different responses to analog treatment.[88,89] Whereas the analog was accumulated to equivalent levels in both cell lines, SSAT was induced to 80-fold higher levels in the MALME-3M cells, and the rate of polyamine pool depletion was significantly greater. Correlating with polyamine pool depletion, MALME-3M cells were much more sensitive than LOX cells to growth inhibition by the analog.

Subsequent structure-function studies revealed that the more aminopropyl moieties contained within the spermine analog, the greater the ability to induce SSAT.[17,18,89] Thus, N[1]-bis(ethyl)norspermine (DENSPM also known as BENSPM) emerged as the most potent analog in this regard. In comparative in vivo studies with other homologs, DENSPM was also found to be the best tolerated in mice and the most effective in reducing the growth of human melanoma xenographs, a relatively slow growing tumor.[124] Analysis of these tumors showed a correlation to the homolog's ability to be retained selectively by the tumor (compared to normal tissue) and to the homolog's ability to induce SSAT activity.[124] Since this correlation was not as convincing in several other solid tumor models,[123] other factors are probably involved. Several studies have shown analog effects on protein synthesis and mitochondrial function.[125,126] A recent report by Igarashi et al[127] showed that the effects of the least toxic bis(ethyl) pentaamine derivative, 1,15-bis(ethylamino)-4,8,12-triazapentadecane (BE-3333), modeled after DENSPM and effective against rapid and slow-growing tumors, reduces polyamine pools as well as cytoplasmic and mitochondrial protein synthesis.

The in vivo advantages of bis(ethylated) polyamine moieties were recognized by others as a viable approach to new and novel antitumor agents and led to the development of additional analogs whose primary mechanism of action was not focused on interference with polyamine biosynthesis. These include N,N^1-bis-[3-(ethylamino)-propyl]-1-7-heptanediamine (BEPH, also known as DE-373) which acts through uncertain mechanisms[100] and 1,19-bis(ethylamino)-5,10,15-triazanonadecane (DE-4444)[128] which was designed to interact dysfunctionally with DNA.[129]

A. SUMMARY OF POLYAMINE ANALOGS

Some of the disadvantages discussed above with biosynthetic inhibitors have been circumvented by the development of polyamine analogs. Treatment with these analogs results in a more rapid depletion of polyamine pools than divisional dilution would predict. This is aided by the combined homeostatic responses including SSAT induction and the down-regulation of polyamine biosynthesis and transport. Additionally, the replacement of analog for the natural polyamines may account for the observed cytotoxicity in select tumor types. These factors along with the relatively nontoxic consequences to normal tissues have contributed to the use of polyamine analogs as single therapeutic agents.

IV. POLYAMINE HOMEOSTASIS

The polyamines are well-known for their ability to regulate their own intracellular concentrations in the millimolar range. The significance of this property undoubtedly relates to the fact that for the most part, polyamines do not incorporate into macromolecules, but remain as positively charged molecules which represent functional entities to the cell. Unlike inorganic cations such as calcium, magnesium or manganese which similarly participate in such functions, the charges of the polyamines are multiple and specifically spaced in an array presumed to be optimized for the interactive roles which they fulfill. Because decreases in polyamine pools interfere with cell growth, and since even subtle increases in certain pools appear to be toxic, cells have developed a complex homeostatic apparatus to sensitively maintain polyamine pools within a relatively narrow range unique to each cell type. The three homeostatic effectors recognized thus far are the biosynthetic enzymes ODC and AdoMetDC, the active polyamine transport mechanism, and the rate limiting enzyme in the back conversion pathway, SSAT (Fig. 7.6). All are specific for their respective polyamine function and sensitively regulated by the polyamines themselves.[28] While biosynthesis and transport have the potential to increase pools, SSAT provides a way to decrease intracellular pools via excretion and/or catabolism. Therefore, biosynthesis and transport are negatively controlled by polyamine pools, and acetylation is positively controlled. In response to polyamine depletion as caused by polyamine inhibitors, biosynthetic enzymes[10] and transport increase[121] in activity while SSAT decreases in activity.[130] Thus, the homeostatic responses act in concert to oppose the goals of the inhibitor strategy. While biosynthetic inhibitors have achieved some success, their utility as antitumor agents is complicated by complex factors related to these homeostatic responses. The component relating to increased transport in response to polyamine depletion appears to be the most serious. Several animal and clinical studies best illustrate the tumors' ability to salvage polyamines from exogenous sources. By using polyamine deprivation strategies involving dietary restriction,[131] gut sterilization with antibiotics,[99] and prevention of back conversion with MDL-72527,[95] DFMO could fully suppress the growth of solid tumors.[98,99,132] Another study by Persson et al[122,133] reported that DFMO can produce a number of cures in animals implanted with L1210 leukemia cells deficient in polyamine transport, while having only a minor effect in mice with the wild-type tumor. Attempts to exploit this transport response by pretreating with DFMO prior to MGBG which utilizes the polyamine transporter system in humans[91,134] or mice[135,136] led to a nonspecific increased accumulation of MGBG in normal tissues as well as the tumor and in some cases intensified toxicities.[23,137] The fact that the MGBG analog, CGP-48664, does not utilize the polyamine transporter for uptake may indicate a potential advantage for its use with DFMO.

In response to polyamine excess or perceived polyamine excess as mimicked by polyamine analogs the homeostatic effectors act

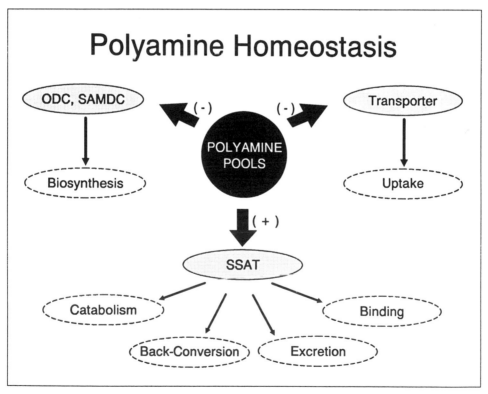

Fig. 7.6. Schematic depicting polyamine homeostasis. The three effectors of polyamine pools are (1) the biosynthetic enzymes, ODC and SAMDC, (2) the transporter, and (3) the catabolic enzyme, SSAT. The first two are negatively regulated by polyamine or polyamine analog treatment, whereas SSAT is positively regulated. In the case of polyamine depletion the first two are positively regulated and SSAT is negatively regulated.(Modified from a scheme originally published by Porter, Regenass and Bergeron, ref #31.)

oppositely.[10,31] Biosynthetic enzyme and transport activities are down-regulated while SSAT activity is up-regulated. In this case, the responses act to enhance the goal of the regulatory strategy. The sensitivity of these systems is illustrated by the rapid response of transport and the biosynthetic enzymes. Following an 1 hour exposure to 10 μM DESPM or SPM, the V_{max} values for SPD and SPM fall by 70% in response to only a 15-20% increase of the total polyamine content.[121] The down-regulation of ODC and AdoMetDC activities showed similar kinetics to these pool perturbations.[120] Consideration of these homeostatic mechanisms may serve to enhance the design and use of inhibitors and analogs as therapeutic agents.

V. CONCLUSIONS

Numerous studies using polyamine metabolic inhibitors or polyamine analogs have furthered our understanding of polyamines contribution to cell growth and other cellular functions. These functions include several homeostatic control mechanisms that are evenly regulated to maintain the total pools within a relatively constant range. Under stressed conditions where polyamine pools are depleted or in excess, the responses of these mechanisms are rapid and in some cases exaggerated. For example, the massive induction in SSAT following analog treatment indicates this site for further study. The development of a selective inhibitor of SSAT to prevent this induction would identify whether its role is as a homeostatic regulator in response to polyamine excess or a contributor to the cytotoxic process. In the case of polyamine transport, while its regulation has compromised inhibitor strategies, its presence is essential for analog accumulation. Thus, there has been a concerted effort to isolate and clone the mammalian transporter in order to better understand the importance of this highly regulated protein in the maintenance of polyamine pools and their accumulation by certain tissues. The ability to modulate this parameter could render a tissue sensitive or resistant to treatment strategies involving polyamines. Future directions will also include defining those parameters critically involved in eliciting a cytotoxic or apoptotic response to polyamine depletion and/or analog treatment. Of equal concern is to define those polyamine functions critical for cell growth, differentiation, apoptosis and other cellular physiologies to continue the design of more selective and effective analogs.

ACKNOWLEDGMENTS

I would like to thank Dr. Kenji Nishioka for the invitation to write this chapter. A special gratitude is extended to Dr. Carl Porter for his constructive editorial comments and conceptual contributions. The typing and library assistance of Julia Radeff and the computer generated chemical structures by Donna Felschow are greatly appreciated.

REFERENCES

1. Pleshkewych A, Kramer DL, Porter CW. Independence of drug action on mitochondria and polyamines in L1210 leukemia cells treated with methylglyoxyl-bis(guanylhydrazone). Cancer Res 1980; 40:4533-40.
2. Porter CW, Kramer DL, Mihich E. Recent clinical and experimental developments with methylglyoxal-bis(guanylhydrazone). In: Mathe G, Mihich E, Reizenstein P, eds. Current Drugs and Methods of Cancer Treatment, New York: Masson Publishing Co. 1983: 71-77.
3. Mamont PS, Duchesne MC, Grove J et al. Antiproliferative properties of DL-α-difluoromethyl ornithine in cultured cells. A consequence of the irreversible inhibition of ornithine decarboxylase. Biochem Biophys Res Commun 1978; 81:58-66.
4. Israel M, Rosenfield JS, Modest EJ. Analogs of spermine and spermidine. I. Synthesis of polymethylene polyamines by reduction of cyanoethylated α,ω-alkylenediamines. J Med Chem 1964; 7:710-16.
5. Israel M, Zoll EC, Muhammad N et al. Synthesis and antitumor evaluation of the presumed cytotoxic metabolites of spermine and N,N' bis(3-aminopropyl)nonane-1,9-diamine. J Med Chem 1973; 16:1-5.
6. Jorstad CM, Harada JJ, Morris DR. Structural specificity of the spermidine requirement of an *Escherichia coli* auxotroph. J Bacteriol 1980; 141:456-63.
7. Porter CW, Bergeron RJ. Spermidine requirement for cell proliferation in eukaryotic cells: Structural specificity and quantitation. Science 1983; 219:1083-85.

8. Porter CW, Bergeron RJ, Stolowich NJ. Biological properties of N^4-spermidine derivatives and their potential in anticancer chemotherapy. Cancer Res 1982; 42:4072-78.

9. Bergeron RJ, McGovern KA, Channing MA et al. Synthesis of N^4-acylated N^1,N^8-bis(acyl)spermidines: An approach to the synthesis of siderophores. J Org Chem 1980; 45:1589-92.

10. Porter CW, Bergeron RJ. Enzyme regulation as an approach to interference with polyamine biosynthesis—an alternative to enzyme inhibition. Adv Enzyme Regul 1988; 27:57-79.

11. Bergeron RJ, Stolowich NJ, Porter CW. Reagents for the selective secondary *N*-acylation of linear triamines. Synthesis 1982; 39:689-92.

12. Bergeron RJ, Garlich JR, Stolowich NJ. Reagents for the stepwise functionalization of spermidine, homospermidine, and bis(3-aminopropyl)amine. J Org Chem 1984; 49:2997-3001.

13. Bergeron RJ, Burton PS, McGovern KA et al. Reagents for the selective acylation of spermidine, homospermidine, and bis[3-aminopropyl]-amine. Synthesis 1981; 9:732-36.

14. Porter CW, Cavanaugh Jr PF, Stolowich N et al. Biological properties of N^4-and N^1,N^8-spermidine derivatives in cultured L1210 leukemia cells. Cancer Res 1985; 45:2050-57.

15. Porter CW, Berger FG, Pegg AE et al. Regulation of ornithine decarboxylase activity by spermidine and spermidine analogue N^1N^8-bis(ethyl)spermidine. Biochem J 1987; 242:433-40.

16. Porter CW, Ganis B, Vinson T et al. Comparison and characterization of growth inhibition in L1210 cells by α-difluoromethylornithine, an inhibitor of ornithine decarboxylase, and N^1,N^8-bis(ethyl)spermidine, an apparent regulator of the enzyme. Cancer Res 1986; 46:6279-85.

17. Libby PR, Bergeron RJ, Porter CW. Structure-function correlations of polyamine analog-induced increases in spermidine/spermine acetyltransferase activity. Biochem Pharmacol 1989; 38(9):1435-42.

18. Libby PR, Henderson M, Bergeron RJ et al. Major increases in spermidine/spermine-N^1-acetyltransferase activity by spermine analogs and their relationship to polyamine depletion and growth inhibition in L1210 cells. Cancer Res 1989; 49:6226-31.

19. Bergeron RJ, McManis JS, Liu CZ et al. Antiproliferative properties of polyamine analogues: A structure activity study. J Med Chem 1994; 37:3464-76.

20. Bergeron RJ, McManis JS, Weimar WR et al. The role of polyamine analogue recognition. J Med Chem 1995; 38:2278-85.

21. Bergeron RJ, Neims AH, McManis JS et al. Synthetic polyamine analogues as antineoplastics. J Med Chem 1988; 31:1183-90.

22. Bergeron RJ, McManis JS, Liu CZ et al. Antiproliferative properties of polyamine analogues: A structure-activity study. J Med Chem 1994; 37:3464-76.

23. Porter CW, Janne J. Modulation of antineoplastic drug action by inhibitors of polyamine biosynthesis. In: McCann PP, Pegg AE, Sjoerdsma A, eds. Inhibition of Polyamine Metabolism. Biological Significance and Basis for New Therapies. Orlando: Academic Press 1987: 203-48.

24. Porter CW, Sufrin JR. Interference with polyamine biosynthesis and/or function by analogs of polyamines or methionine as a potential anticancer chemotherapeutic strategy. Anticancer Res 1986; 6:525-42.

25. Pegg AE. Polyamine metabolism and its importance in neoplastic growth and as a target for chemotherapy. Cancer Res 1988; 48:759-74.

26. Nishioka K. International symposium on polyamines in cancer; Critical role of polyamines in cancer: Basic mechanisms and clinical approaches. Cancer Res 1993; 53:2689-92.

27. Pegg AE, McCann PP. Polyamine metabolism and function in mammalian cells and protozoans. ISI Atlas of Science: Biochemistry 1988: 11-18.

28. Porter CW, Kramer DL, Bernacki RJ et al. Regulation of polyamine biosynthetic activity and homeostasis as a novel antiproliferative strategy. In: Valeriote F, Corbett T. Baker LH, eds. Anticancer Drug Discovery. Boston: Kluwer Academic Publishers 1990: 325-44.

29. Pegg AE, McCann PP. S-adenosylmethionine decarboxylase as an enzyme target for therapy. Pharmac Ther 1992; 56:359-77.

30. Marton LJ, Pegg AE. Polyamines as targets for therapeutic intervention. Ann Rev Pharmcol Toxicol 1995; 35:55-91.

31. Porter CW, Regenass U, Bergeron RJ. Polyamine inhibitors and analogues as potential anticancer agents. In: Dowling RH, Fölsch UR, Löser C eds. Polyamines in the Gastrointestinal Tract 1992: 301-22.

32. McCann PP, Pegg AE. Ornithine decarboxylase as an enzyme target for therapy. Pharmac Ther 1992; 54:195-215.

33. Bey P, Danzin C, Jung M. Inhibition of basic amino acid decarboxylases involved in polyamine biosynthesis. In: McCann PP, Pegg AE, Sjoerdsma A, eds. Inhibition of Polyamine Metabolism. Biological Significance and Basis for New Therapies. Orlando: Academic Press, 1987: 1-31.

34. Danzin C, Bey P, Schirlin D et al. α-Monofluoromethyl and α-difluoromethyl putrescine as ornithine decarboxylase inhibitors: in vitro and in vivo biochemical properties. Biochem Pharmacol 1982; 31-23:3871-78.

35. Khomutov RM, Hyvonen T, Karvonen E et al. 1-Aminooxy-3-aminopropane, a new and potent inhibitor of polyamine biosynthesis that inhibits ornithine decarboxylase, adenosylmethionine decarboxylase and spermidine synthase. Biochem Biophys Res Commun 1985; 130: 596-602.

36. Hyvonen T, Alakuijala L, Andersson L et al. 1-aminooxy-3-aminopropane reversibly prevents the proliferation of cultured baby hamster kidney cells by interfering with polyamine synthesis. J Biol Chem 1988; 263-23:11138-44.

37. Poulin R, Secrist JA, Pegg AE. Effect of 1-amino-oxy-3-aminopropane on polyamine metabolism and growth of L1210 cells. Biochem J 1989; 263:215-21.

38. Hyvonen T, Khomutov AR, Khomutov RM et al. Uptake of ^{3}H labeled 1-aminooxy-3-aminopropane by baby hamster kidney cells. Biochem J 1990; 107:817-20.

39. Mett H, Stanek J, Lopez-Ballester JA et al. Pharmacological properties of the ornithine decarboxylase inhibitor 3-aminooxy-1-propanamine and several structural analogues. Cancer Chemother Pharmacol 1993; 32:39-45.

40. Stanek J, Frei J, Mett H et al. 2-Substituted 3-(aminooxy)propanamines as inhibitors of ornithine decarboxylase: Synthesis and biological activity. J Med Chem 1992, 35:1339-44.

41. Pegg AE, McGovern KA, West L. Decarboxylation of α-difluoromethylornithine by ornithine decarboxylase. Biochem J 1987; 241:305-7.

42. Mamont PS, Danzin C, Kolb M et al. Marked and prolonged inhibition of mammalian ornithine decarboxylase in vivo by esters of (E)-2-(fluoromethyl)dehydroornithine. Biochem Pharmacol 1986; 35(2):159-65.

43. Mamont PS, Siat M, Joder-Ohlenbusch AM et al. Effects of (2R,5R)-6-heptyne-2,5-diamine, a potent inhibitor of *L*-ornithine decarboxylase, on rat hepatoma cells cultured in vitro. Eur J Biochem 1984; 142:457-63.

44. Pera PJ, Kramer DL, Sufrin JR et al. A comparison of the biological effects of four irreversible inhibitors of ornithine decarboxylase in two murine lymphocytic leukemia cell lines. Cancer Res 1986; 46:1148-54.

45. Bartholeyns J, Mamont P, Casara P. Antitumor properties of (2R,5R)-6-heptyne-2,5-diamine, a new potent enzyme-activated irreversible inhibitor of ornithine decarboxylase, in rodents. Cancer Res 1984; 44:4972-77.

46. Danzin C, Casara P, Clavarie N. (2R,5R)-6-heptyne-2,5-diamine, an extremely potent inhibitor of mammalian ornithine decarboxylase. Biochem Biophys Res Commun 1983; 116:237-43.

47. Gerner P, Mamont PS. Restoration of the polyamine contents in rat hepatoma tissue-culture cells after inhibition of polyamine biosynthesis. Eur J Biochem 1986; 156:31-35.

48. Kramer DL, Khomutov RM, Bukin YV et al. Cellular characterization of a new irreversible inhibitor of S-adenosylmethionine decarboxylase and its use in determining the relative abilities of individual polyamines to sustain growth and viability of L1210 cells. Biochem J 1989; 259:325-31.

49. Madhubala R, Secrist JA III, Pegg AE. Effects of inhibitors of *S*-adenosylmethionine decarboxylase on the contents of ornithine decarboxylase and *S*-adenosylmethionine decarboxylase in L1210 cells. J Chem 1988; 254:45-50.

50. Autelli R, Sternborg L, Khomutov RM et al. Regulation of *S*-adenosylmethionine decarboxylase in L1210 leukemia cells. Eur J Biochem 1991; 196:551-56.

51. Stjernborg L, Heby O, Mamont P et al. Polyamine-mediated regulation of *S*-adenosylmethionine decarboxylase expression in mammalian cells. Eur J Biochem 1993; 214:671-76.

52. Bitonti AJ, Byers TL, Bush TL et al. Cure of *Trypanosoma brucei brucei* and *Trypanosoma brucei rhodesiense* infections in mice with an irreversible inhibitor of S-adenosylmethionine decarboxylase. Antimicrobial Agents Chemother 1990; 34:1485-90.

53. Seiler N, Sarhan S, Mamont P et al. Some biological consequences of S-adenosylmethionine decarboxylase inhibition by MDL-73811. Life Chemistry Reports 1991; 9:151-62.

54. Byers TL, Wiest L, Wechter RS et al. Effects of chronic 5'-{[(Z)-4-amino-2-butenyl}methylamino}-5'-deoxyadenosine (AbeAdo) treatment on polyamine and elF-5A metabolism in AbeAdo-sensitive and -resistant L1210 murine leukaemia cells. Biochem J 1993; 290:115-21.

55. Byers TL, Lakanen JR, Coward JK et al. The role of hypusine depletion in cytostasis induced by *S*-adenosyl-*L*-methionine decarboxylase inhibition: New evidence provided by 1-methylspermidine and 1, 12-dimethylspermine. Biochem J 1994; 303:363-68.

56. Guo JQ, Wu YQ, Farmer WL et al. Restricted rotation analogs of S-adenosylmethionine decarboxylase, and potential use as selective antitrypanosomal agents. Bioorg Med Chem Lett 1993; 3:147-52.

57. Wu YQ, Woster PM. Preparation of the pure diastereomeric forms of *S*-(5'-deoxy-5'-adenosyl)-1-ammonio-4-methylsulfonio-2-cyclopentene and their evaluation as irreversible inhibitors of *S*-adenosylmethionine decarboxylase from *Escherichia coli*. Bioorg Med Chem 1993, 1:349-60.

58. Wu YQ, Woster PM. Irreversible inhibition of human S-adenosylmethionine decarboxylase by the pure distereomeric forms

of S-(5'-deoxy-5'-adenosyl)-1-ammonio-4-methylsulfonio-2-cyclo-pentene (AdoMac). Biochem Pharmacol 1995; 49:1125-33.

59. Guo J, Wu YQ, Rattendi D et al. S-(5'-deoxy-5'-adenosyl)-1-aminoxy-4-(methylsulfonio)-2-cyclopentene (AdoMao): An irrevers-ible inhibitor of S-adenosylmethionine decarboxylase with potent in vitro antitrypanosomal activity. J Med Chem 1995; 38:1770-77.

60. Marasco CJ, Kramer D, Miller J et al. Synthesis and evaluation of analogs of *cis*-5'-deoxy-5'-(4-amino-2-butenyl) methylamino-adenosine (MDL-73811) as inhibitors of S-adenosylmethionine de-carboxylase and neoplastic cell growth. Proc Am Assoc Cancer Res 1995; 36:301.

61. Paul B, Dave C, Porter CW. Structural similarities between methylglyoxal-bis(guanylhydrazone), S-adenosyl-L-methionine and spermidine. 178th ACS Meeting 1979: 154.

62. Regenass U, Caravatti G, Mett H et al. New *S*-adenosylmethionine decarboxylase inhibitors with potent antitumor activity. Cancer Res 1992; 52:4712-18.

63. Stanek J, Caravatti G, Frei J et al. 4-Amidinoindan-1-one 2'-amidinohydrazone: A new potent and selective inhibitor of *S*-adenosylmethionine decarboxylase. J Med Chem 1993; 36:2168-71.

64. Regenass U, Mett H, Stanek J et al. CGP-48664, a new S-adenosylmethionine decarboxylase inhibitor with broad spectrum antiproliferative and antitumor activity. Cancer Res 1994; 54: 3201-17.

65. Kramer D, Mett H, Evans A et al. Stable amplification of *S*-adenosylmethionine decarboxylase gene in Chinese hamster ovary cells. J Biol Chem 1995; 270:2124-32.

66. Shirahata A, Morohohi T, Fukai M et al. Putrescine or spermidine binding site of aminopropyltransferases and competitive inhibitors. Biochem Pharmacol 1991; 41:205-12.

67. Coward JK, Pegg AE. Specific multisubstrate adduct inhibitors of aminopropyltransferases and their effect on polyamine biosynthesis in cultured cells. Adv Enzyme Regul 1987; 26:107-13.

68. Shirahata A, Takahashi N, Beppu T et al. Effects of inhibitors of spermidine synthase and spermine synthase on polyamine synthesis in rat tissues. Biochem Pharmacol 1993; 45:1897-1903.

69. Tang KC, Pegg AE, Coward JK. Specific and potent inhibition of spermidine synthase by the transition-state analog, S-adenosyl-3-thio-1,8-diaminoctane. Biochem Biophys Res Commun 1980; 96:1371-77.

70. Pegg AE, Tang KC, Coward JK. Effects of S-adenosyl-1,8-diamino-3-thiooctane on polyamine metabolism. Biochem 1982; 21:5082-89.

71. Tang KC, Mariuzza R, Coward JK. Synthesis and evaluation of some stable multisubstrate adducts as specific inhibitors of spermidine synthase. J Med Chem 1981, 24:1277-84.

72. Sherman ML, Shafman TD, Coward JK et al. Selective inhibition of spermidine biosynthesis and differentiation by S-adenosyl-1,8-diamino-3-thiooctane in murine erythroleukemia cells. Biochem Pharmacol 1986; 35:2633-36.

73. Hibasami H, Sakurai M, Maekawa S et al. Methylthiopropylamine, a potent inhibitor of spermidine synthase and its antiproliferative effect on human lymphoid leukemia molt 4B cells. Anticancer Res 1987; 7:1213-16.

74. Hibasami H, Tanaka M, Nagai J et al. Dicyclohexylamine, a potent inhibitor of spermidine synthase in mammalian cells. FEBS Lett 1980; 116:99-101.

75. Woster PM, Black AY, Duff KJ et al. Synthesis and biological evaluation of S-adenosyl-1,12-diamino-3-thio-9-azadodecane, a multisubstrate adduct inhibitor of spermine synthase. J Med Chem 1989; 32:1300-07.

76. Pegg AE, Coward JK. Effect of N-(n-butyl)-1,3-diaminopropane on polyamine metabolism, cell growth and sensitivity to chloroethylating agents. Biochem Pharmacol 1993; 46:717-724.

77. Baillon JG, Kolb M, Mamont PS. Inhibition of mammalian spermine synthase by N-alkylated-1,3-diaminopropane derivatives in vitro and in cultured rat hepatoma cells. Eur J Biochem 1989; 179:17-21.

78. Pegg AE, Coward JK, Talekar RR et al. Effects of certain 5'-substituted adenosines on polyamine synthesis: Selective inhibitors of spermine synthase. Biochem 1986; 25:4091-97.

79. Pegg AE, Wechter R, Poulin R et al. Effect of S-adenosyl-1,12-diamino-3-thio-9-azadodecane, a multisubstrate adduct inhibitor of spermine synthase, on polyamine metabolism in mammalian cells. Biochem 1989; 28:8446-53.

80. Pegg AE, Wechter R, Pajunen A. Increase in S-adenosylmethionine decarboxylase in SV-3T3 cells treated with S-methyl-5'-methylthioadenosine. Biochem J 1987; 244: 49-54.

81. Pegg AE, Coward JK. Growth of mammalian cells in the absence of the accumulation of spermine. Biochem Biophys Res Commun 1985; 133:82-89.

82. Holm I, Persson L, Pegg AE et al. Effects of S-adenosyl-1,8-diamino-3-thio-octane and S-methyl-5'-methylthioadenosine on polyamine synthesis in Ehrlich ascites-tumour cells. Biochem J 1989; 261:205-10.

83. Seiler N. Functions of polyamine acetylation. Can J Physiol Pharmacol 1987; 65:2024-35.

84. Woster PM. Spermidine/spermine-N^1-acetyltransferase (SSAT)—An emerging target for the design of antitumour agents. Curr Opin Invest Drugs 1993, 2:1291-99.

85. Casero Jr RA, Pegg AE. Spermidine/spermine N^1-acetyltransferase—the turning point in polyamine metabolism. FASEB J 1993; 7:653-61.

86. Huang TL, Dredar SA, Manneh VA et al. Inhibition of N^8-acetylspermidine deacetylase by active-site-directed metal coordinating inhibitors J Med Chem 1992; 35:2414-18.

87. Erwin BG, Persson L, Pegg AE. Differential inhibition of histone and polyamine acetylases by multisubstrate analogues. Biochemistry 1984; 23: 4250-55.

88. Shappell NW, Miller JT, Bergeron RJ et al. Differential effects of the spermine analog, N^1,N^{12}-bis(ethyl)-spermine, on polyamine metabolism and cell growth in human melanoma cell lines and melanocytes. Antican Res 1992; 12:1083-90.

89. Porter CW, Ganis B, Libby PR et al. Correlations between polyamine analogue-induced increases in spermidine/spermine N^1-acetyltransferase activity, polyamine pool depletion, and growth inhibition in human melanoma cell lines. Cancer Res 1991; 51:3715-20.

90. Fogel-Petrovic M, Shappell NW, Bergeron RJ et al. Polyamine and polyamine analog regulation of spermidine/spermine N^1-acetyltransferase in MALME-3M human melanoma cells. J Biol Chem 1993; 268:19118-25.

91. Casero RA, Celano P, Ervin SJ et al. Differential induction of spermidine/spermine N^1-acetyltransferase in human lung cancer cells by the bis(ethyl)polyamine analogues. Cancer Res 1989; 49:3829-33.

92. Pegg AE, Wechter R, Pakala R et al. Effect of N^1, N^{12}-bis(ethyl)spermine and related compounds on growth and polyamine acetylation, content, and excretion in human colon tumor cells. J Biol Chem 1989; 264:11744-49.

93. Saab NH, West EE, Bieszk NC et al. Synthesis and evaluation of unsymmetrical substituted polyamine analogues as modulators of human spermidine/spermine-N^1-acetyltransferase (SSAT) and as potential antitumor agents. J Med Chem 1993, 36-20:2098-3004.

94. McCloskey DE, Casero RA, Woster PM et al. Induction of programmed cell death in human breast cancer cells by an unsymmetrically alkylated polyamine analogue. Cancer Res 1995; 55:3233-36.

95. Bolkenius FN, Seiler N. The role of polyamine reutilization in depletion of cellular stores of polyamines in non-proliferating tissues. Biochim Biophys Acta 1987; 923:125-35.

96. Bey P, Bolkenius FN, Seiler N. N-2,3-Butadienyl-1,4-butanediamine derivatives: Potent irreversible inactivators of mammalian polyamine oxidase. J Med Chem 1985; 28:1-2.

97. Bolkenius FN, Bey P, Seiler N. Specific inhibition of polyamine oxidase in vivo is a method for the elucidation of its physiological role. Biochem Biophys Acta 1985; 838:69-76.

98. Claverie N, Wagner J, Knodgen B et al. Inhibition of polyamine oxidase improves the antitumor effect of ornithine decarboxylase inhibitors. Cancer Res 1987; 7:765-72.

99. Seiler N, Sarhan S, Grauffel C et al. Endogenous and exogenous polyamines in support of tumor growth. Cancer Res 1990; 50:5077-83.

100. Prakash NJ, Bowlin TL, Edwards ML et al. Antitumor activity of a novel synthetic polyamine analogue, N,N'-bis-[3-(ethylamino)-propyl]-1-7-heptane diamine: potentiation by polyamine oxidase inhibitors. Anticancer Res 1990; 10:1281-88.

101. Sufrin JR, Lombardini JB, Kramer DL et al. Methionine analog inhibitors of S-adenosylmethionine biosynthesis as potential antitumor agents. In: Borchardt RT, Creveling CR, Ueland PM, eds. Biological Methylation and Drug Design. Clifton, New Jersey: Humana Press; 373-84.

102. Sufrin JR, Lombardini JB, Keith DD. L-2-Amino-4-methoxy-cis-but-3-enoic acid, a potent inhibitor of the enzymatic synthesis of S-adenosylmethionine. Biochem Biophys Res Commun 1982; 106:251-55.

103. Kramer DL, Sufrin JR, Porter CW. Relative effects of S-adenosylmethionine depletion on nucleic acid methylation and polyamine biosynthesis. Biochem J 1987; 247:259-65.

104. Kramer DL, Sufrin JR, Porter CW. Modulation of polyamine biosynthetic activity by S-adenosylmethionine depletion. Biochem J 1988; 249:581-86.

105. Kotb M, Geller AM. Methionine adenosyltransferase: Structure and function. Pharmac Ther 1993; 59:125-43.

106. Horikawa S, Ishikawa M, Ozasa H et al. Isolation of a cDNA encoding the rat liver *S*-adenosylmethionine synthetase. Eur J Biochem 1989; 184:497-501.

107. Savarese TM, Ghoda LY, Parks Jr RE. Biochemical consideration in the design of analogs of 5'-deoxy-5'-methylthioadensine. In: Cheng YC, Goz B, Minkoff M, eds. Development of Target-Oriented Antiancer Drugs. New York: Raven Press 1983: 129-42.

108. Toohey JI. Methylthio group cleavage from methylthioadenosine. Biochem Biophys Res Commun 1977; 78:1273-80.

109. Nobori T, Szinai I, Amox D et al. Methylthioadenosine phosphorylase deficiency in human non small cell lung cancers. Cancer Res 1993; 53:1089-1101.

110. Nabob T, Mire K, Wu DJ et al. Deletions of the cyclone-dependent kinase-4 inhibitor gene in multiple human cancers. Nature 1994; 368:753-56.

111. Yamanaka H, Kubota M, Carson DA. Synergistic inhibition of polyamine synthesis and growth by difluoromethylornithine plus methylthioadenosine in methylthioadenosine phosphorylase-deficient murine lymphoma cells. Cancer Res 1987; 47:1771-1774.

112. Hoffman RM. Altered methionine metabolism, DNA methylation and oncogene expression in carcinogenesis. Biochim Biophys Acta 1983; 738:49-87.

113. Bacchi CJ, Sufrin JR, Nathan HC. 5'-Alkyl-substituted analogs of 5'-methylthioadenosine as trypanocides. Antimicrobial Agents Chemother 1991; 35:1315-20.

114. Sufrin JR, Speiss AJ, Kramer DL et al. Targeting 5'-deoxy-5'-(methylthio)adenosine phosphorylase by 5' haloalkyl analogues of 5'-deoxy-5'-(methylthio)adenosine. J Med Chem 1991; 34:2600-8.

115. Pegg AE. Recent advances in the biochemistry of polyamines in eukaryotes. Biochem J 1986; 234:249-62.

116. Byers TL, Ganem B, Pegg AE. Cytostasis induced in L1210 murine leukemia cells by the S-adenosyl-L-methionine decarboxylase inhibitor 5'-{[(Z)-4-amino-2-butenyl]methylamino}-5'-deoxyadenosine may be due to hypusine depletion. Biochem J 1992; 287:717-24.

117. Kramer DL, Stanek J, Diegelman P et al. The use of 4-fluoro-L-ornithine to monitor metabolic flux through the polyamine biosynthetic pathway. Biochem Pharmacol 1995; 50:1433-1443.

118. Bergeron RJ, Hawthorn TR, Vinson JRT et al. Role of the methylene backbone in the antiproliferative activity of polyamine analogues on L1210 cells. Cancer Res 1989; 49:2959-64.

119. Porter CW, McManis J, Casero RA et al. Relative abilities of bis(ethyl) derivatives of putrescine, spermidine and spermine to regulate polyamine biosynthesis and inhibit L1210 leukemia cell growth. Cancer Res 1987; 47:2821-25.

120. Porter CW, Pegg AE, Ganis B et al. Combined regulation of ornithine and S-adenosylmethionine decarboxylase by spermine and the spermine analogue N^1N^{12}-bis(ethyl)spermine. Biochem J 1990; 268:207-12.

121. Kramer DL, Miller JT, Bergeron RJ et al. Regulation of polyamine transport by polyamines and polyamine analogs. J Cell Physiol 1993; 155:399-407.

122. Ask A, Persson L, Heby O. Increased survival of L1210 leukemic mice by prevention of the utilization of extracellular polyamines. Studies using a polyamine-uptake mutant, antibiotics and a polyamine-deficient diet. Cancer Lett 1992; 66:29-34.

123. Bernacki RJ, Oberman EJ, Seweryniak KE et al. Preclinical antitumor efficacy of the polyamine analogue N^1,N^{11}-diethylnorspermine administered by multiple injection or continuous infusion. Clinical Cancer Res 1995; 1:847-57.

124. Porter CW, Bernacki RJ, Bergeron RJ. Antitumor activity of N^1, N^{11}-bis(ethyl)norspermine against human melanoma xenografts and possible biochemical correlates of drug action. Cancer Res 1993; 53:581-86.

125. Albanese L, Bergeron RJ, Pegg AE. Investigations of the mechanism by which mammalian cell growth is inhibited by N^1N^{12}-bis(ethyl)spermine. Biochem J 1993; 291:131-37.

126. He Y, Suzuki T, Kashiwagi K et al. Correlation between the inhibition of cell growth by bis(ethyl)polyamine analogues and the decrease in the function of the mitochondria. Eur J Biochem 1994; 221:391-398.

127. Igarashi K, Koga K, He Y et al. Inhibition of the growth of various human and mouse tumor cells by 1,15-bis(ethylamino)-4,8,12-triazapentadecane. Cancer Res 1995; 55:2615-19.

128. Dolan ME, Fleig MJ, Feuerstein BG et al. Effect of 1,19-bis(ethylamino)-5,10,15-triazanonadecane on human tumor xenografts. Cancer Res 1994; 54:4698-4702.

129. Basu HS, Marton LJ. The interaction of spermine and pentamines with DNA. Biochem J 1987; 244:243-46.

130. Shappell NW, Fogel-Petrovic MF, Porter CW. Regulation of spermidine/spermine N^1-acetyltransferase by intracellular polyamine pools. FEBS Lett 1993; 321:179-83.

131. Nakiake S, Kashiwagi K, Terao K et al. Combined use of α-difluoromethylornithine and an inhibitor of S-adenosylmethionine decarboxylase in mice bearing P388 leukemia or Lewis Lung Carcinoma. Jpn J Cancer Res 1988; 79:501-8.

132. Moulinoux JP, Darcel F, Quemener V et al. Inhibition of the growth of U-251 human glioblastoma in nude mice by polyamine deprivation. Cancer Res 1991; 11:175-80.

133. Persson L, Holm I, Ask A et al. Curative effect of difluoromethylornithine on mice bearing mutant L1210 leukemia cells deficient in polyamine uptake. Cancer Res 1988;48:4807-11.

134. Siimes M, Seppanen P, Alhonen-Hongisto L et al. Synergistic action of two polyamine antimetabolites leads to a rapid therapeutic response in childhood leukemia. Int J Cancer 1981; 28:567-70.

135. Kramer DL, Paul B, Porter CW. Effect of pretreatment of L1210 leukemia mice with α-difluoromethylornithine on the selectivity of methylglyoxal-bis(guanylhydrazone) for tumor tissue in L1210 leukemic mice. Cancer Res 1985; 45:2512-2515.

136. Kallio A, Seppanen P, Alhonen-Hongisto L et al. Modulation of the tissue depletion of methylglyoxal bis(guanylhydrazone) in mice by polyamine depletion and by polyamine administration. Cancer Res 1983; 43:324-327.

137. Porter CW, Ozer H, Cowens W et al. Phase II trials of difluoromethylornithine (DFMO) and methylglyoxal-bis(guanylhydrazone) (MGBG) in the treatment of patients with lymphoma and chronic lymphocytic leukemia. In: Proceedings of Biochem. Modulators Advisory Group Mtg, June 13-14, 1983.

CHAPTER 8

POLYAMINE MODULATION OF RESPONSE TO RADIATION AND HYPERTHERMIA

Paul M. Harari, Michael A. Pickart, John M. Buatti,
and Eugene W. Gerner

I. INTRODUCTION

Our gradually advancing understanding of cellular polyamine function and mechanism of action may allow more logical exploitation of the polyamine metabolic pathway for cancer therapy, as perturbation of polyamine metabolism can influence growth behavior of the malignant cell. Further, polyamine modulation may prove valuable in enhancing the effectiveness of therapeutic radiation and/or hyperthermia in cancer treatment. This chapter reviews published data regarding the interaction of endogenous polyamines with ionizing radiation and hyperthermia and highlights several areas in which polyamine modulation of treatment response may warrant further preclinical and clinical development.

Polyamines in Cancer: Basic Mechanisms and Clinical Approaches, edited by Kenji
Nishioka. © 1996 R.G. Landes Company.

II. POLYAMINE MODULATION OF RADIATION RESPONSE

A. POLYAMINE EFFECTS ON CELLS/TISSUES

1. Depletion and radiosensitization

Polyamine depletion via biosynthesis inhibition influences radiosensitivity in selected cell lines. There are certain cell lines that manifest radiosensitization following polyamine depletion with dose enhancement factors ranging between 1.0 and 2.0.[1-5] Several studies have identified alterations in strand break repair and in cell cycle phase distribution consistent with radiosensitization.[1-3] In contrast, there are several other cell lines that demonstrate little or no enhancement of radiosensitivity measured by single dose radiation exposure following polyamine depletion[6,7] but display inhibition of sublethal damage repair (SLDR) and potentially lethal damage repair (PLDR).[8,9] These nonsensitized cell lines have no apparent alteration in strand break repair kinetics, although alteration of cell cycle parameters has been documented.[8,9]

Polyamine analog effects on intrinsic radiosensitivity confirm observations previously identified with biosynthesis inhibitors regarding both radiosensitivity and cell line specificity of the effect.[10,11] However, analog-specific differences in radiosensitivity-modulation may exist within the same cell line (Buatti JM et al, unpublished). Continued investigation of analog-specific heterogeneity of response in the same cell line may improve understanding of the relative impact of different polyamine-dependent functions as they relate to radiosensitivity.

2. Proliferation effects

Polyamines influence cellular growth and proliferation in virtually all pro- and eukaryotic cells.[12-15] Elevated levels of intracellular polyamines are a common finding in rapidly proliferating human tumors, in contrast with lower levels measured in their non-malignant counterparts.[14-16] Whereas activation of polyamine biosynthesis (i.e., ODC), with resultant increases in polyamine levels, is not a reliable predictive marker of malignancy, this is a finding associated with many cancers.[16] High polyamine levels in a variety of cell types and tissues correlate with high proliferation rates. However, a unified molecular description of polyamine involvement in proliferation is yet to be detailed.

Many investigations regarding the role of polyamines in cellular proliferation use inhibitory agents to deplete endogenous polyamine pools. Studies with polyamine biosynthetic enzyme inhibitors suggest an association between polyamine synthesis and DNA synthesis and/or mitosis.[17] A unique aspect of polyamine inhibition studies is the general reversibility of growth inhibition, demonstrating a primarily cytostatic, as opposed to cytotoxic, effect of polyamine inhibition. However, chronic high concentration exposure to polyamine-inhibitory agents eventually induces a cytotoxic effect. A potential therapeutic role for antiproliferative polyamine agents in the approach to rapidly dividing human solid tumors is outlined below.

3. Polyamine modulation of tumor kinetics

Polyamine modulation of tumor growth kinetics in squamous cell carcinoma (SCC) of the head and neck represents a potential clinical application for polyamine agents as radiation therapy adjuvants. SCCs are among the most rapidly growing human solid tumors, with median potential doubling times (T_{pot}) on the order of 4-6 days as measured via flow cytometry.[18] Locoregional disease recurrence is the predominant mode of failure for patients with SCC of the head and neck. Rapidly proliferating head and neck tumor clonogens can repopulate during a course of radiation therapy and compromise tumor control. Clinical data suggest that decreased tumor control results from repopulation during prolongation of the radiotherapy treatment course for rapidly proliferating tumors.[19-21] Local tumor control is reduced by an estimated 3 to 25% per week of treatment prolongation for head and neck tumors.[19,22]

Radiotherapy dose intensification via acceleration and hyperfractionation (altered fractionation schedules) represents a physical means of addressing rapid tumor cell repopulation during therapy. This approach improves locoregional head and neck tumor control rates; however, treatment intensification increases acute toxic effects, most notably, radiation mucositis. An alternative biological approach is to manipulate tumor proliferation kinetics while maintaining constant physical treatment parameters.[23,24] Potential agents of value include cytostatic or antiproliferative compounds. The polyamine biosynthesis inhibitor DFMO represents one such antiproliferative agent. Investigation of cytostatic agents as cancer therapy adjuvants may be particularly well-suited for rapidly proliferating tumors (such as SCCs of the head and neck) that are characterized by high rates of locoregional failure.

The capacity of polyamine inhibitory agents to modulate tumor growth kinetics in human SCCs derived from head and neck tumors has been investigated.[7,23] In vitro studies with DFMO confirm its effectiveness as a growth-inhibitory agent in these SCCs. Generalized slowing of cell cycle progression is identified via flow cytometric analysis of SCC lines treated with DFMO. In vivo, continuous oral administration of DFMO (1.5%) to athymic mice inhibits human SCC xenograft growth.

Polyamine analogs provide an alternative way to manipulate polyamine metabolism (and thereby cell growth).[25-30] Analogs mimic endogenous polyamines, inhibit polyamine biosynthetic pathways, and in some cases, stimulate spermidine and spermine acetylation reactions of the polyamine catabolic pathway, which depletes endogenous longer chain polyamine pools. Specific mechanisms by which polyamine analogs induce antiproliferative effects remain poorly defined. Preliminary studies suggest that polyamine analogs may interact directly with polyamine-binding sites in DNA and chromatin to initiate their activities.[31] Preclinical studies with the polyamine analog 1,19-bis-(ethylamino)-5,10,15-triazanonadecane (BE-4444) have been initiated, with particular attention to its antiproliferative effects in rapidly dividing human SCCs[11] and brain tumors.[32]

Studies examining the effects of the polyamine analog BE-4444 on human SCCs derived from head and neck tumors reveal growth inhibition in all SCC lines tested, with prolongation of cell cycle transit time as measured via flow cytometry.[11] Continuous five day analog exposure produces substantial cytotoxicity (3-4 logs of cell kill) in two of three SCC cell lines studied. This suggests that the antiproliferative effect of BE-4444 is not a necessary correlate of its cytotoxic response in a particular cell line. For example, in

BE-4444 the SCC-13Y cell line effectively inhibits growth and slows the cell cycle but produces little cytotoxicity even after prolonged exposure or high concentrations.

Recent work suggests that the antiproliferative effects of polyamine analogs may correlate with intracellular accumulation and binding to target DNA and chromatin.[31] Transfected cell lines carrying mammalian ODC, which is not suppressed by polyamines, show no correlation between antiproliferative effects of polyamine analogs and either ODC inhibition or polyamine depletion.[28] Studies on human SCC cell lines[11] also suggest that some feature other than ODC inhibition or polyamine depletion induced by the polyamine analog may be important in facilitating subsequent cytotoxicity. If analog binding to specific intracellular targets is a requisite precursor for cytotoxicity, then such binding is either not occurring or is ineffective in selected SCC cell lines.

For the combination of cytostatic agents, such as DFMO or selected polyamine analogs, to provide ultimate therapeutic benefit as an adjuvant to radiation therapy, the effect of these agents on intrinsic radiosensitivity must be investigated. Preliminary studies reveal no apparent effect of DFMO or BE-4444 on in vitro SCC radiosensitivity at concentrations that produce potent ODC inhibition, growth inhibition or polyamine depletion.[7,11] Previous works identify little or no effect of DFMO on single-dose radiation survival in both human and rodent cell lines,[6,8,9] although radiation repair efficiency (sublethal and potentially lethal damage repair, DNA strand break repair) may be inhibited.[8,9] The important finding for future clinical application is that DFMO or BE-4444 treated SCC cells are not rendered more radioresistant than controls. This issue deserves further in vivo examination in dose-limiting normal tissues such as oral mucosa while under the influence of these polyamine agents.

Addition of effective cytostatic agents (e.g., DFMO or polyamine analog) to radiation therapy for rapidly proliferating human tumors may circumvent the need for intensification of radiation dose delivery. In conjunction with additional preclinical studies to investigate the influence of DFMO on normal tissue and tumor radiosensitivity, a pilot clinical trial at the University of Wisconsin is being initiated in which patients receiving conventional radiotherapy for SCCs of the head and neck are administered oral DFMO following pretreatment tumor kinetic analysis. It is believed that administration of cytostatic agents during radiation therapy for patients with rapidly proliferating tumors of the head and neck and other rapidly dividing tumor types may someday provide improved locoregional tumor control.

B. POLYAMINE INTERACTIONS WITH DNA

1. DNA structure/conformation

Polyamines influence the conformation and structural orientation of DNA. Early studies include those on aggregation using dilute solutions of polyamines with large fragments of DNA, and they showed that both spermidine and spermine increase DNA aggregation although at different concentrations.[33,34] Such effects can be mimicked by other cations (Na[+], Mg[++], etc.) at significantly higher concentrations.[33-35] The suggestion has been put forth that this condensation or alteration of conformation stabilizes the DNA.[36-39] These interactions can alter endonuclease digestion of DNA, influence expression of mutated phenotypes, modulate gene expression, and alter ionizing radiation damage and repair of DNA.[31,34,38-43] The influence of polyamines on maintenance and function of mitochondrial DNA has also been studied but remains less clearly defined.[25,44]

Recent investigations suggest potential site-specific polyamine interactions with the DNA molecule including major groove, minor groove, bridging minor groove and phosphate backbone locations.[37] Preliminary analysis suggests that a spermidine-DNA interaction occurring in the major groove may be of significance.[36,37] Dynamic interaction of spermidine in the major groove yields a bend in the DNA (B to Z or A to Z transition) that may facilitate structural changes necessary for transcription, replication or repair-related activities.[34,35,37,45] Specific nucleotide sequence arrangements influence the likelihood of a given polyamine-DNA interaction and hence may control the tertiary structure and resultant functional activity of the molecule.[36,37,45] Polyamine-DNA interaction appears to favor nucleotide heteropolymers as opposed to homopolymers.[37,45,46] Studies with polyamine analogs have increased understanding of the site-specific requirements for polyamine-DNA interactions.[34,38,45] The ability of polyamines to condense DNA correlates with the ability to suppress growth, to repair DNA damage and to rescue cells from effects of polyamine biosynthesis inhibitors.[45,47,48]

Availability of a spectrum of newly synthesized polyamine analogs and improved ability to manipulate nucleotides in vitro and in vivo may better define both specific and nonspecific polyamine-DNA interactions.[48] Complexing of intracellular polyamines to RNA, ATP, protein and phospholipids, along with improved understanding of the influence of polyamines on their structure/conformation, may be important to precisely defining polyamine effects on DNA structure, conformation and hence, function.[49]

2. DNA damage/repair

Studies regarding potential involvement of polyamines in DNA repair processes reveal cell line-specific differences. Several cell lines manifest increased radiosensitivity following polyamine depletion, and the capacity for repair of DNA damage is altered.[1,2] More specifically, the kinetics of radiation-induced strand break repair may be altered by inhibitors of polyamine biosynthesis.[1] Additionally, DNA repair may be hampered following administration of strand-breaking chemotherapeutic agents and DFMO challenge.[50-52] Such studies support a potential influence of polyamines on DNA repair processes.

Evidence also suggests a polyamine influence on cellular processes that indirectly affect repair of DNA following radiation exposure. These processes include cell cycle maturation, gene transcription and apoptosis.[3,53-57] Polyamine depletion can alter the onset of G2-delay following radiation damage, which may increase radiosensitivity by preventing repair during this radioprotective cell cycle checkpoint.[3] Polyamines also alter expression of radiation resistance-associated, radiation-responsive and apoptosis-associated genes that may impact DNA repair processes.[54,55,58-63] However, recent observations indicate that polyamine depletion with DFMO produces radiation protection in an in vivo model of central nervous system injury.[64] Such varied findings across different model systems suggest that polyamine modulation of intrinsic radiosensitivity is not precisely understood and cannot be fully analyzed in isolation without regard to adjacent cellular processes. In conclusion, polyamines influence the conformation and structure of DNA, and this polyamine effect may be important in the modulation of DNA repair following damage induced by ionizing radiation.

3. Thiol influence

Polyamines exhibit radioprotective properties in both pro- and eukaryotes. Potential mechanisms of chemical radioprotection include proton donation and radical scavenging.[65] The relative importance of these two mechanisms depends on the system in which protection is measured. In *Salmonella typhimurium*, nucleophilicity, rather than antioxidant properties of polyamines, may be responsible for protection against chemical mutagenicity.[66] When transforming activity of bacterial DNA is the endpoint, polyamine-dependent radical scavenging may play a significant role with putrescine and spermidine, but not spermine, serving as radioprotectors in the presence of oxygen.[67]

Polyamine structure influences the radio-protective and oxygen radical-protective features of these molecules. The thiol trypanothione (bis-glutathionylspermidine) found in the protozoan *Trypanosoma burcei* but not in mammals is a more effective radioprotector than glutathione, presumably because the spermidine moeity allows this thiol closer contact with DNA.[65] Paraquat, which exerts its effects by causing an oxidative stress response, is more effective in inhibiting the growth of bacterial mutants that lack the ability to synthesize polyamines.[68] The authors of this work on paraquat conclude that polyamines influence bacterial DNA structure, which affects the accessibility of paraquat to the DNA rather than providing radical scavenging activity. The diamine putrescine and the triamine spermidine act as radical scavengers in some bacterial systems,[67] whereas the tetraamine spermine is capable of inhibiting radiation mutagenesis in some mammalian models.[69]

Polyamine contents affect intracellular thiol contents under certain circumstances. DFMO treatment generally depletes intracellular putrescine and spermidine, but not spermine, contents and increases intracellular glutathione content in rat 9L gliosarcoma cells.[70] This increase occurs only after 48 hours of DFMO treatment despite earlier polyamine content suppression. Exogenous spermine treatment inhibits glutathione release from mitochondria, providing protection against toxic reactive oxygen species in these organelles.[71]

Depletion of endogenous putrescine and spermidine contents by DFMO sensitizes some cell types to acute radiation exposures.[8,72] Prager et al[73] manipulated intracellular thiol and polyamine contents to examine the effect of these putative radioprotectors on radioprotection by aminothiols such as the spermidine analog WR1065. Their results indicate that this aminothiol reverses the radiosensitizing effects of polyamine depletion by DFMO but that cysteamine protects control and DFMO-treated cells to the same degree. Thus, whereas intracellular thiols and polyamines can both function to protect cells from acute radiation damage, the mechanism(s) of protection are varied and system dependent.

C. Possible Mechanisms of Action

1. Apoptosis

In 1972, Kerr and colleagues[74] described a mode of cell death in cancer and normal tissues that occurred without inflammation and appeared morphologically distinct from necrosis. They termed this mode of death apoptosis and proposed that the mechanism of this process involved a coordinated set of biochemical events resulting in cell removal. Since that time, Kerr and others have shown that a variety of stresses, including ionizing radiation, hyperthermia and certain cytotoxic drugs, can induce apoptosis.[75]

Recently, specific oncogenes and tumor suppressor genes have been implicated in the mechanisms of apoptosis. The c-*myc* oncogene is one of several genes involved in radiation-induced apoptosis.[76-78] Ionizing radiation can induce c-*myc* gene expression in some cell types[79] or lead to c-*myc* gene amplification in other cell and tissue types.[80] Studies by Cleveland and coworkers have shown that c-*myc* transactivates ODC[81] and that inhibition of ODC blocks c-*myc*-dependent apoptosis in some cell types.[82]

Polyamines have been implicated in apoptosis in several systems. Production of hydrogen peroxide and toxic aldehydes as a consequence of polyamine oxidation causes apoptosis in models of development and differentiation (discussed in detail in chapter 6).[83] In some cell types, longer chain amines, especially spermine, inhibit activation of DNA endonucleases associated with apoptosis. Accumulation of very high putrescine contents, resulting from ODC overexpression, can inhibit cell growth[84] and induce apoptosis by a mechanism that may involve inhibition of hypusine formation in the translation initiation factor eIF-5A.[85] Hypusine is formed by the addition of the butyl amine moiety of spermidine to a lysine in eIF-5A and is essential for cell viability in yeast and animal cells.[86] Thus, although polyamines are implicated in mechanisms of apoptosis, their potential role in radiation- or hyperthermia-induced apoptosis remains to be determined.

2. Modulation of cell cycle proliferation

Following DNA damage induced by ionizing radiation, mammalian cells exhibit two main checkpoints in cell cycle progression at G^1 and G^2 stages. These checkpoints are hypothesized to halt cell cycle progression in order for DNA repair to occur before progression into DNA synthesis or mitosis, respectively.[87-91] The p53 tumor suppressor gene product is implicated in the G^1 cell cycle checkpoint that occurs following DNA damage.[88,89,92] Distinct from G^1 arrest, which is presumed to control a cellular decision to proceed through cell division or undergo apoptosis, G^2 arrest is implicated in resistance and DNA repair following exposure to chemical agents and radiation.[93,94] Alterations in cyclin B protein levels are correlated with G^2 arrest following damage induced by ionizing radiation.[91] A better understanding of these cell cycle checkpoints requires further research regarding the function of various damage-inducible transcripts induced in response to DNA damage following radiation exposure.[95,96] The specific influence of endogenous polyamines on the regulation of such cell cycle checkpoints remains unknown.

Polyamines appear to be a necessary requisite for cellular proliferation in mammalian cells[12,15,97-99] and may influence cellular proliferation via interactions with nucleic acids (see Section II.B.1), transcription factors, or other proteins that affect gene expression. Examples include the *Escherichia coli* single strand-binding protein,[100] casein kinase II[101,102] and the topoisomerases.[12] Casein kinase II demonstrates increased activity following mitogenic stimulation[103] and may act upon myc oncoproteins believed to be important in cell proliferation, whereas topoisomerases may affect gene expression through influence on DNA supercoiling.[12] Post-transcriptional mechanisms that control cell cycle regulation under polyamine influence[12] may also exist that function similarly to the autoregulatory expression of antizyme,[104] a polyamine-inducible protein that binds and inhibits ODC.

Polyamine depletion by biosynthesis inhibition is a useful method for studying polyamine regulatory effects on cell cycle events. Several polyamine inhibitory agents induce antiproliferative effects in normal cells and cause a G^1 cell cycle block.[17] This G^1 block is often absent in transformed and malignant cells.[17,53,105-107] Normal cells may require polyamines for routine passage into S phase; however, this transition may be perturbed when suboptimal polyamine concentrations are present. Selected tumor cells may be unable to halt cell cycle progression in the absence of polyamines and thus proceed through G^1. Their subsequent arrest in S phase suggests a requirement for polyamines in DNA synthesis. Recent studies with a polyamine auxotrophic mutant, CHO-P22, which has no detectable ODC activity, supports the above hypothesis.[105] Polyamine depleted cell cultures accumulate in S phase while continuing to incorporate bromodeoxyuridine without increasing their DNA content. These results from both normal and malignant cells suggest regulation of the G^1-to-S transition by a polyamine-dependent checkpoint; however, not all available data corroborate this hypothesis.[108-112]

Polyamines may play a regulatory role in proliferative processes such as release from quiescence and mitogen/hormone activation.[42,113-116] Cells making the transition from G^0 to G^1 generally display a rapid increase in ODC activity, polyamine levels and growth-related gene expression. Studies reveal that proliferation-inhibition (via DFMO-induced polyamine depletion in human colon carcinoma cells) results in a greater than 90% reduction in transcription of c-*myc*, c-*fos* and *H2A* genes.[42] It is further suggested that these effects may require modulation of specific endogenous polyamines.[115] For example, reduction in c-*myc* mRNA levels are observed following depletion of spermidine levels alone, whereas reduction in c-*fos* mRNA requires depletion of both spermidine and spermine. Similar results are observed in polyamine-depleted IEC-6 cells derived from rat intestinal crypt cells.[116] DFMO treatment prevents increased expression of c-*myc* and c-*jun* mRNA as well as increased expression of c-*fos* following release from serum deprivation. Thomas et al observed that DFMO inhibits growth stimulation by estradiol of G^1-synchronized MCF-7 breast cancer cells.[114] Studies of polyamine biosynthesis suppression by antiestrogens[113] further suggest that polyamines may play a role in hormone-stimulated initiation of proliferation.

The role of polyamines as regulatory agents during early activation of proliferation is challenged by Morris[117] who suggests that if a regulatory role for polyamines in growth processes exists, it should occur well after mitogenic stimulation due to the delayed kinetics of polyamine accumulation. Recent reports may support this view and suggest that induction of ODC expression is downstream of both c-*myc*[81,118] and c-*fos*[119] expression. Carefully designed experiments are needed to clarify the relationship of ODC induction and growth-related gene expression during the activation of proliferation.

The influence of polyamines on cell cycle regulation of exponentially growing cells is not well defined. Polyamines may be involved in the degradation of mitotic cyclins and thereby facilitate progression through the cell cycle.[120] In this study by Thomas and Thomas, DFMO-induced depletion of polyamines in MCF-7 breast cancer cells blocked degradation of cyclin B1 mRNA. Accumulating evidence supports a role for polyamines in modulating expression of gene transcripts that influence cellular proliferation, and this may overlap with the role of polyamines in modulating cellular responses to ionizing radiation.

3. Effects on gene expression

Ionizing radiation induces expression of a number of genes in eukaryotic cells, some of which may determine whether cells live or undergo apoptosis.[76] In certain cell types, the oncogene c-*myc* is induced by ionizing radiation,[79] and myc expression is associated with resistance to radiation in some models.[77,121] Also, c-*myc* expression is affected by polyamines.[54] Because c-*myc* is induced by radiation, is implicated in radiation-induced apoptosis, and is affected by polyamine content, which affects radiation survival responses, one may hypothesize that polyamines modulate cellular responses to ionizing radiation by affecting specific gene expression, including but not limited to, *c-myc* expression.

The effects of polyamines on specific gene expression explain why depletion of these amines affects radiation survival responses in some cell types. It is well documented that *c-myc* is regulated in a highly tissue-specific manner.[122] If polyamines affect unique aspects of *c-myc* or other gene regulatory mechanisms (i.e., transcription initiation or attenuation, translation, post-translational processes), then modulation of these amines may affect responses directed by *c-myc* or other genes in those tissues actively employing polyamine-dependent regulation. In Colo 320 cells, polyamine depletion suppresses *c-myc* RNA contents[54] and enhances expression of a novel RNA similar to an anti-sense *c-myc* transcript.[123] It is not known whether this anti-sense transcript affects expression of sense *c-myc*, nor is cell type or tissue-specific expression of this polyamine-dependent message defined.

III. POLYAMINE MODULATION OF HYPERTHERMIA RESPONSE

A. BRIEF HYPERTHERMIA BACKGROUND

The rationale for the use of hyperthermia (41-45°C) in cancer therapy has been reviewed elsewhere.[124] Briefly, hyperthermic temperatures above 41°C are cytotoxic. Hyperthermic cytotoxicity is enhanced by factors characteristic of tumors (e.g., acid pH) and not normal tissues, and hyperthermic temperatures interact synergistically with radiotherapy and certain chemotherapeutic agents. Synergistic interactions with radiotherapy may occur due to inhibition of radiation repair mechanisms. Synergistic interactions with chemotherapy agents are a consequence of several mechanisms, including hyperthermia-induced membrane changes leading to increased drug uptake, temperature-dependent increases in damage production and suppression of drug-induced damage repair.

Hyperthermic temperatures above 41°C induce expression of genes encoding the so-called heat shock proteins that cause metabolic changes in cells that induce recovery of normal functions or cell death.[125] Non-lethal hyperthermic exposures induce transient, non-heritable resistance to subsequent toxic heat stresses.[126] This resistance is termed thermotolerance.[127]

B. EFFECTS ON CELLS AND TISSUES

Hyperthermia inhibits ODC activity[128] and causes loss of cellular polyamines into the extracellular environment.[129] Depletion of endogenous polyamines by DFMO enhances hyperthermia-induced cytotoxicity in hamster cells.[130-132] This effect, like the effects of polyamine depletion on cellular radioresponses, is cell line dependent. In one human tumor cell line, polyamine depletion has little effect on acute hyperthermic survival responses but increases the rate of thermotolerance decay.[133] In animals with spontaneously arising tumors, the combination of DFMO and hyperthermia did not improve tumor response over hyperthermia therapy alone.[134] When systemic hyperthermia is combined with the spermidine analog, methylglyoxal bisguanylhydrazone (MGBG), potent tumoricidal and normal tissue toxicities occur in domestic animal models.[135]

Exogenous, as well as endogenous, polyamine contents affect hyperthermic survival responses. Oxidation of the longer chain amines, spermidine and spermine by extracellular copper-dependent amine oxidases (CuAOs) found in serum additives to tissue culture cells produce toxic aldehydes and hydrogen peroxide.[136] Oxidation of extracellular polyamines at both normothermic and hyperthermic temperatures reduces intracellular glutathione levels and leads to marked cell killing.[137] The relevance of this mechanism to tumor and normal tissue responses to hyperthermia is unclear. It has recently been proposed that CuAOs might be used in a gene therapy context.[138] Artificial expression of these enzymes in tumors containing high levels of polyamines, treated with hyperthermia, could lead to tumoricidal activity via polyamine oxidation.

C. POSSIBLE MECHANISMS OF ACTION

Polyamines modify cell and tissue responses to hyperthermia by at least two distinct mechanisms. One mechanism involves oxidation of the long chain amines spermidine and spermine or their acetyl derivatives.[136] Extracellular oxidation of spermidine and spermine is mediated by CuAOs and produces hydrogen peroxide and toxic aldehydes like acrolein. Intracellular oxidation of N^1-acetyl derivatives of spermidine and spermine, predominantly in peroxisomes, is mediated by the flavin adenine dinucleotide (FAD)-dependent polyamine oxidase (PAO) and produces acetoamidopropanal and hydrogen peroxide. The acetylated aldehyde is not toxic to cells, and hydrogen peroxide produced by PAO action is generally detoxified by peroxisomal peroxide and oxygen-radical detoxifying enzymes. Heat shock-induced endogenous polyamine catabolism can result in decreased cell viability when intracellular glutathione contents are suppressed.[139]

Hyperthermic enhancement of cytotoxicity by polyamine depletion is not a consequence of production of toxic aldehydes or oxygen radicals but may involve polyamine catabolism. Heat and certain chemical stresses induce spermidine acetylation in bacteria and both spermidine and spermine acetylation in rodent and human cells.[140-142] In mammals, the mechanism of heat shock induction is the post-transcriptional activation of spermidine/spermine N^1-acetyltransferase (SSAT).[143] In bacteria, the acetyltransferase is constitutively expressed and induction occurs via a mechanism involving heat shock-induced intracellular spermidine compartment change.[142] When heat shock-induced polyamine catabolism occurs in peroxisomes, with their high levels of catalase, the hydrogen peroxide produced is detoxified, and putrescine is produced. Because putrescine synthesis is generally required for optimal cell growth, but heat shock inhibits ODC activity, polyamine catabolism may be an alternate, stress-inducible recovery mechanism for putrescine production.

IV. CONCLUSIONS AND FUTURE DIRECTIONS

A. POLYAMINES AND CELLULAR STRESS RESPONSES

Polyamines are involved in a wide variety of cellular and tissue-specific stress responses. Stress responses in animal cells influenced by polyamines include those induced by heat shock, ionizing radiation and certain chemicals. Polyamines are also involved in tissue-specific responses to injury, including a variety of healing responses in the gastrointestinal tract[144] and ischemia in the brain.[145] In this latter regard, it is notable that oxygen deprivation induces expression of a transcript encoding eIF-5A, the spermidine-modified translation factor, in yeast.[146]

Polyamines are ubiquitous in nature and appear to be essential for optimal growth of both pro- and eukaryotic cells. They participate in a variety of cellular stress responses. Whether their participation in cellular stress responses can be manipulated to either prevent or treat human cancer remains to be determined.

B. POLYAMINE MODULATION AS A RADIATION THERAPY ADJUVANT

Newly synthesized polyamine analogs induce a spectrum of polyamine pathway alterations that allow insight into mechanisms by which polyamines affect cell growth and proliferation. Preclinical in vitro studies indicate activity in a variety of human tumor types including malignant gliomas,[31,73] skin melanomas,[147] pancreatic adenocarcinomas,[148] colon adenocarcinomas[149] and SCC.[11] Preclinical in vivo studies in tumor-xenografted athymic mice demonstrate potent antitumor activity of the analog N^1,N^{11}-bis(ethyl)norspermine (BENSPM) in melanomas[150] and of BE-4444 in human malignant gliomas, lung, and colon squamous cell carcinomas.

Combining an antiproliferative agent in adjuvant fashion with curative radiation therapy for rapidly dividing human tumors is a new concept now being examined with the ultimate objective of improving locoregional tumor control and survival. The polyamine pathway is a potentially valuable arena for such examination in light of the ubiquitous distribution of polyamines in mammalian cells and their central involvement in cellular growth. Preliminary studies of antiproliferative polyamine agents on normal tissue responses to ionizing radiation suggest no enhancement of the acute radiation response. Such studies are required to examine potential enhancement of normal tissue reactions to radiation that might negate the potential benefit of reduced tumor cell proliferation rate during administration of antiproliferative polyamine agents.

Whether polyamine biosynthesis inhibitors and/or polyamine analogs will ultimately prove valuable as adjuncts to curative radiotherapy in rapidly proliferating human tumors remains to be defined. Our steadily improving understanding of specific mechanisms of action and subsequent cellular effects of endogenous polyamines on DNA structure/conformation, DNA repair, response to ionizing radiation, modulation of cell cycle kinetics and associated gene expression will enable more research-driven use of polyamine agents in cancer therapy.

ACKNOWLEDGMENTS

This work has been supported in part by grants from the National Cancer Institute, CA 66786 (PMH), CA 30052, CA 23074 and CA 59024 (EWG), and by Career Development Awards from the American Cancer Society (PMH, JMB) and the Radiological Society of North America (PMH).

REFERENCES

1. Snyder RD. Inhibition of x-ray-induced DNA strand break repair in polyamine-depleted HeLa cells. Int J Radiat Biol 1989; 55:773-82.
2. Snyder RD, Lachmann PJ. Hyperthermia, polyamine depletion and inhibition of x-ray-induced DNA strand break repair. Radiat Res 1989; 120:121-28.
3. Snyder RD, Schroeder KK. Radiosensitivity of polyamine-depleted HeLa cells and modulation by the aminothiol WR-1065. Radiat Res 1994; 137:67-75.
4. Arundel CM, Nishioka K, Tofilon PJ. Effects of α-difluoromethyl-ornithine-induced polyamine depletion on the radiosensitivity of a human colon carcinoma cell line. Radiat Res 1988; 114:634-40.
5. Courdi A, Milano G, Bouclier M et al. Radiosensitization of human tumor cells by α-difluoromethylornithine. Int J Cancer 1986; 38:103-7.
6. Seidenfield J, Deen DF, Marton LJ. Depletion of intracellular polyamine content does not alter the survival of 9L rat brain tumor cells after X-irradiation. Int J Radiat Biol 1980; 38:223-29.
7. Petereit DG, Harari PM, Contreras L et al. Combining polyamine depletion with radiation therapy for rapidly dividing head and neck tumors: Strategies for improved locoregional control. Int J Radiat Oncol Biol Phys 1994; 28:891-98.
8. Stea B, Buatti JM, Stringer DE et al. Inhibition of polyamine synthesis suppresses growth and gamma-ray-induced sublethal and potentially lethal damage recovery in human tumor cells in culture. Radiat Oncol Invest 1993; 1:41-49.

9. Gerner EW, Tome ME, Fry SE et al. Inhibition of ionizing radiation recovery processes in polyamine-depleted Chinese hamster cells. Cancer Res 1988; 48:4881-85.

10. Chen CZ, Hu LJ, Bergeron RJ et al. Radiopotentiation of human brain tumor cells by the spermine analog N^1N^{14}-bis(ethyl) homospermine. Int J Radiat Oncol Biol Phys 1994; 29:1041-47.

11. Harari PM, Pickart MA, Contreras L et al. Slowing proliferation in head and neck tumors: Growth inhibitory effects of the polyamine analog 1,19-bis-(ethylamino)-5,10,15-triazanonadecane (BE-4444) on human squamous cell carcinomas. Int J Radiat Oncol Biol Phys 1995: 32:687-694.

12. Marton LJ, Morris DR. Molecular and cellular functions of the polyamines. In: McCann PP, Pegg AE, Sjoerdsma A, eds. Inhibition of Polyamine Metabolism: Biological Significance and Basis for New Therapies. Orlando: Academic Press, Inc., 1987:79-105.

13. Bitonti AJ, McCann PP. Inhibition of polyamine biosynthesis in microorganisms. In: McCann PP, Pegg AE, Sjoerdsma A, eds. Inhibition of Polyamine Metabolism: Biological Significance and Basis for New Therapies. Orlando: Academic Press, Inc., 1987:259-73.

14. Luk GD, Casero Jr RA. Polyamines in normal and cancer cells. Adv Enzyme Regul 1987; 26:91-105.

15. Pegg AE, McCann PP. Polyamine metabolism and function in mammalian cells and protozoans. ISI Atlas of Sci: Biochem 1988: 11-18.

16. Hixson LJ, Garewal HS, McGee DL et al. Ornithine decarboxylase and polyamines in colorectal neoplasia and mucosa. Cancer Epidemiol Biomarkers Prev 1993; 2:369-74.

17. Heby O, Jänne J. Polyamine antimetabolites: Biochemistry, specificity, and biological effect of inhibitors of polyamine synthesis. In: Morris DR, Marton LJ, eds. Polyamines in Biology and Medicine. New York: Marcel Dekker, Inc., 1981:243-310.

18. Wilson GD, McNally NJ, Dische S et al. Measurement of cell kinetics in human tumours in vivo using bromodeoxyuridine incorporation and flow cytometry. Br J Cancer 1988; 58:423-31.

19. Fowler JF, Lindstrom MJ. Loss of local control with prolongation in radiotherapy. Int J Radiat Oncol Biol Phys 1992; 23:457-67.

20. Peters LJ, Ang KK, Thames HD. Accelerated fractionation in the radiation treatment of head and neck cancer. A critical comparison of different strategies. Acta Oncol 1988; 27:185-94.

21. Withers HR, Taylor JM, Maciejewski B. The hazard of accelerated tumor clonogen repopulation during radiotherapy. Acta Oncol 1988; 27:131-46.

22. Thames HD, Peters LJ, Withers HR et al. Accelerated fractionation vs hyperfractionation: Rationales for several treatments per day. Int J Radiat Oncol Biol Phys 1983; 9:127-38.

23. Harari PM, Contreras L, Pickart MA et al. Modulation of proliferation kinetics in human squamous cell carcinomas of the head and neck. Arch Otolaryngol Head Neck Surg 1993; 119:738-42.

24. Kinsella TJ, Gould MN, Mulcahy RT et al. Integration of cytostatic agents and radiation therapy: A different approach to "proliferating" human tumors. Int J Radiat Oncol Biol Phys 1991; 20:295-302.

25. Albanese L, Bergeron RJ, Pegg AE. Investigations of the mechanism by which mammalian cell growth is inhibited by N^1N^{12}-bis(ethyl)spermine. Biochem J 1993; 291:131-37.

26. Bergeron RJ, Neims AH, McManis J et al. Synthetic polyamine analogues as antineoplastics. J Med Chem 1988; 31:1183-90.

27. Bowlin TL, Prakash NJ, Edwards ML et al. Participation of T-lymphocytes in the curative effect of a novel synthetic polyamine analogue, N,N-bis-[3-(ethylamino)-propyl]-1,7-heptanediamine, against L1210 leukemia in vivo. Cancer Res 1991; 51:62-66.

28. Ghoda L, Basu HS, Porter CW et al. Role of ornithine decarboxylase suppression and polyamine depletion in the antiproliferative activity of polyamine analogs. Mol Pharmacol 1992; 42:302-6.

29. Porter CW, McManis J, Caserom RA et al. Relative abilities of bis(ethyl) derivatives of putrescine, spermidine and spermine to regulate polyamine biosynthesis and inhibit cell growth. Cancer Res 1987; 47:2821-25.

30. Prakash NJ, Bowlin TL, Edwards ML et al. Antitumor activity of a novel synthetic polyamine analogue, N,N-bis-[3-(ethylamino)-propyl]-1-7-heptanediamine: Potentiation by polyamine oxidase inhibitors. Anticancer Res 1990; 10:1281-88.

31. Basu HS, Sturkenboom MCJM, Delcros JG et al. Effect of polyamine depletion on chromatin structure in U-87 MG human brain tumor cells. Biochem J 1992; 282:723-27.

32. Basu HS, Pellarin M, Feuerstein BG et al. Interaction of a polyamine analogue, 1,19-bis-(ethylamino)-5,10,15-triazanonadecane (BE-4444), with DNA and effect on growth, survival and polyamine levels in seven human brain tumor cell lines. Cancer Res 1993; 53:3948-55.

33. Gosule LC, Schellman JA. DNA condensation with polyamines. J Mol Biol 1978; 121:311-26.

34. Srivenugopal KS, Wemmer DE, Morris DR. Aggregation of DNA by analogs of spermidine; enzymatic and structural studies. Nucleic Acids Res 1987; 15:2563-80.

35. Sen D, Crothers DM. Condensation of chromatin: Role of multivalent cations. Biochemistry 1986; 25:1495-1503.

36. Schmid N, Behr JP. Location of spermine and other polyamines on DNA as revealed by photoaffinity cleavage with poly-aminobenzene-diazonium salts. Biochemistry 1991; 30:4357-61.

37. Feuerstein BG, Williams LD, Basu HS et al. Implications and concepts of polyamine-nucleic acid interactions. J Cell Biochem 1991; 46:37-47.

38. Basu HS, Wright WD, Deen DF et al. Treatment with a polyamine analog alters DNA-matrix association in HeLa cell nuclei: A nucleoid halo assay. Biochemistry 1993; 32:4073-76.

39. Hanna M, Szostak JW. Suppression of mutations in the core of the Tetrahymena ribozyme by spermidine, ethanol and by substrate stabilization. Nucleic Acids Res 1994; 22:5326-31.

40. Cress AE, Kurath KM, Hendrix MJ et al. Nuclear protein organization and the repair of radiation damage. Carcinogenesis 1989; 10:939-43.

41. Hanawalt, PC. Preferential repair of damage in actively transcribed DNA sequences in vivo. Genome 1989; 31:605-11.

42. Celano P, Baylin SB, Casero Jr RA. Polyamines differentially modulate the transcription of growth-associated genes in human colon carcinoma cells. J Biol Chem 1989; 264:8922-27.

43. Cozzarelli NR. DNA topoisomerases. Cell 1980; 22:327-28.

44. Vertino PM, Beerman TA, Kelly EJ et al. Selective cellular depletion of mitochondrial DNA by the polyamine analog N^1N^{12}-bis(ethyl)spermine and its relationship to polyamine structure and function. Mol Pharmacol 1991; 39:487-94.

45. Basu HS, Feuerstein BG, Deen DF et al. Correlation between the effects of polyamine analogues on DNA conformation and cell growth. Cancer Res 1989; 49:5591-97.

46. Ban C, Ramakrishnan B, Sundaralingam M. Crystal structure of highly distorted chimeric decamer r(C)d(CGGCGCCG)-spermine complex: Spermine binding to phosphate only and minor groove tertiary base-pairing. Nucleic Acids Res 1994; 22:5466-76.

47. Bergeron RJ, Hawthorne TR, Vinson T et al. Role of the methylene backbone in the antiproliferative activity of polyamines analogues on L1210 cells. Cancer Res 1989; 49:2959-64.

48. Bergeron RJ, McManis JS, Liu CZ et al. Antiproliferative properties of polyamine analogues: A structure-activity study. J Med Chem 1994; 37:3464-76.

49. Watanabe S, Kusama-Eguchi K, Kobayashi H et al. Estimation of polyamine binding to macromolecules and ATP in bovine lymphocytes and rat liver. J Biol Chem 1991; 266:20803-809.

50. Dorr RT, Liddil JD, Gerner EW. Modulation of etoposide cytotoxicity and DNA strand scission in L1210 and 8226 cells by polyamines. Cancer Res 1986; 46:3891-95.

51. Oredsson SM, Deen DF, Marton LJ. Influence of polyamine depletion by α-difluoromethylornithine, an enzyme-activated irreversible inhibitor of ornithine decarboxylase, on alkylation- and carbo-

moylation-induced cytotoxicity in 9L rat brain tumor cells in vitro. Cancer Res 1983; 43:4606-9.

52. Hunter KJ, Deen DF, Pellarin M et al. Effect of α-difluoromethylornithine on 1,3-bis(2-chloroethyl)-1-nitrosourea and cis-diamminedichloroplatinum(II) cytotoxicity, DNA interstrand cross-linking, and growth in human brain tumor cells in vitro. Cancer Res 1990; 50:2769-72.

53. Anehus S, Pohjanpelto P, Baldetorp B et al. Polyamine starvation prolongs the S and G_2 phases of polyamine-dependent (arginase-deficient) CHO cells. Mol Cell Biol 1984; 4:915-22.

54. Celano P, Baylin SB, Giardiello FM et al. Effect of polyamine depletion on c-*myc* expression in human colon carcinoma cells. J Biol Chem 1988; 263:5491-94.

55. Celano P, Berchtold CM, Giardiello FM et al. Modulation of growth gene expression by selective alteration of polyamines in human colon carcinoma cells. Biochem Biophy Res Commun 1989; 165:384-90.

56. Coffino P, Poznanski A. Killer polyamines? J Cell Biochem 1991; 45:54-58.

57. Brune B, Hartzell P, Nicotera P et al. Spermine prevents endonuclease activation and apoptosis in thymocytes. Exp Cell Res 1991; 195:323-29.

58. Weichselbaum RR, Hallahan DE, Sukhatme V et al. Biologic consequences of gene regulation after ionizing radiation exposure. J Natl Cancer Inst 1991; 83:480-84.

59. Sullivan NF, Willis AE. Elevation of c-*myc* protein by DNA strand breakage. Oncogene 1989; 4:1497-1502.

60. Fitzgerald TJ, Santucci MA, Das I et al. The v-abl, c-fms, or v-myc oncogene induces gamma radiation resistance of hematopoietic progenitor cell line 32d CL 3 at clinical low dose rate. Int J Radiat Oncol Biol Phys 1991; 21:1203-10.

61. Illiakis G, Metzger L, Muschel RJ et al. Induction and repair of DNA double strand breaks in radiation-resistant cells obtained by transformation of primary rat embryo cells with oncogenes H-ras and v-myc. Cancer Res 1990; 50:6575-79.

62. Monti MG, Marverti G, Ghiaroni S et al. Spermine protects protein kinase C from phopholipid-induced inactivation. Experientia 1994; 50:953-57.

63. Askew DS, Ashmun RS, Simmons BC et al. Constitutive c-myc expression in an IL-3-dependent myeloid cell line suppresses cell cycle arrest and accelerates apoptosis. Oncogene 1991; 6:1915-22.

64. Fike JR, Gobbel GT, Marton LJ et al. Radiation brain injury is reduced by the polyamine inhibitor α-difluoromethylornithine. Radiat Res 1994; 138:99-106.

65. Awad S, Henderson GB, Cerami A et al. Effects of trypanothione on the biological activity of irradiated transforming DNA. Int J Radiat Biol 1992; 62:401-7.

66. De Flora S, Rosenkranz HS, Klopman G. Structural basis of antimutagenicity of chemicals towards 4-nitroquinoline 1-oxide in *Salmonella typhimurium*. Mutagenesis 1994; 9:39-45.

67. Held KD, Awad S. Effects of polyamines and thiols on the radiation sensitivity of bacterial transforming DNA. Int J Radiat Biol 1991; 59:699-710.

68. Minton KW, Tabor H, Tabor CW. Paraquat toxicity is increased in Escherichia coli defective in the synthesis of polyamines. Proc Nat Acad Sci USA 1990; 87:2851-55.

69. Shigematsu N, Schwartz JL, Grdina DJ. Protection against radiation-induced mutagenesis at the hprt locus by spermine and N,N"-(dithiodi-2,1-ethanediyl)bis-1,3-propanediamine (WR-33278). Mutagenesis 1994; 9:355-60.

70. Hunter KJ, Deen DF, Marton LJ. Changes in the glutathione content of rat 9L cells induced by treatment with the ornithine decarboxylase inhibitor α-difluoromethylornithine. Cancer Res 1987; 47:5270-73.

71. Rigobello MP, Toninello A, Siliprandi D et al. Effect of spermine on mitochondrial glutathione release. Biochem Biophys Res Commun 1993; 194:1276-81.

72. Williams JR, Casero Jr RA, Dillehay LE. The effect of polyamine depletion on the cytotoxic response to PUVA, gamma rays and UVC in V79 cells in vitro. Biochem Biophys Res Commun 1994; 201:1-7.

73. Prager A, Terry NH, Murray D. Influence of intracellular thiol and polyamine levels on radioprotection by aminothiols. Int J Radiat Biol 1993; 64:71-81.

74. Kerr JFR, Wyllie AH, Currie AR. Apoptosis: A basic biological phenomenon with wide-ranging implication in tissue kinetics. Br J Cancer 1972; 26:239-57.

75. Kerr JF, Winterford CM, Harmon BV. Apoptosis. Its significance in cancer and cancer therapy. Cancer 1994; 73:2013-26.

76. Boothman DA, Meyers M, Fukunaga N et al. Isolation of x-ray-inducible transcripts from radioresistant human melanoma cells. Proc Nat Acad Sci USA 1993; 90:7200-4.

77. Ling CC, Chen CH, Li WX. Apoptosis induced at different dose rates: implication for the shoulder region of cell survival curves. Radiother Oncol 1994; 32:129-36.

78. Chen CH, Zhang J, Ling CC. Transfected c-myc and c-Ha-ras modulate radiation-induced apoptosis in rat embryo cells. Radiat Res 1994; 139:307-15.

79. Wilson RE, Taylor SL, Atherton GT et al. Early response gene signaling cascades activated by ionizing radiation in primary human B cells. Oncogene 1993; 8:3229-37.

80. Jin Y, Burns FJ, Garte SJ. Oncogene amplification detected by *in situ* hybridization in radiation-induced skin cancers in rats. Radiat Res 1992; 132:193-99.

81. Bello-Fernandez C, Packham G, Cleveland JL. The ornithine decarboxylase gene is a transcriptional target of c-Myc. Proc Nat Acad Sci USA 1993; 90:7804-8.

82. Packham G, Cleveland JL. Ornithine decarboxylase is a mediator of c-myc-induced apoptosis. Mol Cell Biol 1994; 14:5741-47.

83. Parchment RE. The implications of a unified theory of programmed cell death, polyamines, oxyradicals and histogenesis in the embryo. Int J Dev Biol 1993; 37:75-83.

84. Tome ME, Fiser SM, Gerner EW. Consequences of aberrant ornithine decarboxylase regulation in rat hepatoma cells. J Cell Physiol 1994; 158:237-44.

85. Byers TL, Lakanen JR, Coward JK et al. The role of hypusine depletion in cytostasis induced by S-adenosyl-L-methionine decarboxylase inhibition: New evidence provided by 1-methylspermidine and 1,12-dimethylspermine. Biochem J 1994; 303:363-68.

86. Park MH, Wolff EC, Folk JE. Is hypusine essential for eukaryotic cell proliferation? Trends Biochem Sci 1993; 18:475-79.

87. Fornace AJ, Alamo I, Hollander MC. DNA-damage inducible transcripts in mammalian cells. Proc Natl Acad Sci USA 1988; 85:8800-4.

88. Kastan MB, Zhan Q, El-Deiry WS et al. A mammalian cell cycle checkpoint pathway utilizing p53 and GADD45 is defective in ataxia telangiectasia. Cell 1992; 71:587-97.

89. Kuerbitz SJ, Plunkett BS, Walsh WV et al. Wild-type p53 is a cell cycle checkpoint determinant following irradiation. Proc Natl Acad Sci USA 1992; 89:7491-95.

90. Meyers M, Schea R, Seabury H et al. Role of X-ray-induced genes and proteins in adaptive survival responses. In: Sugahara T, Sagan LA, Aoyama T, eds. Low Dose Irradiation and Biological Defense Mechanisms: Austerdam, The Netherlands: Elsevier Science Publishers BV, 1992:263-66.

91. Muschel RJ, Zhang HB, Iliakis G et al. Cyclin B expression in HeLa cells during the G_2 block induced by ionizing radiation. Cancer Res 1991; 51:5113-17.

92. Kastan MB, Onyekwere O, Sidransky D et al. Participation of p53 protein in the cellular response to DNA damage. Cancer Res 1991; 51:6304-11.

93. Lau CC, Pardee AB. Mechanism by which caffeine enhances lethality of nitrogen mustard. Proc Natl Acad Sci USA 1982; 79:2942-46.

94. Schlegel R, Pardee AB. Caffeine-induced uncoupling of mitosis from the completion of DNA replication in mammalian cells. Science 1986; 232:1264-66.

95. Boothman DA, Meyers M, Lee SW. Isolation of x-ray-inducible transcripts from radioresistant human melanoma cells. Proc Nat Acad Sci USA 1993; 90:7200-4.

96. Boothman DA, Majmudar G, Johnson T. Immediate x-ray-inducible responses from mammalian cells. Radiat Res 1994; 138:S44-46.

97. Tabor CW, Tabor H. Polyamines. Annu Rev Biochem 1984; 53:749-90.

98. Rupniak HT, Paul D. Polyamines and the control of the cell cycle in animal cells. In: Morris DR, Marton LJ, eds. Polyamines in Biology and Medicine. New York: Marcel Dekker, Inc., 1981:315-25.

99. Pegg AE. Polyamine metabolism and its importance in neoplastic growth and as a target for chemotherapy. Cancer Res 1988; 48:759-74.

100. Wei T, Bujalowski W, Lohman TM. Cooperative binding of polyamines induces the Escherichia coli single-strand binding protein-DNA binding mode transitions. Biochemistry 1992; 31: 6166-74.

101. Lüscher B, Kuenzel EA, Krebs EG et al. Myc oncoproteins are phosphorylated by casein kinase II. EMBO J 1989; 8:1111-19.

102. Lüscher B, Christenson E, Litchfield DW et al. Myb DNA binding inhibited by phosphorylation at a site deleted during oncogenic activation. Nature 1990; 344:517-22.

103. Sommercorn J, Mulligan JA, Lozeman FJ et al. Activation of casein kinase II in response to insulin and to epidermal growth factor. Proc Natl Acad Sci USA 1987; 84:8834-38.

104. Matsufuji S, Matsufuji T, Miyazaki Y et al. Autoregulatory frameshifting in decoding mammalian ornithine decarboxylase antizyme. Cell 1995; 80:51-60.

105. Pohjanpelto P, Nordling S, Knuutila S. Flow cytometric analysis of the cell cycle in polyamine-depleted cells. Cytometry 1994; 16:331-38.

106. Koza RA, Herbst EJ. Deficiencies in DNA replication and cell-cycle progression in polyamine-depleted HeLa cells. Biochem J 1992; 281:87-93.

107. Schaefer EL, Seidenfeld J. Effects of polyamine depletion on serum stimulation of quiescent 3T3 murine fibroblast cells. J Cell Physiol 1987; 133:546-52.

108. Hessels J, Kingma AW, Muskiet FAJ et al. Growth-inhibition of 2

solid tumors in mice, caused by polyamine depletion, is not attended by alterations in cell-cycle phase distribution. Int J Cancer 1991; 48:697-703.

109. Hessels J, Kingma AW, Ferwerda H et al. Microbial flora in the gastrointestinal tract abolishes cytostatic effects of α-difluoromethylornithine in vivo. Int J Cancer 1989; 43:1155-64.

110. Andersson G, Heby O. Polyamines in ehrlich ascites tumour growth. In: Gaugas JM, ed. Polyamines in Biomedical Research. Chichester, England: John Wiley and Sons, 1980:51-61.

111. Seidenfeld J, Block AL, Komar KA et al. Altered cell cycle phase distributions in cultured human carcinoma cells partially depleted of polyamines by treatment with difluoromethylornithine. Cancer Res 1986; 46:47-53.

112. Milam KM, Deen DF, Marton LJ. Cell proliferation and polyamine metabolism in 9L cells treated with (2R,5R)-6-heptyne-2,5-diamine or α-difluoromethylornithine. Cell Tissue Kinetics 1989; 22:269-77.

113. Thomas T, Trend B, Butterfield JR et al. Regulation of ornithine decarboxylase gene expression in MCF-7 breast cancer cells by antiestrogens. Cancer Res 1989; 49:5852-57.

114. Thomas T, Thomas TJ. Estradiol control of ornithine decarboxylase mRNA, enzyme activity, and polyamine levels in MCF-7 breast cancer cells: Therapeutic implications. Breast Cancer Res Treat 1994; 29:189-201.

115. Celano P, Berchtold CM, Giardiello FM et al. Modulation of growth gene expression by selective alteration of polyamines in human colon carcinoma cells. Bioch Biophys Res Commun 1989; 165:384-90.

116. Wang JY, McCormack SA, Viar MJ et al. Decreased expression of protooncogenes c-fos, c-myc, and c-jun following polyamine depletion in IEC-6 cells. Amer J Physiol 1993; 265:G331-38.

117. Morris DR. A new perspective on ornithine decarboxylase regulation: Prevention of polyamine toxicity is the overriding theme. J Cell Biochem 1991; 46:102-5.

118. Wagner AJ, Meyers C, Laimins LA et al. c-Myc induces the expression and activity of ornithine decarboxylase. Cell Growth Differ 1993; 4:879-83.

119. Wrighton C, Busslinger M. Direct transcriptional stimulation of the ornithine decarboxylase gene by fos in PC12 cells, but not in fibroblasts. Mol Cell Biol 1993; 13:4657-69.

120. Thomas T, Thomas TJ. Regulation of cyclin B1 by estradiol and polyamines in MCF-7 breast cancer cells. Cancer Res 1994; 54:1077-84.

121. McKenna WG, Weiss MC, Endlich B et al. Synergistic effect of the v-myc oncogene with H-ras on radioresistance. Cancer Res 1990; 50:97-102.

122. Marcu KB, Bossone SA, Patel AJ. myc function and regulation. Annu Rev Biochem 1992; 61:809-60.

123. Celano P, Berchtold CM, Kizer DL et al. Characterization of an endogenous RNA transcript with homology to the antisense strand of the human c-myc gene. J Biol Chem 1992; 267:15092-96.

124. Shimm DA, Gerner EW. Hyperthermia in the treatment of malignancies. In: Lehmann JF, ed. Therapeutic Heat and Cold. 4th ed. Baltimore: Williams and Wilkins, 1990:674-99.

125. Carper SW, Duffy JJ, Gerner EW. Heat shock proteins in thermotolerance and other cellular processes. Cancer Res 1987; 47:5249-55.

126. Gerner EW, Schneider MJ. Induced thermal resistance in HeLa cells. Nature 1975; 256:500-2.

127. Gerner EW. Thermotolerance. In: Storm FK, ed. Hyperthermia in Cancer Therapy. Boston: GK Hall, 1983:141-62.

128. Noterman JA, Gerner EW. Thermal stability of ornithine decarboxylase. Natl Cancer Inst Mongr 1982; 61:69-71.

129. Gerner EW, Russell DH. The relationship between polyamine accumulation and DNA replication kinetics in synchronized CHO cells after heat shock. Cancer Res 1977; 37:482-89.

130. Fuller DJ, Gerner EW. Delayed sensitization to heat by inhibitors of polyamine biosynthetic enzymes. Cancer Res 1982; 42:5046-49.

131. Fuller DJ, Gerner EW. Sensitization of Chinese hamster ovary cells to heat shock by α-difluoromethylornithine. Cancer Res 1987; 47:816-20.

132. Mivechi NF, Dewey WC, Feuerstein BG et al. Relationship between heat sensitivity and polyamine levels after treatment with α-difluoromethylornithine (DFMO). Radiat Res 1986; 108:269-81.

133. Roizin-Towle L, Yarlett N, Pirro JP et al. Hyperthermia studies in polyamine-altered human lung carcinoma cells. Radiat Res 1990; 124:S80-87.

134. Laskowitz DT, Elion GB, Dewhirst MW et al. Effects of glutathione or polyamine depletion on in vivo thermosensitization. Int J Hyperthermia 1992; 8:199-208.

135. Klein MK, Dewhirst MW, Fuller DJ. Whole body hyperthermia and heat-sensitizing drugs: A pilot study in canine lymphoproliferative disease. Int J Hyperthermia 1987; 3:187-98.

136. Harari PM, Fuller DJ, Gerner EW. Heat shock stimulates polyamine oxidation by two distinct mechanisms in mammalian cell cultures. Int J Radiat Oncol Biol Phys 1989; 16:451-57.

137. Russo A, Mitchell JB, DeGraff W et al. Depletion of cellular glutathione by exogenous spermine in V79 cells: Implications for spermine-induced hyperthermic sensitization. Cancer Res 1985; 45:4910-14.

138. Agostinelli E, Przybytkowski E, Mondovi B et al. Heat enhancement of cytotoxicity induced by oxidation products of spermine in Chinese hamster ovary cells. Biochem Pharmacol 1994; 48:1181-86.

139. Harari PM, Tome ME, Fuller DJ et al. Effects of diethyldithiocarbamate and endogenous polyamine content on cellular responses to hydrogen peroxide cytotoxicity. Biochem J 1989; 260:487-90.

140. Harari PM, Fuller DJ, Carper SW et al. Polyamine biosynthesis inhibitors combined with systemic hyperthermia in cancer therapy. Int J Radiat Oncol Biol Phys 1990; 19:89-96.

141. Fuller DJ, Carper SW, Clay L et al. Polyamine regulation of heat shock induced spermidine N^1-acetyltransferase activity. Biochem J 1990; 267:601-5.

142. Carper SW, Willis DG, Manning KA et al. Spermidine acetylation in response to a variety of stresses in *Escherichia coli*. J Biol Chem 1991; 266:12439-41.

143. Gerner EW, Kurtts T, Fuller DJ et al. Stress induction of the spermidine/spermine N^1-acetyltransferase by a post-transcriptional mechanism in human and rodent cells. Biochem J 1993; 294: 491-95.

144. Konturek JW, Brzozowski T, Konturek SJ. Epidermal growth factor in protection, repair, and healing of gastroduodenal mucosa. J Clin Gastroenterol 1991; 13:S88-97.

145. Gilad GM, Gilad VH, Wyatt RJ. Accumulation of exogenous polyamines in gerbil brain after ischemia. Mol Chem Neuropathol 1993; 18:197-210.

146. Kang HA, Schwelberger HG, Hershey JW. The two genes encoding protein synthesis initiation factor eI-5A in Saccharomyces cerevisiae are members of a duplicated gene cluster. Mol Gen Genet 1992; 233:487-90.

147. Porter CW, Ganis B, Libby PR et al. Correlations between polyamine analogue-induced increases in spermidine/spermine N^1-acetyltransferase activity and growth inhibition in human melanoma cell lines. Cancer Res 1991; 51:3715-20.

148. Chang BK, Porter CW, Bergeron RJ. Cellular responses to polyamine analogues and inhibitors in human pancreatic adenocarcinoma cell lines. J Cell Pharmacol 1991; 2:133-137.

149. Pegg AE, Wechter R, Pakala R et al. Effect of N^1, N^{12}-bis-(ethyl)spermine and related compounds on growth and polyamine acetylation, content, and excretion in human colon tumor cells. J Biol Chem 1989; 264:11744-11749.

150. Porter CW, Bernacki RJ, Miller J et al. Antitumor activity of N^1,N^{11}-bis(ethyl)norspermine against human melanoma xenografts and possible biochemical correlates of drug action. Cancer Res 1993; 53:581-586.

CHAPTER 9

NUTRITIONAL MODIFICATIONS, POLYAMINES, AND CANCER

V. Bruce Grossie Jr., Kenji Nishioka

I. INTRODUCTION

The requirement for polyamines (putrescine, spermidine, and spermine) to support cell growth is well established and is the subject of numerous chapters in this book. It has been well established that an increase in polyamine synthesis is associated with rapidly growing tissues such as tumors.[1] In addition, the polyamine content of the urine, plasma, and/or erythrocytes (RBCs) is considered to be a marker for tumor proliferation in the cancer patient.[2-6] Although the polyamine concentration in both plasma and RBCs was increased in cancer patients, the concentration in the RBC was much greater than that in the plasma.[5] This subject will be discussed in detail in the next chapter. The focus of this chapter is the relationship between nutritional support of the cancer patient and polyamine metabolism with specific reference to the role of polyamines in total parenteral nutrition (TPN) enhanced tumor growth.

II. TOTAL PARENTERAL NUTRITION AND CANCER

The nutritional status of a cancer patient is important to the efficacy of treatment. The presence of the disease, as well as its treatment, often results in weight loss, malnutrition, and cachexia

Polyamines in Cancer: Basic Mechanisms and Clinical Approaches, edited by Kenji Nishioka. © 1996 R.G. Landes Company.

which are negative prognostic factors for the survival of cancer patients.[7-9] Cachexia is a complex problem, however, and is only partially the result of decreased intake. To test the hypothesis that improving the nutritional status of cancer patients through TPN would improve the ability of malnourished patients to withstand conventional cancer therapy, Copeland and coworkers[10,11] gave TPN to malnourished cancer patients who had lost >10% of their ideal or usual body weight and had a serum albumin concentration below 3.0 g/100 ml. These authors[10] concluded that the combination of TPN with chemotherapy resulted in a 36% response rate for patients who might otherwise have not received adequate therapy due to malnutrition. For patients with >6.5% weight loss, Lanzotti et al[11] reported that 5 of 10 receiving TPN responded to chemotherapy while none of the 12 non-TPN patients responded. Subsequent randomized trials, however, have not shown any increase in treatment efficacy when TPN is administered with standard treatment. Some reports suggest that TPN will benefit only a small subset of the cancer population.[12-14]

Although Copeland et al[10] reported no TPN related stimulation of the tumor growth rate in the 58 patients, concern still remains that the administration of this aggressive form of nutritional therapy to cancer patients has potential for tumor growth stimulation. Many animal and human studies have failed to fully resolve this question—does the aggressive administration of nutrients through TPN feed the tumor as well as the host?

III. TPN AND RBC POLYAMINES

A. RBC POLYAMINE CONCENTRATION AND TUMOR GROWTH

The association of an increased RBC polyamine content with tumor cell proliferation[4,5] suggested that this might be useful as a marker to detect changes in tumor cell proliferation during TPN. Ota et al,[15,16] therefore, compared the RBC polyamine concentrations of malnourished cancer patients (n = 25) with noncancer patients with benign bowel disease (n = 7) before and after 7-10 days of TPN. Preoperative TPN resulted in an increased RBC putrescine concentration for cancer but not noncancer patients. While this strongly suggested an increased tumor polyamine synthesis and tumor growth stimulation, the source of the increase in RBC polyamines could not be determined.

To evaluate the effect of tumor growth rate on the RBC polyamine concentrations of the tumor-bearing host, a series of experiments using transplantable tumors in rats was initiated. These studies were designed to evaluate the hypothesis that an increase in RBC polyamine concentration was associated with a higher tumor growth rate. Two transplantable tumors in the male Fischer 344 rat were used.[17] These tumors were inoculated subcutaneously (SC) in the rat and grew without metastasis or regression within the time of the experiments. These results confirmed that an increase in RBC polyamines occurred when the tumor was rapidly growing and decreased to control levels when a tumor entered the plateau phase of the growth curve. The transplantable sarcoma grew exponentially and was associated with a continuous increase in the concentration of polyamines in the RBCs. A transplantable Ward colon tumor, on the other hand, grew exponentially until approximately nine grams, when its growth began to slow. The concentration of polyamines in RBCs of rats with the Ward colon tumor increased above the control only transiently at the time the tumor had reached the plateau phase.[17] These results suggested that increased RBC polyamine concentrations would correlate with tumor growth rates.

Although TPN consistently results in an increase in RBC polyamine concentration, the effect of TPN on tumor growth is dependent on the growth characteristics of the tumor.[18] TPN does not enhance the growth of a transplantable sarcoma which is growing in exponential phase. The growth rate is enhanced by TPN, however, if the growth rate of the sarcoma has been decreased by a feeding of a restricted-intake of chow for 14 days.[18] TPN also enhances the growth of a transplantable Ward colon tumor, the growth of which begins to reach a plateau in growth at approximately nine grams. The mechanism of this differential response has not been determined but may be related to the arginine content or polyamine synthesis of the tumors in response to TPN.

B. POLYAMINE INHIBITION AND TPN-INDUCED TUMOR GROWTH

To evaluate the effect of TPN on tumor growth and the relationship of polyamine synthesis, TPN alone or with the polyamine inhibitor 2-difluoromethylornithine (DFMO) was given to rats with a transplantable sarcoma or colon tumor. For the initial experiment, rats with a transplantable sarcoma were fed a restricted intake of chow (RI) for 14 days to induce malnutrition; we had previously shown that this will also slow the growth of the sarcoma. This RI regimen was followed by six days of TPN alone or with the polyamine inhibitor DFMO (1000 mg/kg/d). DFMO was added directly to the nutrient solution and administered for the entire period of TPN. Tumor growth was significantly increased during the six day course of TPN alone, while the tumor growth of rats receiving TPN with DFMO was equal that of the control which continued to receive the restricted intake of chow during the same period of time. Tumor ornithine decarboxylase (ODC) activity and tumor putrescine content followed the same pattern as the tumor growth—a decrease when rats were fed the restricted intake, an increase following six days of TPN, and a significant reduction when DFMO was added to the TPN regimen. The weights and ODC activity of normal tissues was significantly affected by the nutritional status of the rats but not by administration of DFMO, suggesting a greater response of the tumor to polyamine perturbations compared to that of normal tissues.

The effect of TPN on tumor growth and polyamines was further evaluated using the Ward colon tumor growing subcutaneously in the Fischer 344 rat. The tumor was inoculated SC as previously described.[17] When the tumors were 1-4 grams, TPN alone or with 1,500 mg/kg of DFMO was administered for 12 days. After 12 days the tumors were measured, rats anesthetized, and blood collected from the abdominal aorta. The results, Figure 9.1, are shown in relationship to the growth curve of this tumor. Although the tumor was measured only before and after TPN, the tumor weights of the control fed chow corresponded with previous tumor growth curve for rats fed chow ad libitum. The final tumor weight was significantly increased after 12 days of TPN alone, while the growth of the tumor of rats receiving TPN +

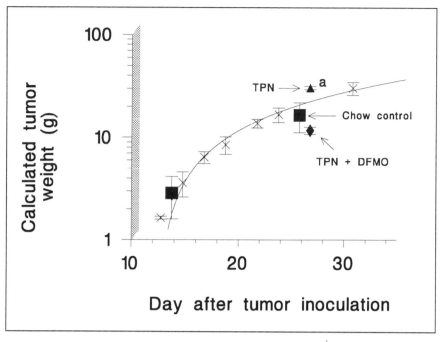

Fig. 9.1. Initial and final weights of a Ward colon tumor compared with the growth curve of rats fed chow. The growth pattern of the tumor was evaluated by two-dimensional measurement every other day (n = 5). The final weight of the control (n = 9) (solid squares) was comparable to that expected from the growth pattern of the tumor. The final tumor weights for rats (n = 6) receiving TPN (solid triangles) were significantly (P < 0.05) greater than the controls. The final tumor weights (solid rectangle) of rats receiving TPN + DFMO (1500 mg/kg/d) (n = 9) were lower than those for TPN rats.

DFMO was similar to that of the control (Fig. 9.1). The RBC polyamine concentrations were significantly altered by TPN and DFMO (Table 9.1). Urine polyamines, however, showed a much different pattern (Table 9.1). Putrescine and a spermine content were significantly increased with TPN while the concentration of all major polyamines was decreased when DFMO was added to the regimen. Plasma polyamine concentrations showed an even different pattern with only putrescine being increased. These results support the hypothesis that RBCs are significant reservoirs for the major polyamines during polyamine depletion. They also suggest that polyamine synthesis is an important parameter in the increase in growth of transplantable tumors in rats but may not totally explain a TPN-related increase in tumor growth.

Table 9.1. Effect of TPN alone or with DFMO on erythrocyte and urinary polyamine concentrations

	Regimen	Putrescine[3]	Spermidine	Spermine
Erythrocytes1	chow	0.504 ± 0.155	67.5 ± 30.0	2.67 ± 0.72
	TPN	1.085 ± 0.549a	96.8 ± 31.2	4.91 ± 2.26
	TPN/DFMO	0.545 ± 0.171	142.3 ± 44.7	33.77 ± 17.21
Plasma1	chow	0.71 ± 0.17	1.10 ± 0.20	0.051 ± 0.021
	TPN	1.72 ± 0.42a	1.30 ± 0.30	0.033 ± 0.005
	TPN/DFMO	0.10 ± 0.02b	0.20 ± 0.10	0.045 ± 0.018
Urine2	chow	40.2 ± 11.3	50.5 ± 25.4	1.67 ± 0.67
	TPN	103.7 ± 29.4a	106.0 ± 91.7	1.98 ± 1.12
	TPN/DFMO	4.6 ± 3.2b	5.7 ± 4.0	0.68 ± 0.58

[1]Blood was drawn from the abdominal aorta into a heparinized vacutainer tube and placed on ice. The plasma was separated from the erythrocytes by centrifugation.
[2]Urine was collected in a 50 ml tube with 0.5 ml 1.0N HCl for 24 hours.
[3]Mean ± SD, nmols/ml. Means differ significantly ($P < 0.05$) [a] vs chow, [b] vs TPN.

IV. AMINO ACID MANIPULATIONS OF TPN

Amino acid defined as TPN was formulated with Aminess as the source of essential amino acids (E). The nonessential amino acids: (N) alanine, glycine, proline, and serine were then added in equal amounts. The regimens were completed by adding arginine (A), ornithine (O), or citrulline (C) at isonitrogenous concentrations (Table 9.2).

A. TUMOR GROWTH AND RBC POLYAMINE CONCENTRATION

Arginine is the major polyamine precursor amino acid that is routinely included in TPN formulations to stimulate the urea cycle and ammonia metabolism. It is not considered to be an essential amino acid for the adult mammal. Although ornithine is the direct polyamine precursor amino acid and a direct metabolite of arginine, the results of several studies suggest that a diet with ornithine substituted for arginine does not support growth as well as the arginine diet does. Gonzales and Byus[19] also reported that ornithine substituted for arginine sustained the early, but not late, growth of a carcinogen induced mammary tumor.

We[20] demonstrated that substituting ornithine for arginine in a TPN regimen will eliminate the TPN-related increase in tumor growth. The RBC polyamine concentrations were increased, however, when both the arginine- and ornithine-containing regimens were administered. The plasma arginine concentration, on the other hand, was significantly increased when arginine was a component of the regimen and significantly lower when ornithine was substituted at equimolar and isonitrogenous concentrations in the TPN regimen. In another study, an isonitrogenous substitution of citrulline for arginine in the TPN regimen resulted in a significant increase in the growth of the colon tumor (Fig. 9.2) which was equivalent to that of an arginine-containing regimen. RBC polyamine levels were similarly increased (Fig. 9.3); plasma concentrations of arginine, however, increased to a significantly greater concentration (Fig. 9.4). Citrulline is a metabolite of ornithine and carbamyl phosphate but has been shown to better substitute for arginine than ornithine in supporting arginine requirements of the cell. These results suggest that the increased growth of the Ward

Table 9.2. Composition of parenteral regimens

Amino acid	ENA	ENO	ENC
Arginine[1]	1300	-0-	-0-
Ornithine (as acetate)[1]	-0-	1972	-0-
Citrulline[1]	-0-	-0-	1742
Leucine[2]	—	825	—
Methionine[2]	—	825	—
Phenylalanine[2]	—	825	—
Lysine (as acetate)[2]	—	600	—
Valine[2]	—	600	—
Isoleucine[2]	—	525	—
Threonine[2]	—	375	—
Tryptophan[2]	—	188	—
Histidine[2]	—	412	—
Alanine[1]	—	2070	—
Glycine[1]	—	1030	—
Proline[1]	—	680	—
Serine[1]	—	500	—

[1]Added to Aminess as individual amino acids (mg/100ml) and filter sterilized using a 0.22 micron filter. The respective amino acid solutions were added to D50W (1:1) and TPN electrolytes (20 ml/L), potassium phosphates (6 ml/L), and multivitamin (MVI-12, 2 ml/L). TPN was administered at 50 ml/day for eight days.
[2]Component amino acids of Aminess.

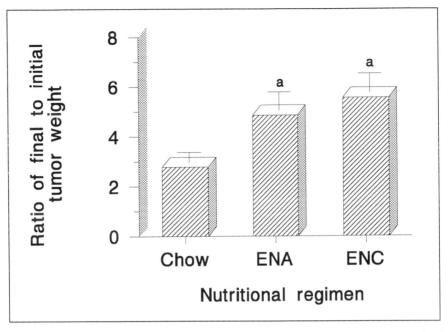

Fig. 9.2. Effect of substituting citrulline (ENC) for arginine (ENA) on the tumor growth of Ward colon tumor. The regimens were administered for eight days at which time the tumor growth change was determined. Mean ± SD differ significantly (P < 0.05)[a] vs chow.

colon tumor is dependent on arginine but a further increase in the plasma arginine concentrations has little effect.

B. TUMOR GROWTH AND TUMOR POLYAMINE CONTENT

If the enhanced growth of tumors during TPN were polyamine related, an increase in tumor content would be expected. The tumor polyamine content of the Ward colon tumor was not affected by the different TPN regimens, while the tumor and plasma arginine and ornithine were significantly altered.[20,21] As reviewed above, TPN does not affect the growth of the transplantable sarcoma for rats previously fed chow ad libitum.[18] The effects of amino acid modification on the tumor amino acid and polyamine content were evaluated and compared with the colon tumor. As shown in Table 9.3, an arginine-containing parenteral regimen resulted in an increase in sarcoma tumor putrescine which was further increased when ornithine was substituted for arginine. However, spermidine and spermine levels were not affected. The tumor (sarcoma) arginine content was not altered by TPN with arginine

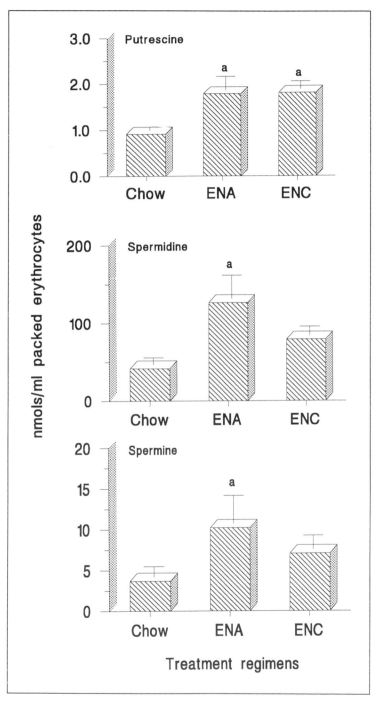

Fig. 9.3. Effect of substituting citrulline (ENC) for arginine (ENA) on the erythrocyte polyamine concentrations. Mean ± SD differ significantly (P < 0.05)[a] vs. chow.

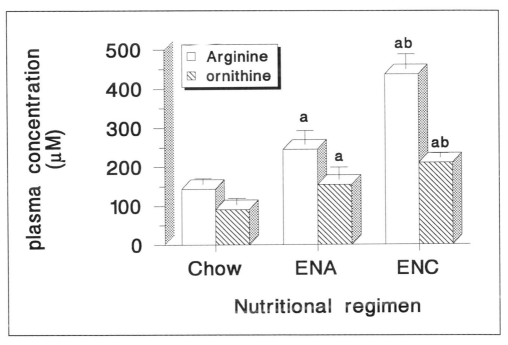

Fig. 9.4. Effect of substituting citrulline (ENC) for arginine (ENA) on the plasma arginine and ornithine concentrations of Ward colon tumor bearing rats. Mean ± SD differ significantly (P < 0.05)[a] vs chow[b] vs ENA.

Table 9.3. Effect of amino acid modification of TPN on sarcoma tumor polyamine content

Regimen[1]	Putrescine[2,3]	Spermidine[2,3]	Spermine[2,3]
chow	185 ± 52	591 ± 85	282 ± 19
ENA	270 ± 55[a]	632 ± 62	303 ± 25
ENO	394 ± 38[a,b]	686 ± 85	282 ± 12

[1]The controls were fed chow ad libitum. ENA and ENO were formulated with arginine and ornithine respectively as in Table 9.1.
[2]Mean ± SD. nmols/gram wet tumor tissue.
[3]Means differ significantly (P < 0.05) [a] vs chow, [b] vs. ENA.

*Table 9.4. Effect of amino acid modification on plasma and tumor
arginine and ornithine of sarcoma bearing rats*

Tissue	Regimen[1]	Arginine[2,3]	Ornithine[2,3]
Plasma	chow	211 ± 59	101 ± 37
	ENA	375 ± 135^a	154 ± 27
	ENO	132 ± 109^b	320 ± 109^b
Tumor	chow	350 ± 32	69.1 ± 8.3
	ENA	383 ± 72	75.0 ± 20.0
	ENO	202 ± 29^b	185.1 ± 16.8^b

[1]The controls were fed chow ad libitum. ENA and ENO were formulated with arginine and ornithine respectively as in Table 9.1.
[2]Mean $\pm$ SD. nmols/ml (plasma) or gram wet tissue (tumor).
[3]Results are mean $\pm$ SD. Means differ significantly ($P < 0.05$) [a] vs chow, [b] vs. TPN.

(Table 9.4). These results suggest that the increased putrescine content of the tumor is not associated with TPN-stimulation of tumor growth.

C. ORNITHINE AND DFMO-INDUCED THROMBOCYTOPENIA

The dose-limiting toxicity of DFMO is thrombocytopenia.[22] Grossie et al[22,23] demonstrated that the thrombocytopenia induced by a high dose DFMO, administered by a continuous infusion, could be blocked by giving concomitant ornithine. This was dependent on the molar ratio of ornithine:DFMO; at a molar ratio of ≥ 0.2, but not at 0.035, there was no thrombocytopenia, and the antitumor activity against a Ward colon tumor and sarcoma was not altered. At a ratio of 0.7, however, the antitumor activity was also being reversed. These rats were fed chow ad libitum, which could be expected to be a good source of polyamines. This, in conjunction with the polyamine from gut microflora, would result in a significant polyamine reserve not depleted by IV DFMO.[25] A study was designed to determine the effect of ornithine in TPN, which would by-pass the gut. The ornithine concentration used previously (Table 9.2) and DFMO at 1,500 mg/kg/d x 4 days were given to Ward colon tumor bearing rats. Although the molar ratio of ornithine: DFMO was > 4.0, the reduction in tumor putrescine content was not affected by concomitant ornithine.[26] These results suggest that the antitumor activity of DFMO, when administered with a parenteral regimen, would not be affected by a concomitant infusion of ornithine.

V. CONCLUSION

Polyamines play a significant role in the growth of neoplastic, as well as normal, cells. Inhibition of polyamine synthesis with inhibitors such as DFMO results in a decrease in tumor growth with little or no effect on normal tissue. This is due to the uncontrolled growth pattern of even the slowest growing tumor along with an increased need for polyamines. The relationship of enhanced polyamine synthesis during TPN, however, is more complex. Our results show that TPN enhanced tumor growth depends on an increase in the content of arginine as well as the presence of polyamines. Whether this suggests that arginine is a limiting amino acid for protein synthesis or other roles of arginine is under investigation.

ACKNOWLEDGMENTS

The authors thank Ms. Pat Thomas for her assistance in preparing this chapter and to Elaine White for her editorial review.

REFERENCES
1. Tabor CW, Tabor H. Polyamines. Ann Rev Biochem 1984; 53:749-90.
2. Russell DH. Increased polyamine concentrations in the urine of human cancer patients. Nature (New Biol) 1971; 233:144-45.
3. Nishioka K, Romsdahl MM. Elevation of putrescine and spermidine in sera of patients with solid tumors. Clin Chim Acta 1974; 56:155-61.
4. Nishioka K, Romsdahl MM, McMurtrey MJ. Serum polyamine alterations in surgical patients with colorectal carcinoma. J Surg Oncol 1977; 9:555-62.
5. Takami H, Nishioka K. Raised polyamines in erythrocytes from melanoma-bearing mice and patients with solid tumors. Br J Cancer 1980; 41:751-56.
6. Takami H, Romsdahl MM, Nishioka K. Polyamines in blood-cells as a cancer marker. Lancet 1979, 912-13.
7. Warren S. The immediate cause of death in cancer. Amer J Med Sci 1932; 184:610-15.

8. Lanzotti VJ, Thomas DR, Boyle LE et al. Survival with inoperable lung cancer-an integration of prognostic variables based on simple clinical criteria. Cancer 1977; 39:303-13.

9. DeWys WD, Begg C, Lavin PT et al. The impact of malnutrition on treatment results in breast cancer. Cancer Treat Rep 1981; 65 (Suppl 1):87-91.

10. Copeland EM, III, MacFadyen Jr BV, Lanzotti VJ et al. Intravenous hyperalimentation as an adjunct to cancer chemotherapy. Am J Surg 1975; 129:167-73.

11. Lanzotti VJ, Copeland EM III, George SL et al. Cancer chemotherapeutic resonse and intravenous hyperalimentation. Cancer Chemother Rep 1975; 59:437-39.

12. Nixon DW, Moffitt S, Lawson DH et al. Total parenteral nutrition as an adjunct to chemotherapy of metastatic colorectal cancer. Cancer Treat Rep 1981; 56:121-28.

13. Popp MB, Fisher RI, Simon RM et al. A prospective randomized study of adjuvant parenteral nutrition in the treatment of diffuse lymphoma: Effect of drug tolerance. Cancer Treat Rep 1981; 65:129-35.

14. Popp MD, Fisher RI, Wesley R et al. A prospective randomized study of adjuvant parenteral nutrition in the treatment of advanced diffuse lymphoma: Influence on survival. Surgery 1981; 90:195-203.

15. Ota DM, Nishioka K, Folkes M et al. Nutritional parameters affecting erythrocyte polyamine levels in cancer patients. J Clin Oncol 1984; 2:1157-64.

16. Ota DM, Nishioka K, Grossie B et al. Erythrocyte polyamine levels during intravenous feeding of patients with colorectal carcinoma. Eur J Cancer Clin Oncol 1986; 22:837-42.

17. Grossie Jr VB, Nishioka K, Ota DM et al. Relationship of erythrocyte polyamine levels and growth rate of transplantable tumors in rats. Cancer Res 1986; 46:3464-68.

18. Grossie Jr VB, Ota DM, Chang T-H et al. Differential effect of parenteral nutrition on tumor growth and erythrocyte polyamine levels in the rat. J Parent Enter Nutr 1989; 13:590-595.

19. Gonzales GG, Byus CV. Effect of dietary arginine restriction upon ornithine and polyamine metabolism during two-stage epidermal carcinogenesis in the mouse. Cancer Res 1991; 51:2932-39.

20. Grossie Jr VB, Nishioka K, Ajani JA et al. Substituting ornithine for arginine in total parenteral nutrition eliminates enhanced tumor growth. J Surg Oncol 1992; 50:161-67.

21. Grossie Jr VB, Nishioka K. A parenteral nutrition regimen with ornithine substituted for arginine alters the amino acid, but not polyamine, content of the Ward colon tumor. (submitted for publication).

22. Grossie Jr VB, Ota DM, Nishioka K et al. The effect of intravenous difluoromethylornithine on the polyamine metabolism of normal tissues and a transplantable fibrosarcoma. Cancer Res 1987; 47:1836-40.
23. Grossie Jr VB, Ota DM, Ajani JA et al. Reduction of difluoromethylornithine induced thrombocytopenia in rats with ornithine while maintaining antitumor activity. Cancer Res 1989; 49:4159-62.
24. Grossie Jr VB, Ota DM, Ajani JA et al. Amelioration of thrombocytopenia with concomitant ornithine in sarcoma-bearing rats receiving high dose difluoromethylornithine. Invest New Drugs 1991; 9:321-26.
25. Quemener V, Blanchard Y, Chamaillard C et al. Polyamine deprivation: A new tool in cancer treatment. Anticancer Res 1994; 14:443-48.
26. Grossie Jr VB, Nishioka K. Ornithine (ORN) in parenteral nutrition (TPN) ameliorates difluoromethylornithine (DFMO)-induced thrombocytopenia without affecting tumor putrescine (PUT) reduction. FASEB J 1996; 9:51309.

CHAPTER 10

CIRCULATING POLYAMINES AS BIOLOGICAL MARKERS FOR CANCER

Jacques-Philippe Moulinoux, Véronique Quemener,
Jean-Guy Delcros and Bernard Cipolla

I. INTRODUCTION

Processes of malignant neoplasia are characterized by the dysregulation of cellular proliferation homeostasis. Disregarding the fact that certain cancer cells have innate or acquired characteristics which distinguish them from normal histologically homologous cells, malignant cancer cell division occurs according to processes similar in their major aspects to those found in normal cells. From a strictly medical point of view, the diagnostic problems which exist in cancer disease arise from this biological fact.

How can one detect a malignant proliferative process occurring within a normal organism which is itself undergoing constant renewal? The metabolism of the polyamines is one of several metabolic cascades which are linked to cell proliferation. The characteristics of polyamine metabolism make it a target for antiproliferative drugs and a source of new signals in the blood which indicate the presence of proliferative processes.[1-5]

During past years we have tried to gather information on extracellular polyamines, blood polyamines in particular, and we have

Polyamines in Cancer: Basic Mechanisms and Clinical Approaches, edited by Kenji Nishioka. © 1996 R.G. Landes Company.

tried to answer the following two questions: (1) What is the diagnostic significance of blood polyamines? (2) Is it possible to use the information obtained from blood polyamine determination in antiproliferative cancer therapy?

II. DIAGNOSTIC SIGNIFICANCE

The first studies trying to ascertain the implications of polyamine levels in biological fluids of the organism were begun in 1971 by D.H. Russell.[6] After these initial experiments there ensued various bioclinical studies investigating the diagnostic significance of polyamine determinations, without any well defined goal in mind.[1] Were new screening methods, new biological criteria for spreading disease, or a new "tumor marker" the goal?[5] The term of "tumor marker" caused confusion. Were the markers diagnosing the presence of a malignant process (amount of cancer tissue), or were they rather an index estimating the aggressiveness of the tumor with respect to the organism (malignant hyperplasia)? With the exception of the works of L.J. Marton et al,[7-9] who showed that the measurement of polyamine levels in the cerebrospinal fluid assured a better follow-up of children with operated medulloblastoma, these first attempts were a failure. The absence of a clear, clinically based goal, and an oversimplified scheme of the blood compartment carrying "free" polyamines in the plasma caused problems in the clinical interpretation of circulating polyamine levels. By the end of the 1970s the unclear biochemical view of the potential role of polyamines as markers for cancer led to an almost total disinterest in their diagnostic use.

A. POLYAMINE BLOOD COMPARTMENTALIZATION

Striving for better understanding of the potential of polyamines as tumor markers, the determining of the distribution of polyamines in peripheral blood should have been the first step. The amount of free polyamines in the plasma, estimated after protein precipitation with acid, represents only approximately 2% of the total pool of circulating polyamines.[1,10-11] Nevertheless, almost all clinical studies concentrated exclusively on the seric compartment.[1] What are the characteristics of circulating polyamine transporters known at this time? A "transporter" of extracellular polyamines is an element present in a biological fluid, which is capable of carrying polyamines from one cell to another, in a specific or nonspecific fashion, without any transport-related enzymatic activity which might be inherent to the transporter.[5] Circulating polyamine transporters can be classified at least into two principal groups, those which are proteins, and those which are peripheral blood cells, mainly red blood cells (RBCs).

One major type of proteins that could be involved in polyamine transport are the antipolyamine antibodies. Anti-polyamine antibodies exist in very low quantities in normal human serum as well as in rabbit serum.[12-14] The existence of immunocomplexes containing polyamines in human sera supports their potential role as polyamine transporter.[15-16] Enzyme-linked immunosorbent assay (ELISA) methods have been used for measurements of antipolyamine antibodies and immunocomplexes in human serum from patients with bronchopulmonary cancer.[17] However the data are too fragmentary to attribute any biological significance to these parameters.

Even though free polyamines are not considered as immunogenic because of their small size, it has been demonstrated that injection of free spermine or spermidine induces specific antipolyamine antibodies in rabbits.[18] Antibody formation by "free" polyamines may be explained by the presence of transglutaminases which catalyze amide bond formation between polyamines and glutamate residues of proteins. We found that factor XIII, the blood transglutaminase, catalyzes the covalent binding of polyamines to fibronectin and antiproteases, namely α-2 macroglobuline, α-1 antitrypsine, α-1 antichymotrypsine and antithrombine III.[19] But there is no evidence that these modifications occur in vivo. The existence of proteins with bound polyamines in the plasma of mice was demonstrated using an immunoaffinity technique using antipolyamine antibodies. Among those proteins, certain ones were specifically associated with malignant cellular proliferation. They were present in the plasma of mice with cancer, absent in normal plasma and differed from those induced during acute inflammatory reaction.[20] Neither the nature of the polyamines or the proteins, nor the type of the bond between the polyamines and the proteins have been elucidated.

In plasma, polyamines are associated not only with proteins but also with lipoproteins. Apolipoprotein B, the major protein found in chylomicrons (VLDL and LDL) is also a substrate for cellular and plasma transglutaminase.[21] A liposperminc complex has been found in the serum of cancer patients.[22] In addition to their covalent binding to proteins, polyamines may also bind noncovalently to lipids.[23] In tumor carrying mice we have observed that free or weakly bound polyamines, mainly spermine, are present in purified lipoprotein particles.[24] The content of polyamines associated with lipoprotein particles is different in tumor bearing animals as compared with normal mice. This suggests that modifications of polyamine concentrations influence the charge of the lipoproteins and induce modifications of the ^{1}H NMR spectral in plasma.[25] In cancer patients, changes in the distribution of noncovalently bound polyamines to plasma lipoproteins might be an explanation for the "Fossell index" of cancer.[26]

The proportion of "free" plasma polyamines, and those bound to a transporter, does not exceed 2% of the total blood polyamine pool as has been mentioned. Therefore, polyamine transport by transporters present in plasma is quantitatively of minor importance. However, one cannot exclude that these "free" polyamines have a role in the regulation of cell proliferation. More than 95% of circulating spermidine and spermine is transported by RBCs.[10,11,27] The internalization of polyamines by RBCs involves band III proteins [28,29] and is an energy dependent process.[11,30] We have shown that normal RBCs have a strong affinity for spermidine, at least 30-times stronger than that for putrescine, therefore, the accumulation inside the RBCs of polyamines is not dependent on the size of the molecules.[11] The uptake of these organic polycations does not depend on the existence of negative charges on the surface of the RBC. Sialic acid residues produce a negatively charged layer on the stroma. Digestion by neuraminidase (which removes virtually all of the sialic acid residues) increases the transport of spermidine into the RBC.[30,31] One must also remember that more than 98% of spermidine and spermine exists in a free form in the cytosol of an RBC;[10,11] the RBC is therefore an ideal transporter of spermidine and spermine.

III. COMPARTMENTALIZATION OF THE POLYAMINES IN BLOOD: DIAGNOSTIC SIGNIFICANCE AND THERAPEUTIC IMPLICATIONS

One may wonder if the polyamine blood compartments described above could be used to (1) detect the existence of a malignant process or (2) measure the magnitude of malignant hyperplasia. It seems premature at present to draw conclusions with respect to the clinical significance of the plasma protein-bound polyamines. This is in part due to methodological problems.[15-17] The determination of protein-bound polyamines in plasma may become a useful tool in the future in the initial diagnosis of the presence of a tumor and in the follow-up of cancer patients under treatment. Logically, the protein compartment should correspond to "qualitative" aspects of the cancer, and a *contrario,* the RBC polyamine pool is rather a reflection of the proliferation. The RBC polyamine level is an index of the hyperplastic status of the tumor: animals with grafted tumors show regularly increased RBC polyamine content; in these animal models the RBC spermidine level correlated not only with the tumor progression, but also with the polyamine content of the proliferating tissue.[29,32,33] Figure 10.1 shows the relationship between the evolution of the RBC spermidine level and the tumor volume (3LL Lewis lung carcinoma); within the second and third week, when the tumor volume increases considerably, the RBC spermidine content increases proportionately. Between the third and fourth week, when the increase in tumor volume is less rapid, the spermidine level increases only slightly as will be shown later, a large proportion of the spermidine found in the RBCs originating from the tumor.[29]

Animals submitted to partial hepatectomy also showed an increase in their RBC polyamine content.[33] As in tumor-grafted animals, during liver regeneration the RBC spermidine levels correlated not only with the rate of cell proliferation, but also with the polyamine content of the proliferating tissue. This led us to consider RBC spermidine levels as markers of cell proliferation rate, but not as a "tumor marker."[5] From a clinical point of view, it is essential to distinguish the time of tumor diagnosis and the time of treatment.

A. Initial Diagnosis

Except for those patients with untreated solid tumors having long doubling times (colon, thyroid), as a general rule RBC polyamine levels arc proportional to the grade of malignancy.[32,34-37] Nevertheless, even though the RBC polyamine levels are increased in cancer patients in a statistically significant manner, they do not permit the diagnosis of the presence of a malignant process. Spermidine and spermine can only provide an element of statistical value; RBC polyamines are in proportion with the tumor stage. As is shown in Figure 10.2, polyamine determinations at the time of tumor diagnosis confirm this tendency in prostatic cancer patients.[37] The fact that RBC polyamines are not useful for initial diagnosis can be explained by the fact that RBC polyamine con-

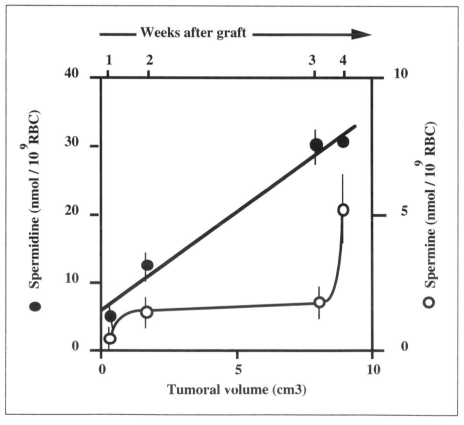

Fig. 10.1. Relationship between the RBC polyamine levels and the tumor volume in 3LL grafted mice (from ref 28).

centrations reflect the level of tumor hyperplasia which evolves in a noncontinuous manner, with growth phases and stationary phases. Therefore, at diagnosis, a given patient may correspond to one of the two situations and exhibit the corresponding levels of erythrocytic polyamines. A marker of cell proliferation might represent only a statistical probability of the presence of a neoplastic process

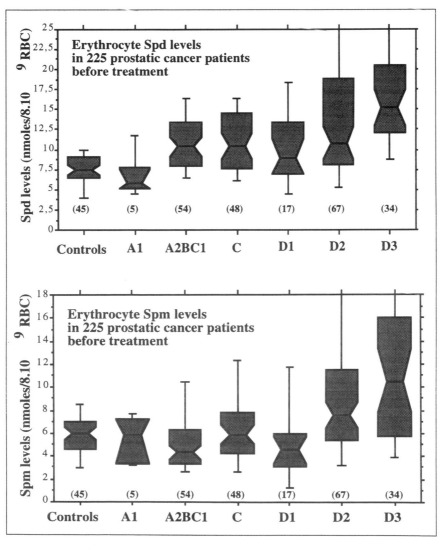

Fig. 10.2. RBC Spd and Spm levels in patients with prostatic carcinoma before treatment (from ref. 37).

at the time of the initial diagnosis, but it may be of prognostic value. This, in fact, was what we observed in patients with prostatic adenocarcinoma (solid tumor/adult patient)[38,39] and in children suffering from acute lymphoblastic leukemia (ALL).[40,41]

1. Cancer of the prostate

In a multivariate analysis of 97 patients with newly diagnosed, untreated, stage D2 prostatic carcinoma, the initial performance status, hemoglobin (Hb), prostate specific antigen (PSA) levels, tumor Gleason grade, extent of the disease on the bone scan, and RBC spermidine and spermine levels with progression were correlated. In pretreatment performance status, Hb and spermidine and spermine levels were correlated with tumor progression, Hb and spermine being the most significant independent variables. Concerning cause-specific survival and hormonal escape, only Hb and RBC spermine levels were significant independent variables.

Polyamine levels allowed us to discriminate, at diagnosis, those patients with a high risk of rapid hormonal relapse; 50% of patients with a spermine level > 9 nmol (abnormal level) relapsed seven months after the diagnosis (mean survival time: 14 months). In contrast, 50% of patients with a spermine level < 9 nmol (normal level) relapsed only 29 months after the diagnosis (mean survival time = 34 months) (Fig. 10.3). At diagnosis PSA levels do not differentiate high risk patients from low risk patients. A better appreciation of the aggressiveness of the tumor by polyamine analysis will lead to the initiation of earlier first treatments and more "aggressive" treatments. The modalities of this more aggressive treatment remain to be determined, but results obtained by polyamine deprivation on Dunning MAT-LyLu adenocarcinoma of the prostate in rats led us to consider this treatment as an important therapeutic tool for patients in hormonal escape.[42]

2. Children with ALL

Using multivariate analysis, we have established in ALL children, at diagnosis, the clinical usefulness of RBC polyamine levels if they are used together with other bioclinical criteria. The importance of elevated spermine levels in concomitance with elevated leukocyte number, Hb content and other criteria lies in the fact

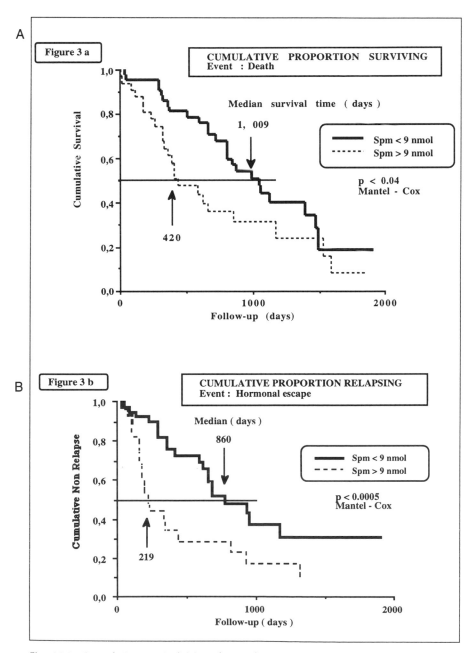

Fig. 10.3. *Cumulative survival (a) and cumulative non relapse (b) according to RBC spermine level of less than 9 or 9 or more nmol/8 x10⁹ RBC.*

that these parameters are the basis for the initial classification of the patients, which in turn decides the choice of the initial treatment. This study revealed the existence of five subpopulations instead of the three obtained when only usual bioclinical parameters are considered. Most importantly, the initial RBC polyamine levels revealed a subpopulation of relapsing. This high risk subpopulation was undetectable when using only the usual criteria, because the children of this high risk subpopulation were distributed among the three usual clinical populations. Therefore, the treatment of these patients was not adapted to their proliferative status.

B. LONG-TERM THERAPEUTIC FOLLOW-UP

The RBC polyamine levels are not markers of malignant transformation, but they can be exploited in the follow-up of cancer patients as their increase is one sign among others of tumor recurrence. During the follow-up of patients operated for malignant supratentorial glioma, 40% of patients with recurring glioblastoma exhibited abnormal RBC polyamine levels in the first six months preceding the first clinical and radiological signs of such a recurrence.[36] This observation led to two concepts, one being the "biological" recurrence (the increase in RBC polyamine content), the other being the "clinical" recurrence (clinical and/or radiological signs of recurrence) of the tumor, the former preceding the latter. This seems to be true for prostatic adenocarcinoma patients as well.

To explore this concept further, we looked for an animal model which mimics the clinical situation. Ethylnitrosourea induced tumors in the offspring of pregnant rats seemed suitable because, in analogy to the clinical situation, tumors exhibited undetermined time of appearance in a nonpredetermined proportion of the animals.[43] RBC polyamines were determined over a period of seven months in 154 rats. Our data clearly demonstrated the appearance of elevated spermidine concentrations in advance of tumor occurrence; in 71% of the rats which later developed a tumor, abnormal spermidine levels (> 40 nmol/8 x 10^9 RBC) preceded by 35 ± 31 days the first clinical symptoms for the presence of a tumor. In 29% of the animals abnormal RBC spermidine concentrations were observed at the time of tumor diagnosis. Elevation of spermine concentrations (>6 nmol/8 x 10⁹ RBC) was less frequent. Figure 10.4 shows a typical pattern of the evolution of the RBC polyamine levels in a rat which developed a tumor. In this example, abnormal spermidine levels (>40 nmol/8 x 10⁹ RBC) were observed 40 days before the tumor was diagnosed.

In this experimental model, RBC polyamine levels do not allow us to discriminate between malignant and nonmalignant tumors. This confirms earlier findings which showed that RBC polyamines are markers of the cell proliferation rate, but not for the presence of a malignant tumor.[5] RBC polyamine concentrations are solely an index of the intensity of hyperplastic processes that can be clinically used for the early detection of proliferative phases of tumors, thus allowing timely therapeutic measures.

From a bioclinical standpoint, and considering patients operated upon for glioblastoma, the proliferative phase corresponds to the cellular reconstruction of the tumor mass ("biological recurrence") and would logically be sensitive to chemotherapy, whereas a tumor mass fully reconstituted ("clinical and/or radiological recurrence") and therefore having already proliferated, would seem to require surgery and/or radiotherapy. The therapeutic use of RBC

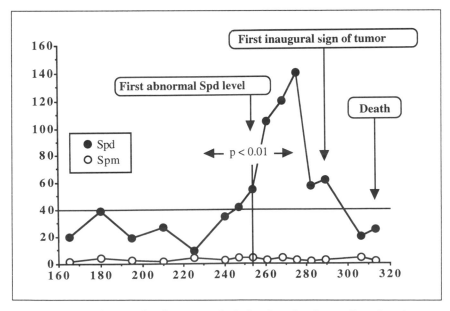

Fig. 10.4. RBC polyamine levels in a rat which developed a chemically induced tumor.

polyamine levels as early markers of biological tumor recurrence was tested in glioblastoma patients.[35,42] Patients operated on for glioblastoma and treated according to their individual degree of hyperplasia as determined by their RBC polyamine levels exhibited a significant increase in their survival time.[36,44] Even though we can probably not use RBC polyamines' levels as an index of hyperplasia to all types of solid tumors (e.g., slow growing colon carcinoma), it seems logical to treat a cancer patient when the disease is in its proliferative phase.

Another interesting clinical exploitation of the hyperplastic index came from follow-up studies in children with bone marrow grafts. We observed that in 100% of the cases, the first signs of bone marrow regeneration were preceded one to three weeks by an increase in RBC spermidine levels. Therefore, the measurement of the RBC polyamine levels allows the early appreciation of bone marrow graft survival.[45,46]

Polyamine analogs may permit us to quantify the intensity of the malignant cell proliferation in patients suffering from a solid tumor. We had noted that after IP injection of trace amounts of ^{14}C putrescine, labeled spermidine accumulated in the RBC of 3LL-bearing mice in proportion with tumor growth.[36] Since 2-methylputrescine is an excellent substrate of spermidine synthase, we attempted to use this nonradioactive putrescine analog instead of ^{14}C putrescine.[47] As observed with ^{14}C putrescine, 24 hours after IP injection of 2-methylputrescine, methylspermidine accumulated only in RBC of the tumor-bearing mice, not in tumor-free animals, and the concentration of the methyl derivative correlated directly with tumor progression. Not only 2-methylputrescine but other nonradioactive putrescine analogs which are subtrates of spermidine synthase may be considered for use as tumor markers. Nevertheless, not all putrescine analogs are appropriate, even though they are subtrates of this enzyme. For example, we failed to detect any accumulation of 6-fluoro- or 6,6-difluorospermidine in RBC from 3LL-bearing mice after administration of 2-fluoro- or 2,2-difluoroputrescine. The decreased basicity of the fluorinated analogs makes them probably less suitable for binding to anionic sites than the natural polyamines, so that they are displaced by spermidine and do not accumulate in RBC.

IV. CONCLUSION

Circulating polyamines are "markers" of cellular proliferation. As demonstrated by polyamine depletion of the tumor-bearing animals,[42,48-51] extracellular polyamines participate in supporting the state of malignant proliferation, and de facto, play important roles in the homeostatic control of cellular growth. Therefore, circulating polyamines have characteristics which are similar to those observed for intracellular polyamines;[52] proliferating cells contain increased amounts of polyamines, their concentrations vary as a function of the cell cycle, and these molecules are vital elements for the cell. In a clinical context, especially with respect to therapy, one must consider polyamine metabolism in its entirety,[53] at the level of the whole organism, and not only in its intracellular aspects.

ACKNOWLEDGMENTS

We are indebted to Pr. N. Seiler for helpful comments on the manuscript. These works were supported by the CNRS, the Association pour la Recherche sur le Cancer (ARC), and the Ligue Nationale Française Contre le Cancer.

REFERENCES

1. Scalabrino G, Ferioli ME. Polyamines in mammalian tumors. Adv Cancer Res 1981; 35:152–268; 1982, 36:2–102.
2. Pegg AE. Polyamine metabolism and its importance in neoplastic growth and as target for chemotherapy. Cancer Res 1988; 48:759-74.
3. Bachrach U, Heimer YM. In: Bachrach U, Heimer YM, eds. The Physiology of Polyamines Vol. 1; Vol.2. Boca Raton, Florida, USA: CRC Press, 1989.
4. Quemener V, Khan NA, Moulinoux J-P. Polyamines and cancer. Cancer J 1990; 3:45–52.
5. Moulinoux J-P, Quemener V, Khan NA. Biological significance of circulating polyamines. Cell Molec Biol 1991; 37:773–83.
6. Russell DH. Increased polyamine concentrations in the urine of human cancer patients. Nature 1971; 233:144–45.
7. Marton LJ, Heby O, Wilson CB. Increased polyamine concentrations in the CSF of patients with brain tumors. Int J Cancer 1974; 14:731–35.
8. Marton LJ, Heby O, Levin VA et al. The relationship of polyamines in the CSF to the presence of central nervous system tumors. Cancer Res 1976; 36:973–77.

9. Marton LJ, Edwards MS, Levin VA et al. CSF polyamines: a new and important means of monitoring patients with medulloblastoma. Cancer 1981; 47:757–60.

10. Moulinoux J-P, Quemener V, Chevet D. Red cell free polyamine concentrations in patients on maintenance hemodialysis. Life Sci 1981; 29:955–62.

11. Moulinoux J-P, Quemener V, Quash G-A. In vitro studies on the entry of polyamines into normal red blood cells. Biochimie 1984a; 66:385–93.

12. Roch A-M, Quash G-A, Ripoll J-P et al. Evidence for natural antibodies (IgG) to polyamines in human sera. Recent Results Cancer Res 1979; 67:56–62.

13. Bartos D, Bartos F, Campbell RA et al. Antibody to spermine: A natural biological constituent. Science 1980; 208:1178–81.

14. Furiuchi K, Ezoe H, Obara T et al. Evidence for a naturally occuring anti-spermine antibody in normal rabbit serum. Proc Natl Acad Sci USA 1980; 77:2904–8.

15. Roch A-M, Quash G-A, Ripoll H et al. Protein-bound polyamines and immune complexes containing polyamines in human plasma. In: Caldarera CM, Sappia V, Bachrach U et al, eds. Adv Polyamine Res, Vol. 3. New York: Raven Press, 1981: 225–35.

16. Roch A-M, Quash G-A. Development of immunolatex procedures for measuring bound polyamines. In: Campbell RA, Morris DR, Bartos D, DAves GD, Bartos F, eds. Advances in Polyamine Research, Vol. 2. New York: Raven Press, 1978: 55–63.

17. Roch AM, Delcros JG, Ripoll JP et al. A novel covalent enzyme-linked immunoassay (CELIA) for simultaneously measuring free and immune complex bound antibodies of defined specificity. I. Application to naturally occuring anti-polyamine antibodies in human sera. J Immunol Methods 1990; 133:1–11.

18. Atanassov CL, Delcros JG, Muller S et al. Immunization of rabbits with spermine induces antibodies to self antigens. Int Arch Allergy Immunol 1993; 102:46–55.

19. Roch A-M, Thomas V, Quash G-A et al. A quantitative and qualitative study of the transglutaminase-mediated insertion of polyamines into plasma proteins from patients with broncho-pulmonary cancer. Int J Cancer, 1984, 33, 787–793.

20. Delcros JG, Roch A-M, Thomas V et al. Protein-bound polyamines in the plasma of mice grafted with the Lewis lung carcinoma. FEBS Lett 1987; 220:236–42.

21. Coccuzi E, Miacentini M, Beninati S et al. Post-translational modification of apolipoprotein B by transglutaminases. Biochem J 1990; 265:707–13.

22. Quash G-A, Wilson MB. Polyamines in human serum. W I Med J 1967; XVI:81–91.

23. Schuber F. Influence of polyamines on membrane functions. Biochem J 1989; 260:1–10.
24. Quemener V, Leray G, Moulinoux J-P et al. Polyamine transport by plasma lipoproteins is modified in tumor-bearing mice. Submitted to J Lipid Res.
25. Leray G, Quemener V, Le Rumeur E et al. Proton NMR spectroscopy of plasma lipoproteins in the experimental Lewis lung carcinoma. Anticancer Res 1992; 12:1227–32.
26. Fossel ET, Carr JM, McDonagh JM. Detection of malignant tumors: water-suppressed proton nuclear magnetic resonance spectroscopy of plasma. N Engl J Med 1986; 315: 1369–76.
27. Rennert OM, Shukla JB. Polyamines in health and disease. In: Campbell RA et al, eds. Adv Polyamine Res. Vol. 2. New York: Raven Press, 1978: 195–201.
28. Moulinoux J-P, Quemener V, Khan NA et al. Spermidine uptake by erythrocytes from normal and Lewis lung carcinoma grafted mice I. Anticancer Res 1989; 9:1057–62.
29. Moulinoux J-P, Quemener V, Khan NA et al. Spermidine uptake by erythrocytes from normal and Lewis lung carcinoma grafted mice II. Anticancer Res 1989; 9:1063–68.
30. Khan NA, Quemener V, Moulinoux J-P. Spermidine binding sites at the cell surface of normal and desialated human erythrocytes. Biochem Arch 1989; 5:321–29.
31. Khan NA, Quemener V, Moulinoux J-P. Inhibition of adenylate cyclase activity by polyamines in human erythrocyte plasma membranes. Life Sci 1989; 46:43–47.
32. Moulinoux J-P, Quemener V, Roch A-M et al. Red blood cell polyamines in mice bearing the Lewis lung carcinoma (3LL) and in patients with bronchopulmonary cancers. Int J Cancer 1984; 34:277–81.
33. Moulinoux J-P, Quemener V, Chambon Y. Evolution of red blood cell polyamine levels in partially hepatectomized rats. Eur J Cancer 1987; 23:237–44.
34. Moulinoux J-P, Quemener V, Chatel M et al. Polyamines in brain tumors: A correlative study between tumor, spinal fluid and red blood cell free polyamine levels. J Neuro-Oncol 1984; 2:153–58.
35. Moulinoux J-P, Delamaire D, Quemener V et al. Diagnosis value of erythrocyte polyamines and histaminemia in malignant hepatic tumors. Clin Chim Acta 1985; 145:77–87.
36. Moulinoux J-P, Quemener V, Havouis R et al. Erythrocyte polyamines: Their diagnostic and therapeutic importance in human neuro-oncology. Adv Exp Med Biol 1989; 50:331–44.
37. Cipolla B, Moulinoux J-P, Quemener V et al. Erythrocyte polyamine levels in human prostatic carcinoma. J Urol 1990; 144:1164–66.

38. Cipolla B, Guille F, Moulinoux J-P et al. Polyamine and prostatic carcinoma: clinical and therapeutic implications. Eur Urol 1993; 24:124–31.

39. Cipolla B, Guille F, Moulinoux J-P et al. Erythrocyte polyamines and prognosis in stage D2 prostatic carcinoma patients. J Urol 1994; 151: 629–33.

40. Quemener V, Le Gall E, Edan C et al. Red blood cell polyamine levels in children with acute leukemia: their clinical interest in disease staging and monitoring of therapy efficiency. Cancer J 1986; 4:174–78.

41. Quemener V, Bansard F, Bouet F et al. Erythrocyte polyamine levels: a new and important criterion for the treatment of acute lymphoblastic leukemia in children. Cancer J 1993; 6:208–12.

42. Moulinoux J-P, Quemener V, Cipolla B et al. The growth of MAT-LyLu rat prostatic adenocarcinoma can be prevented in vivo by polyamine deprivation. J Urol 1991; 146:1408–12.

43. Quemener V, Havouis R, Khan N et al. Determination of erythrocyte polyamines as predictive method in tumor diagnosis. An animal study with chemically induced tumors. Anticancer Res 1996; (in press).

44. Théron J, Moulinoux J-P, Casasco A et al. Intra-arterial chemotherapy with BCNU. Correlation between tumor growth and red blood cell polyamine levels. In: Brain Oncology: Biology, Diagnosis and Therapy. Boston: Martinus Nijhoff Publishers, 1987: 409-12.

45. Bergeron C, Bouet F, Quemener V et al. Clinical importance of erythrocyte polyamine level determination during bone marrow transplantation in children. Anticancer Res 1989; 9:1757–60.

46. Bergeron C, Le Moine P, Le Berre C et al. Erythrocyte polyamine levels: An indication of successful engraftment of bone marrow in children. Bone Marrow Transplant 1995; 16:27-37.

47. Moulinoux J-P, Quemener V, Havouis R et al. Accumulation of polyamine analogs in red blood cells: A potential index of tumor proliferation rate. Anticancer Res 1991; 11:2143–46.

48. Moulinoux J-P, Darcel F, Quemener V et al. Inhibition of the growth of U-251 human glioblastoma in nude mice by polyamine deprivation. Anticancer Res 1991; 11:175–80.

49. Seiler N, Sarhan S, Grauffel C et al. Endogenous and exogenous polyamines in support of tumor growth. Cancer Res 1990; 50: 5077-83.

50. Quemener V, Moulinoux J-P, Bergeron C et al. Tumor growth inhibition by polyamine deprivation. In: Dowling RH, Fölsch UR, Löser C, eds. Polyamines in the Gastrointestinal Tract. Lancaster: Kluwer Academic Publishers, 1992: 375–85.

51. Quemener V, Blanchard Y, Chamaillard L et al. Polyamine deprivation: A new tool in cancer treatment. Anticancer Res 1994; 14:443–48.

52. Khan NA, Quemener V, Moulinoux J-P. Characterization of polyamine transport pathways. In: Carter C, ed. The Neuropharmacology of Polyamines. Neuroscience Perspectives, London: Academic Press, 1994: 37–60.

53. Seiler N. Formation, catabolism and properties of the natural polyamines. In: Carter C, ed. The Neuropharmacology of Polyamines. Neuroscience Perspectives, London: Academic Press, 1994: 1–36.

CHAPTER 11

CLINICAL STUDIES OF POLYAMINES AND THEIR ANTIMETABOLITES

Kenji Nishioka, Michele Follen Mitchell and Jaffer A. Ajani

I. INTRODUCTION

The objectives of this chapter are to review clinical studies of polyamines and their antimetabolites based on various re views and discussions from previous chapters and to evaluate future directions of polyamine studies as they apply to cancer research. Since values of polyamines as human tumor markers have been discussed in chapters 9 and 10 and recently by Bachrach,[1] this aspect will be excluded in this chapter except aspects of ODC activity and polyamine levels in tumor tissues as possible markers for malignancy. In addition, chapter 8 reviewed aspects related to radiotherapy and hyperthermia and thus will also be excluded from this chapter. As a result, we will focus primarily on therapeutic and chemopreventive clinical trials of polyamine antimetabolites.

A. ODC AND POLYAMINES IN HUMAN TISSUES AS BIOLOGICAL MARKERS FOR MALIGNANCY

In 1984, Luk and Baylin demonstrated that the ODC activity of normal-appearing colonic mucosa was significantly greater in patients with familial polyposis than in normal controls.[2] This investigation also included unaffected first-degree relatives of patients

Polyamines in Cancer: Basic Mechanisms and Clinical Approaches, edited by Kenji Nishioka. © 1996 R.G. Landes Company.

with familial polyposis; a bimodal distribution of ODC activity was reported. One peak was in the range of normal controls while the other overlapped with ODC activity of normal-appearing mucosa from affected patients. They concluded that ODC activity of normal-appearing mucosa could identify family members who carried the genotype. This study stimulated further evaluations of polyamine metabolism in various tumor tissue particularly in colonic tissues. As a result, extensive studies on this subject have been carried out.[3-28] Although the majority of studies were performed using tissues from patients with gastrointestinal malignancies, this population also included patients with breast cancer,[4] head and neck cancers[9,21] and lung cancer.[13] Except for the result reported by Moorehead et al[6] who showed lower ODC activity in rectal tumors than in normal-appearing rectal mucosa, other investigators have demonstrated that tumor tissues and polyps contain increased levels of either ODC activities or polyamine levels or both, compared to normal tissues. In our human colon mucosa study, in addition, we observed that ODC activity in normal-appearing mucosa varied throughout the large intestine, with significantly greater activities in the distal segment of the large bowel.[18] The higher ODC activity detected in the sigmoid colon and rectum correlates with the higher incidence of tumor development in this region of the large bowel. Kingsnorth et al reported that breast cancer polyamine levels are a biological marker of tumor aggressiveness and can be used as a prognostic indicator of early recurrence that is independent of node status.[4]

To determine if ODC activity of normal-appearing mucosa could identify family members who carry the genotype, many investigators examined normal mucosa from high risk groups.[13,15,20,26,27] They failed to observe increased levels of ODC activities in normal mucosa from high risk groups of subjects and concluded that ODC activity is an unreliable marker for the identification of populations at high risk. However, Okuzumi et al reported that mucosa from the cancer-bearing stomach had high ODC activity compared to gastric mucosa without cancer.[19] Therefore, further examination of this issue may be required in different tumor groups.

II. THERAPEUTIC CLINICAL STUDIES

In this section, we will discuss the following items: DFMO, methylacetylenic putrescine, deoxyspergualin, MGBG, a combination of DFMO and MGBG, DFMO plus interferon and MGBG plus other chemotherapeutic agents.

A. DFMO

As discussed in chapter 7, DFMO, also called eflornithine, is an enzyme-activated irreversible inhibitor of ODC. The antitumor activity of this agent has been extensively documented in both in vitro and in vivo animal tumor models. Pharmacokinetic properties of this agent with oral and intravenous administrations indicated that peak plasma concentrations are reached within 6 hours after oral doses, and a mean half-life for oral and intravenous doses is 199 minutes. Mean renal clearance was determined as 0.99 ml/min/kg, accounting for 83% of drug elimination. DFMO kinetics follow a dose-linear model with a bioavailability of 54-58%.[29]

Dunzendorfer examined clinical effects of DFMO in a preliminary study in two patients with invasive and metastatic carcinoma of the bladder and three patients with metastatic renal cancer. Multiple oral doses of 18-24 g/day for up to two months were given. A moderate anti-growth effect was observed. The toxic side effects noted were gastrointestinal toxicity, erythropenia and audiovestibular symptoms, which were all reversible.[30] Maddox et al examined intravenous DFMO (5.5-64 g/m²) in their phase I trial with patients with refractory leukemia.[31] Drug toxicities including ototoxicity, nausea, vomiting and anorexia were mild. No patients achieved a remission but they noted stabilization or decrease in circulating blast cells in some patients. Abeloff et al examined oral administration of this agent in their Phase II trial.[32] Previously treated patients with advanced small cell lung cancer and previously untreated patients with metastatic colon were included in this study. Thrombocytopenia, reversible hearing loss and gastrointestinal side effects were noted with minor therapeutic effects in the small cell lung cancer patients. Meyskens et al, based on their clonogenic assay result, decided to examine this agent in their phase II study for the treatment of metastatic melanoma.[33] They observed one complete response in a patient and stabilization in seven patients of 21 evaluable patients. They observed significant ototoxicity and thrombocytopenia in this oral administration. These data, however, indicated that DFMO as a single agent may be an effective therapy for melanoma. Lipton et al treated 10 patients with metastatic disease to the liver in their phase I study employing continuous hepatic arterial infusion of DFMO.[34] Two of nine evaluable patients had an objective partial response. Stable disease was recorded in three patients. Ototoxicity was encountered in all patients who received a daily dose of DFMO equal to or greater than 1.0 g/m^2. Interestingly no signs of thrombocytopenia or hepatic toxicity were observed. In our study, patients with metastatic colorectal carcinoma received continuous infusion of DFMO at a median dose of 8 $g/m^2/day$ (range, 6-14) for 28 days.[35,36] We observed significant decreases in erythrocyte and plasma polyamine levels following DFMO administration. Sustained suppression of circulating polyamine levels was also achieved with continuous DFMO infusion. We also observed a correlation between steady-state plasma DFMO levels and lowering of platelet count. Of 32 evaluable patients, none achieved a partial or complete response; however, three patients achieved a minor response and 14 had stable disease. The most frequent toxic effects included thrombocytopenia (which was dose-limiting, 8 g/m^2), malaise, nausea, vomiting, reversible ototoxicity and diarrhea. Our data suggested that continuous-infusion DFMO therapy is feasible and results in only mild gastrointestinal toxicity. Another interesting study was performed by Levin et al in the DFMO treatment of recurrent gliomas.[37] Eighty patients (36 glioblastoma multiform patients and 44 anaplastic glioma patients) were assessed for response. Antitumor activity (partial response, minor response and stable disease) was seen in 45% of the patients with anaplastic glioma, but in only 17% of patients with glioblastoma multiform. Although it is difficult to find studies of combination of clinical DFMO treatment with other chemotherapeutic agents, this same group previously carried out treatment of recurrent gliomas with 1,3-bis(2-chloroethyl)-1-nitrosourea (BCNU) and DFMO.[38] Of 21 evaluable patients, two had a partial response and 10 had stable disease. The combination was well tolerated with dose-limiting toxicity being myelo-suppression and hearing loss.

In an attempt to define biochemical markers of ODC inhibition by DFMO, we determined erythrocyte and plasma polyamine levels. We observed significant decreases in these measurements following DFMO treatment as mentioned above. Haegele et al examined urinary polyamine and decarboxylated AdoMet (one of the products of AdoMetDC reaction) levels.[39] They concluded that urinary excretion of decarboxylated AdoMet represents a valid biochemical indicator of ODC inhibition in humans, whereas urinary polyamines are of no value. Horn et al examined urinary polyamine levels of a control group of patients with solid tumors who received conventional chemotherapy and of a study group of patients with similar malignancies who received oral DFMO in addition to the conventional chemotherapy.[40] DFMO activity appeared to be reflected by a long-term decrease in urinary polyamine levels. The above clinical investigations suggest that as a single agent DFMO is promising for malignant melanoma, liver metastasis (continuous hepatic arterial infusion) and recurrent anaplastic glioma.

B. METHYLACETYLENIC PUTRESCINE (MAP)

This is also an enzyme-activated irreversible inhibitor of ODC. Cornbleet et al carried out a phase I study of this agent given to nine patients with advanced malignancies.[41] Oral doses of 375 and 750 mg/day were well tolerated. The next dose of 1,500 mg caused myelosuppression and renal toxicity. No objective responses were observed in five patients having stable disease and four patients having progressive disease during the study period. The plasma elimination half-life was between 3.9 and 9.2 hours in six patients (mean, 5.6 hours). In this study they also detected increased levels of urinary excretion of decarboxylated AdoMet while no consistent changes in the excretion of urinary polyamines were observed.

C. DEOXYSPERGUALIN

Spergualin was isolated in 1982 and exhibited immunosuppressive as well as antitumor activities. Deoxyspergualin is an analog of the polyamine spergualin with preclinical evidence of activity in murine and human tumor models.[42] Havlin et al have recently

conducted a phase I study of this agent.[43] This study examined a
120 hour continuous infusion schedule in 56 patients with refractory solid tumors ranging from 80 to 2,792 mg/m²/day. Dose-
limiting toxicity was reversible hypotension. Other dose-dependent
effects noted were pruritus and circumoral paresthesias. Myelosuppression and gastrointestinal toxicities were mild. This agent
was rapidly cleared from the plasma with a mean terminal half-life
of 1.9 hours. Immunological studies revealed a non-dose-depen-
dent increase in the number of cells, predominantly the T suppressor (CD8) phenotype, posttreatment. In three patients, a mild
increase in lymphokine activated killer cell activity was noted. Two
patients with refractory head and neck cancer had minor response.

D. MGBG

Methylglyoxal bis(guanylhydrazone) or mitoguazone is usually
abbreviated as MGBG or methyl-GAG. Traditionally, basic scientists used the term MGBG while clinical investigators often preferred methyl-GAG. As discussed in chapter 7, unlike DFMO,
MGBG has longer clinical history, as its antitumor activity was
discovered before its capability to inhibit AdoMetDC was documented.[44] This agent was synthesized and reported by Freelander
and French in 1958 to show antitumor activity against murine
leukemia L1210.[45,46] Regelson et al then conducted a clinical study
of parenteral MGBG treatment.[47] This was followed by intravenous (IV) treatment of this agent by Freireich et al.[48-50] Though
these early stage clinical studies were extensively reviewed by
Mihichi[51] briefly, the daily administration of MGBG induced a
strikingly high number of complete remissions in acute myelocytic
leukemia. However, this treatment also generated severe mucositis
and other toxicities, some of which were fatal. Thus very few clinical studies of MGBG were conducted in the early 1970s.[52,53] As a
result, Knight et al adopted weekly IV administration.[54] New clinical trials subsequently utilized a weekly administration schedule;
this approach was also supported by the pharmacokinetic results
obtained by other studies.[55-59] No in vivo metabolism of this agent
was found. An average terminal half-life was 4.1 hours. The cumulative urinary excretion over 72 hours was approximately 15%
indicating that MGBG is mostly retained in the patient. Cerebral

and cerebellar uptake of this agent were observed. Though MGBG was taken up by brain tumors, the concentration of MGBG was minimal in the cerebrospinal fluid. Investigators conducted a large number of clinical phase I and phase II studies of MGBG as a single agent.[60-97] These investigations also dealt with patients with a wide variety of cancers: lymphoma, Hodgkin's disease, multiple myeloma, small cell carcinoma of the lung, nonsmall cell lung cancer, renal cell carcinoma, breast, colon, esophagus, ovary, head and neck, prostate, soft tissue sarcoma, pancreas, stomach and bladder. Toxic side effects noted include mucositis, nausea, vomiting, fatigue, diarrhea, neuropathy, myalgia, skin rash, myopathy, myelosuppression, paresthesia and thrombocytopenia. Although only minimal clinical activities were observed in some solid tumor types, the investigators found excellent responses against recurrent and refractory lymphomas and Hodgkin's disease. As a result, von Hoff is currently treating patients with AIDS-associated non-Hodgkin's lymphomas, obtaining encouraging initial results.[98]

E. DFMO PLUS MGBG

Quite a few clinical trials were conducted using this combination. In fact, the first clinical trial of DFMO was carried out using this agent. Based on an experimental result indicating DFMO pretreatment enhances the uptake of the second agent, MGBG,[99] a clinical study was initiated in childhood leukemia.[100,101] Pretreatment of patients with oral DFMO definitely stimulated the accumulation of subsequent MGBG infused into blast cells (intracellular MGBG levels in mononuclear leukocytes were monitored) and resulted in therapeutic synergism with a rapid disappearance of the circulating blast cells. Since then this combination regimen has been attempted in some other tumor types including adult leukemia, multiple myeloma, prostate and brain tumors.[102-111] Some of the clinical studies of this combination, however, brought out new concerns of increased toxic side effects without any therapeutic gain. For instance, Splinter and Romijn showed that of 28 evaluable patients with advanced solid tumors, only two had partial remission with severe side effects.[105] They observed new toxicities of this combination (e.g., hemolysis and jaundice) which they had not observed previously. The other noted toxicities include nausea, diarrhea, fatigue, myelosuppression, thrombocytopenia, mucositis and ototoxicity. Warrell et al conducted sequential administration of DFMO followed by MGBG in patients with advanced diseases.[102] They also experienced apparently enhanced toxicity of MGBG with minimum therapeutic effects. Gastaut et al also observed a similar trend in their treatment schedule of acute leukemia and blastic phase of chronic myeloid luekemia.[106] Two groups also used this combination for treatment of prostate cancer. The results were marginal at best.[103,104]

Maddox et al utilized this combination in patients with leukemia or multiple myeloma.[108-110] Though pretreatment of patients may increase the toxicity of subsequent MGBG treatment, they confirmed that DFMO pretreatment increases uptake of MGBG. However, they observed that DFMO treatment needed to be extended until polyamines are depleted in the target cell. One interesting observation they made in their studies was that myeloid maturation was induced.

This combination induced an impressive response in phase I-II study in the treatment of recurrent primary brain tumors.[107] Dose-limiting toxicities were gastrointestinal and myelotoxicities and tinnitis. As described above (section IIA), DFMO alone was very effective against recurrent gliomas.[37] Therefore, the main active component in this combination may be DFMO. In fact, in the glioma study the initial random allocation of patients to the DFMO/MGBG arm was stopped because of two cases of lethal hepatic necrosis. Overall, however, this combination of DFMO/MGBG does not appear very promising. Redgate et al have recently suggested use of internal radioemitters such as tritiated putrescine or thymidine to enhance the effectiveness of a polyamine-based approach.[111]

F. DFMO WITH INTERFERON

Based on promising experimental results of this combination,[112-115] a phase I study was attempted.[116,117] Though some responses including a complete remission in malignant melanoma were observed, the overall response was less than expected. This approach is still being investigated using different experimental systems.[118-122]

G. MGBG Plus Other Chemotherapeutic Agent(s)

Many clinical investigations have been conducted using MGBG in combination with other agents. These include a variety of tumor types: acute nonlymphocytic leukemia, Hodgkin's disease, non-Hodgkin's lymphoma, renal cell adenocarcinoma, esophageal squamous cell carcinoma, squamous cell carcinoma of head and neck and nonsmall cell lung cancer.[123-149] Notable clinical activities were observed in esophageal cancer and head and neck cancer. In the study conducted by Vogl et al, 18 patients with esophageal cancer were treated with a regimen combining MGBG, methotrexate, bleomycin and cisplatin.[126] Nine of 14 evaluable patients responded. Treatment was well tolerated in all patients but one, who developed signs of severe methotrexate toxicity. Kelsen et al also treated patients with esophageal cancer.[128] They used a combination of MGBG, vindesine and cisplatin. Of 39 evaluable patients 16 had complete or partial remission. The risks of pulmonary damage were decreased by the substitution of MGBG for bleomycin. With regards to head and neck cancer, Takasugi et al reported 39% response rate to MGBG/cisplatin treatment in patients with squamous cell carcinoma of the head and neck in 1986.[129] This response rate was not different from results obtained with either agent alone. Forastiere et al, however, reported 65% response rate with this MGBG/cisplatin combination in 1988.[136] In 1994, Urba et al showed 84% response rate employing MGBG/cisplatin/5-fluorouracil combination.[147]

The majority of studies were carried out in patients with lymphoma or Hodgkin's disease. This is reasonable as MGBG has definite clinical activity as a single agent against lymphomas as described above (section II.C). MGBG is one of the active agents in many standard regimens developed against malignant lymphoma and Hodgkin's disease including current salvage treatment.[124,127,130-132,134,135,137,139-144,146,148,149]

III. CHEMOPREVENTIVE CLINICAL STUDIES

Chemoprevention refers to the use of chemical agents to prevent or delay the development of cancer in healthy populations of high risk individuals because of familial background, previous cancer treatment or increased exposure to an etiologic agent. These groups also include individuals with premalignant lesions. Since these chemopreventive agents are normally administered to healthy individuals for a long period of time, we need to be alert to the long-term toxicities of these agents.[150] In this section, therefore, we focus on examining the feasibility of interfering with the polyamine metabolic pathway as a target for chemopreventive intervention.

Field cancerization refers to a multicentric origin of tumor over a wide area of epithelial tissue recognized in patients with certain types of cancers.[151] These multifocal tumors of different origins can be indicative of exposure to environmental carcinogens or genetic disorders in patients.

In addition to cellular proliferation and differentiation, polyamines are involved in neoplastic transformation (chapter 4), cellular maintenance including apoptosis (chapter 6) and angiogenesis, which is essential for cancer growth and metastasis. Based on these findings, our hypothesis with regard to polyamine-directed chemoprevention is two pronged: to inhibit neoplastic transformation against ongoing field cancerization and to remove cells already transformed through apoptosis. Polyamine-directed suppression of angiogenesis also helps to inhibit tumor growth and metastasis.[152-154] Toward this hypothesis, we have demonstrated that we can induce apoptosis in a human colon carcinoma cell line and HL-60 cells in vitro.[155] McCloskey et al have also showed that they can induce apoptosis in human breast cancer cells by an unsymmetrically alkylated polyamine analog.[156] The ability of DFMO as a chemopreventive agent has been tested in many animal carcinogenesis models as has been recently reviewed:[157] papilloma (two stage chemical carcinogenesis),[158] colon,[159-162] bladder,[163,164] trachea,[165] tongue,[166] breast[167,168] and liver.[169] In these models, animals were treated with an initiation agent or a carcinogen, and DFMO as a single chemopreventive agent or in combination with another agent was introduced. One interesting observation made demonstrated specificity of DFMO in the rat colon.[170] A single DFMO dose of 100 mg/kg inhibited tumor cell proliferation while normal colonic epithelia was not affected. To affect normal cell proliferation, 400 mg/kg DFMO was required indicating a specific differential effect of DFMO. We also have made similar observations in our fibrosarcoma-bearing rat model. In the range of IV infused DFMO dose (400-1,700 mg/kg/day) we used, DFMO significantly reduced tumor growth without affecting weights of normal tissues (kidney, spleen and liver).[171] Furthermore, when malnourished tumor-bearing animals were treated with a total parenteral nutrition regimen in combination with DFMO, we were able to preferentially replete normal tissues.[172] While DFMO almost totally inhibited ODC activity in the tumor, ODC activities in both liver and kidney were unaffected. These observations may relate to findings made by O'Brien et al[173] reporting differences in enzymatic properties and structure between normal epidermis and epidermal tumors, suggesting possible differences in ODCs between normal and tumor cells. Clarification of this issue requires further extensive biochemical and molecular biological studies.

Based on these encouraging animal experimental results, clinical phase I studies were initiated. In addition to determining the minimal effective dose of DFMO, various biomarkers to monitor the chemopreventive effects have been examined. Creaven et al examined daily oral dose of DFMO (0.2-6.4 g/m^2) given for six months.[174] Subjects were free of disease following surgery for malignancy or in a defined high-risk group for cancer. The highest nontoxic dose was determined to be 1.6 g/m^2/day. The dose-limiting toxicity was ototoxicity. This group also examined urinary and erythrocyte polyamine levels during this trial.[175] They found that urinary polyamine levels are better markers than erythrocyte polyamine levels for monitoring the effects of DFMO. One subject with familial polyposis who had high erythrocyte and urinary polyamine levels prior to DFMO treatment showed a significant decline in urinary polyamines and responded to DFMO treatment with nearly complete resolution of the polyps in the rectal stump. As discussed above in section II.A, it may also be interesting to measure urinary decarboxylated AdoMet levels as a biomarker of DFMO effect. Love et al conducted a randomized phase I study of DFMO to determine the lowest daily oral dose that can achieve at least 50% inhibition of ODC activity induced by TPA in human skin with minimal clinical toxicity.[176] They treated a similar group of patients for up to 12 months with a dose range of

0.5-3.0 g/m²/day. They concluded that the lowest effective daily DFMO oral dose is 0.5 g/m²/day. Meyskens et al carried out a dose de-escalation study of DFMO in patients who underwent colonoscopy for removal of a colon polyp.[177] Their aim was to determine the lowest dose of DFMO that would deplete target tissue (colorectal mucosa) levels of polyamines in humans who had undergone prior removal of colon polyps while producing minimal toxic effects. These subjects were treated orally with single, daily doses of DFMO ranging from 3.0 to 0.1 g/m² for four weeks. Polyamine analyses of colorectal biopsy specimens showed that DFMO treatment caused a decrease in both putrescine content and the ratio of spermidine to spermine for all dose groups down to 0.25 g/m²/day.[178] None of the patients receiving either 0.25 or 0.5 g/m²/day experienced ototoxicity in this trial. Thus their lowest effective dose is 0.25 g/m²/day. The above three groups also measured plasma DFMO levels. The first two groups determined plasma DFMO half-life, which showed 3.5[176] and 4.7[174] hours. The pharmacokinetics were linear. These results were very similar to those obtained in the earlier study (section II.A).[29]

Our phase I chemoprevention study has been conducted in patients with cervical intraepithelial neoplasia grade 3 (CIN III) for the following reasons:

(a.) cervical cancer remains an important health problem in women (the second most common malignancy in women worldwide); and

(b.) the cervix is an excellent model for demonstrating the carcinogenic progression from mildly dysplastic lesions through severely dysplastic lesions to invasive cancer. Cervical lesions can be followed with colposcopy and Papanicolaou smear. Therefore, the cervix is a unique organ that is well suited to the development of chemoprevention trials;

(c.) CIN III is the most advanced premalignant dysplasia, a precursor of invasive cervical cancer.[179,180]

In addition, some polyamine studies of cervical cancer are already available.[181-183] Thirty patients were placed on five doses of DFMO (1.0, 0.5, 0.25, 0.125 and 0.06 g/m²/day) for 31 days. DFMO was well tolerated and modulated polyamine biosynthesis markers[184] at doses down to 0.125 g/m²/day. While the purpose of a phase I study is not response, a 50% histological response (five complete histological responses and 10 histological regressions of the lesions to CIN I or II) is very encouraging.

Potential prospective DFMO intervention chemopreventive studies in organs other than the colon[185] and the cervix[179,180] include the prostate[186,187] and the bladder.[188] Pretreatment studies of Barrett's esophagus, a premalignant lesion for adenocarcinoma, have been already conducted.[189-191]

IV. FUTURE DIRECTIONS

Traditionally, results obtained from basic research of polyamines have been efficiently translated into clinical studies. This has been one of the most unique characteristics of this field of research.[192,193] In addition to many new agents which have been designed to inhibit specific enzymes involved in polyamine metabolism and catabolism, a group of new polyamine analogs (chapter 7) which are presumably dysfunctional but yet bind to specific polyamine sites in cells and can compete with natural polyamines in cellular transport are now available. These new compounds may be more effective in therapeutic and chemopreventive trials and may also open up further opportunities for combination regimens.

One of the major problems in developing new polyamine-related agents against cancer is that we still do not know exact mechanisms of action of natural polyamines inside cells. From this point of view, new knowledge and information obtained from basic research of polyamines are always welcome. Further knowledge about the roles of polyamines in differentiation, apoptosis, neoplastic transformation and the immune system is critically important to make progress in developing effective polyamine-related antitumor agents.

In our recent publication, we discussed an issue related to survival without tumor shrinkage and reevaluated survival gain by cytostatic effect of chemotherapy.[194] In other words, the survival time of most patients with solid tumors depends on survival by an induced cytostatic phase rather than on tumor reduction. Thus, aggressive chemotherapy may not be very useful and may even be harmful to patients by suppressing immune system function and inducing toxic side effects and cachexia. Supporting this viewpoint is the observation that immunotherapy often prolongs survival times despite no tumor reduction.[195] To further validate our viewpoint, we have studied in rats a preliminary cytostatic therapeutic regimen using DFMO, which successfully delayed tumor regrowth after BCNU treatment.[196]

We have recently studied the correlation of response with plasma pharmacokinetics and polyamine levels in patients with acute myelogenous leukemia receiving amonafide.[197] In this study, we used plasma polyamine concentrations as a measure of tumor sensitivity (pharmacodynamic effect). Combined examination of dynamic changes in polyamine levels with drug pharmacokinetic parameters and clinical responses appears to yield new information.

Since polyamine-related agents have an entirely different mechanism of action from other conventional anticancer drugs, and many new compounds are in the pipeline, the future of research dealing with polyamine-related agents is bright, and the harvest of this long research effort will be realized soon.

REFERENCES

1. Bachrach U. Polyamines as markers of malignancy. Prog Drug Res 1992; 39:9-33.
2. Luk GD, Baylin SB. Ornithine decarboxylase as a biologic marker in familial colonic p olyposis. N Engl J Med 1984; 311:80-83.
3. Kingsnorth AN, Lumsden AB, Wallace HM. Polyamines in colorectal cancer. Br J Surg 1984; 71:792-94.
4. Kingsnorth AN, Wallace HM, Bundred NJ et al. Polyamines in breast cancer. Br J Surg 1984; 71:352-6.
5. LaMuraglia GM, Lacaine F, Malt RA. High ornithine decarboxylase activity and polyamine levels in human colorectal neoplasia. Ann Surg 1986; 204:89-93.
6. Moorehead RJ, Hoper M, McKelvey STD. Assessment of ornithine decarboxylas activity in rectal mucosa as a marker for colorectal adenoma and carcinoma. Br J Surg 1987; 74:364-65.
7. Porter CW, Herrera-Ornelas L, Pera P et al. Polyamine biosynthetic activity in normal and neoplastic human colorectal tissues. Cancer 1987; 60:1275-81.
8. Herrera-Ornelas L, Porter C, Pera P et al. A comparison of ornithine decarboxylase and S-adenosylmethionine decarboxylase activity in human large bowel mucosa, polyps, and colorectal adenocarcinoma. J Surg Res 1987; 42:56-60.

9. Dimery IW, Nishioka K, Grossie Jr VB et al. Polyamine metabolism in carcinoma of the oral cavity compared with adjacent and normal oral mucosa. Am J Surg 1987; 54:429-33.

10. Narisawa T, Takahashi M, Niwa M et al. Increased mucosal ornithine decarboxylase activity in large bowel with multiple tumors, and adenoma. Cancer 1989; 63:1572-76.

11. Garewal HS, Sampliner R. Barrett's esophagus: A model premalignant lesion for adenocarcinoma. Prev Med 1989; 18:749-56.

12. Löser C, Fölsch UR, Paprotny C et al. Polyamines in human gastric and esophageal cancer. Scand J Gastroenterol 1989; 24:1193-99.

13. Cohen DJ, Verma AK. Ornithine decarboxylase activity as a biochemical marker in individuals predisposed to lung cancer. J Invest Surg 1989; 2:103-6.

14. Löser C, Fölsch UR, Paprotny C et al. Polyamines in human gastrointestinal malignancies. Digestion 1990; 46(Suppl 2):430-38.

15. Braverman DZ, Stankiewicz H, Goldstein R et al. Ornithine decarboxylase: An unreliable marker for the identification of populations at risk for colonic neoplasia. Am J Gastroenterol 1990; 85:723-26.

16. Löser C, Fölsch UR, Paprotny C et al. Polyamine concentrations in pancreatic tissue, serum, and urine of patients with pancreatic cancer. Pancreas 1990; 5:119-27.

17. Löser C, Fölsch UR, Paprotny C et al. Polyamines in colorectal cancer. Evaluation of polyamine concentrations in the colon tissue, serum, and urine of 50 patients with colorectal cancer. Cancer 1990; 65:958-66.

18. Nishioka K, Grossie Jr VB, Chang T-H et al. Colorectal ornithine decarboxylase activity in human mucosa and tumors: Elevation of enzymatic activity in distal mucosa. J Surg Oncol 1991; 47:117-20.

19. Okuzumi J, Yamane T, Kitao Y et al. Increased mucosal ornithine decarboxylase activity in human gastric cancer. Cancer Res 1991; 51:1448-51.

20. Love RR, Surawicz TS, Morrissey JF et al. Levels of colorectal ornithine decarboxylase activity in patients with colon cancer, a family history of nonpolyposis hereditary colorectal cancer, and adenoma. Cancer Epidemiol Biomarker Prev 1992; 1:195-98.

21. Weiss Jr RL, Calhoun KH, Ahmed AE et al. Ornithine decarboxylase activity in tumor and normal tissue of head and neck cancer patients. Laryngoscope 1992; 102:855-57.

22. Di Leo A, Linsalata M, Cavallini A et al. Sex steroid hormone receptors, epidermal growth factor receptor, and polyamines in human colorectal cancer. Dis Colon Rectum 1992; 35:305-09.

23. Elitsur Y, Moshier JA, Murthy R et al. Polyamine levels, ornithine decarboxylase (ODC) activity, and ODC-mRNA expression in normal and cancerous human colonocytes. Life Sci 1992; 50:1417-24.

24. Russo F, Linsalata M, Messa C et al. Polyamines and estrogen-receptor concentrations in human colorectal carcinomas. Ital J Gastroenterol 1992; 24:8-12.

25. Linsalata M, Russo F, Cavallini A et al. Polyamines, diamine oxidase, and ornithine decarboxylase activity in colorectal cancer and in normal surrounding mucosa. Dis Colon Rectum 1993; 36:662-67.

26. Hixon LJ, Garewal HS, McGee DL et al. Ornithine decarboxylase and polyamines in colorectal neoplasia and mucosa. Cancer Epidemiol Biomarker Prev 1993; 2:369-74.

27. Hixon LJ, Emerson SS, Shassetz LR et al. Source of variability in estimating ornithine decarboxylase activity and polyamine contents in human colorectal mucosa. Cancer Epidemiol Biomarker Prev 1994; 3:317-23.

28. Higuchi CM, Wang W. Comodulation of cellular polyamines and proliferation: Biomarker application to colorectal mucosa. J Cell Biochem 1995; 57:256-61.

29. Haegele KD, Alken RG, Grove J et al. Kinetics of α-difluoromethylornithine: An irreversible inhibitor of ornithine decardoxylase. Clin Pharmacol Ther 1981; 30:210-7.

30. Dunzendorfer U. The effect of α-difluoromethylornithine on tumor growth, acute phase reactants, β-2-microglobulin and hydroxproline in kidney and bladder carcinoma. Urol Int 1981; 36:128-36.

31. Maddox AM, Keating MJ, McCredie KE et al. Phase I evaluation of intravenous difluoromethylornithine—a potent inhibitor. Invest New Drugs 1985; 3:287-92.

32. Abeloff MD, Rosen ST, Luk GD et al. Phase II trials of α-difluoromethylornithine, an inhibitor of polyamine synthesis, in advanced small cell lung cancer and colon cancer. Cancer Treat Rep 1986; 70:843-45.

33. Meyskens FL, Kingsley EM, Glattke T et al. A phase II study of α-difluoromethylornithine (DFMO) for the treatment of metastatic melanoma. Invest New Drugs 1986; 4:257-62.

34. Lipton A, Harvey HA, Glenn J et al. A phase I study of hepatic arterial infusion using difluoromethylornithine. Cancer 1989; 63:433-37.

35. Ajani JA, Ota DM, Grossie Jr VB et al. Alterations in polyamine metabolism during continuous intravenous infusion of α-difluoromethylornithine showing correlation of thrombocytopenia with α-difluoromethylornithine plasma levels. Cancer Res 1989; 49:5793-97.

36. Ajani JA, Ota DM, Grossie Jr VB et al. Evaluation of continuous α-difluoromethylornithine therapy for colorectal carcinoma. Cancer Chemother Pharmacol 1990; 26:223-26.

37. Levin VA, Prados MD, Yung WKA et al. Treatment of recurrent gliomas with eflornithine. J Natl Cancer Inst 1992; 84:1432-37.

38. Prados M, Rodriguez L, Chamberlain M et al. Treatment of recurrent gliomas with 1,3,-bis(2-chloroethyl)-nitrosourea and α-difluoromethylornithine. Neurosurg 1989; 24:806-9.

39. Haegele KD, Splinter TAW, Romijn JC et al. Decarboxylated-S-adenosylmethionine excretion: A biochemical marker of ornithine decarboxylase inhibition by α-difluoromethylornithine. Cancer Res 1987; 47:890-95.

40. Horn Y, Spigel L, Marton LJ. Urinary polyamine levels in cancer patients treated with D,L-α-difluoromethylornithine, an inhibitor of polyamine biosynthesis. J Surg Oncol 1989; 41:177-82.

41. Cornbleet MA, Kingsnorth A, Tell GP et al. Phase I study of methylacetylenic putrescine, an inhibitor of polyamine biosynthesis. Cancer Chemother Pharmacol 1989; 23:348-52.

42. Takeuchi T. Antitumor antibiotics discovered and studied at the Institute of Microbial Chemistry. J Cancer Res Clin Oncol 1995; 121:505-10.

43. Havlin KA, Kuhn LG, Koeller J et al. Deoxyspergualin: Phase I clinical, immunologic and pharmakokinetic study. Anticancer Drug 1995; 6:229-36.

44. Williams-Ashman HG, Schenone A. Methylglyoxal bis(guanylhydrazone) as a potent inhibitor of mammalian and yeast S-adenosylmethionine decarboxylase. Biochem Biophys Res Commun 1972; 46:288-95.

45. Freedlander BL, French FA. Carcinostatic action of polycarbonyl compounds and their derivatives. II. Glyoxal bis(guanylhydrazone) and derivatives. Cancer Res 1958; 18:360-63.

46. French FA, Freedlander BL, Blanz EJ. Chemotherapy studies on transplanted mouse tumors. Cancer Chemother Screening Data XI. Cancer Res 1961; 21:343-58.

47. Regelson W, Holland JF. Initial clinical study of parenteral methylglyoxal bis(guanylhydrazone) diacetate. Cancer Chemother Rev 1961; 11:81-6.

48. Freireich EJ, Frei III E, Karon M. Methylglyoxal bis(guanylhydrazone): A new agent active against acute myelocytic leukemia. Cancer Chemother Rep 1962; 16:183-6.

49. Levin RH, Brittin GM, Freireich EJ. Differnet patterns of remission in acute myelocytic leukemia. A comparison of the effects of methylglyoxal bis(guanylhydrazone) and 6-mercaptopurine. Blood 1963; 21:689-97.

50. Levin RH, Henderson E, Karon M et al. Treatment of acute leukemia with methtlglyoxal bis(guanylhydrazone) (methyl GAG). Clin Pharmacol Ther 1964; 6:31-42.

51. Mihich E. Current studies with methylglyoxal bis(guanylhydrazone). Cancer Res 1963;23:1375-89.

52. Falkson G. Methyl-GAG (NSC-32946) in the treatment of esophagus cancer. Cancer Chemother Rep 1971; 55:209-12.

53. Shnider BI, Colsky J, Jones R et al. Effectiveness of methyl-GAG: A Southwest oncology group pilot study. Cancer Chemother Rep 1974;58:689-95.

54. Knight WA III, Livingston RB, Fabian C et al. Phase I-II trial of mitoguazone in patients with relapsed small cell carcinoma of the lung. Cancer Treat Rep 1979; 63:1933-37.

55. Marsh KC, Liesmann J, Patton TF et al. Plasma levels and urinary excretion of methyl-GAG following iv infusion in man. Cancer Treat Rep 1981; 65:253-7.

56. Rosenblum MG, Stewart DJ, Yap BS et al. Penetration of methylglyoxal bis(guanylhydrazone) into intracerebral tumors in humans. Cancer Res 1981; 41:459-62.

57. Rosenblum MG, Keating MJ, Yap BS et al. Pharmacokinetics of [^{14}C]methylglyoxal-bis-guanylhydrazone) in patients with leukemia. Cancer Res 1981; 41:1748-50.

58. Stewart DJ, Rosenblum MG, Luna M et al. Disposition of methylglyoxal bis(guanylhydrazone) (MGBG, NSC-32946) in man. Cancer Chemother Pharmacol 1981; 7:31-5.

59. Dunzendorfer U, Balis ME, Whitmore WF. Some aspects of clearance of mitoguazone in cancer patients and experimental cancer models. Arzneimittel-Forschung 1986; 36:506-8.

60. Knight WA III, Livingston RB, Fabian C et al. Phase I-II trial of methyl-GAG: A Southwest Oncology Group pilot study. Cancer Treat Rep 1979; 63:1933-7.

61. Chapman R, Kelsen D, Gralla R et al. Phase II trial of methylglyoxal-bis-(guanylhydrazone) in non-small-cell lung cancer. Cancer Clin Trials 1981; 4:389-91.

62. Fuks JZ, Van Echo DA, Aisner J et al. Phase II trial of methyl-G (methylglyoxal bis-guanylhydrazone) in patients with metastatic renal cell carcinoma. Cancer Clin Trials 1981; 4:411-4.

63. Myers JW, Knight WA III, Livingston RB et al. Phase I-II trial of methyl-GAG in advanced colon cancer. A Southwest Oncology Group study. Cancer Clin Trials 1981; 4:277-9.

64. Todd RF III, Garnick MB, Canellos GP et al. Phase I—II trial of methyl-GAG in the treatment of patients with metastatic renal adenocarcinoma. Cancer Treat Rep 1981; 65:17-20.

65. Zeffren J, Yagoda A, Watson RC et al. Phase II trial of methyl-GAG in advanced renal cancer. Cancer Treat Rep 1981; 65:525-7.

66. Yap HY, Blumenschein GR, Schell F et al. Phase II evaluation of methyl-GAG in patients with refractory metastatic breast cancer.

Cancer Treat Rep 1981;65:465-7.

67. Warrell Jr RP, Lee BJ, Kempin SJ et al. Effectiveness of methyl-GAG (methylglyoxal-bis[guanylhydrazone]) in patients with advanced malignant lymphoma. Blood 1981; 57:1011-4.

68. Child JA, Bono AV, Fossa SD et al. An EORTC phase II study of methyl-glyoxal bis-guanylhydrazone in advanced renal cell cancer. Eur J Cancer Clin Oncol 1982; 18:85-7.

69. Samson MK, Baker LH, Cummings G et al. Phase II trial of methyl-GAG (NSC-32946) in squamous cell and adenocarcinoma of the lung. Am J Clin Oncol 1982; 5:631-3.

70. Child JA. Methyl-GAG in advanced renal cell carcinoma. Prog Clin Biol Res 1982; 100:663-7.

71. Knight WA III, Loesch DM, Leichman LP et al. Methyl-GAG in advanced colon cancer: A phase II trial of the Southwest Oncology Group. Cancer Treat Rep 1982; 66:2099-100.

72. Kelsen D, Chapman R, Bains M et al. Phase II study of methyl-GAG in the treatment of esophageal carcinoma. Cancer Treat Rep 1982; 66:1427-9.

73. Kelsen DP, Yagoda A, Warrell R et al. Phase II trials of methylglyoxal-bis- (guanylhydrazone). Am J Clin Oncol 1982; 5:221-5.

74. Hart RD, Ohnuma T, Holland JF et al. Methyl-GAG in patients with malignant neoplasms: A phase I re-evaluation. Cancer Treat Rep 1982; 66:65-71.

75. Warrell Jr RP, Burchenal JH. Methylglyoxal bis(guanylhydrazone) (Methyl- Gag): Current status and future prospects. J Clin Oncol 1983; 1:52-65.

76. Knight WA III, Fabian C, Costanzi JJ. Methyl-glyoxal bis guanyl hydrazone (methyl-GAG, MGBG) in lymphoma and Hodgkin's disease. A Phase II trial of the Southwest Oncology Group. Invest New Drugs 1983; 1:235-7.

77. Vance RB, Knight WA III, Chen TT et al. Phase II evaluation of MGBG in non-small cell carcinoma of the lung. A Southwest Oncology Group study. Invest New Drugs 1983; 1:89-93.

78. Scher H, Chapman R, Kelsen D. Phase II trial of mitoguazone in patients with relapsed small cell carcinoma of the Lung. Cancer Treat Rep 1984; 68:561-2.

79. Vogl SE, Pagano M, Horton J. Phase II study of methylglyoxal bis(guanylhydrazone) (NSV 3296) in advanced ovarian cancer. Am J Clin Oncol 1984; 7:733-36.

80. Thongprasert B, Bosl GL, Geller NL et al. Phase II trial of mitoguazone in patients with advanced head and neck cancer. Cancer Treat Rep 1984; 68:1301-2.

81. Knight WA III, O'Bryan RM, Samal B et al. Methyl-glyoxal bis guanyl hydrazone (methyl-GAG, MGBG) in advanced breast cancer. A Phase II trial of the Southwest Oncology Group. Invest New Drugs 1984; 2:71-3.

82. Scher HI, Yagoda A, Ahmed T et al. Methylglyoxal-bis(guanyl-hydrazone) in hormone-resistant adenocarcinoma of the prostate. J Clin Oncol 1985; 3:224-28.

83. Chun H, Bosl GL. Phase II trial of mitoguazone in patients with refractory germ cell tumors. Cancer Treat Rep 1985; 69:461-2.

84. Sordillo PP, Magill GB, Welt S. Phase II trial of methylglyoxal bis(guanylhydrazone) (methyl-GAG) in patients with soft-tissue sarcomas. Am J Clin Oncol 1985; 8:316-18.

85. Inamasu MS, Oishi N, Chen TT. Phase II study of mitoguazone in pancreatic cancer: A Southwest Oncology Group study. Cancer Treat Rep 1986; 70:531-32.

86. Forastiere AA, Natale RB, Wheeler RR. Phase II trial of methyl-glyoxal bis(guanylhydrazone) (MGBG) in advanced head and neck cancer. Cancer 1986; 58:2585-8.

87. Luedke DW, Maddox W, Birch R et al. Mitoguazone in advanced squamous cell carcinoma of head and neck origin: A phase II trial of the Southeastern Cancer Study Group. Cancer Treat Rep 1986; 70:529-30.

88. Ravry MJ, Omura G-A, Hill GJ et al. Phase II evaluation of mitoguazone in cancers of the esophagus, stomach, and pancreas: A Southeastern Cancer Study Group trial. Cancer Treat Rep 1986; 70:533-4.

89. Moor MR, Graham SD, Birch R. Phase II evaluation of mito-guazone in metastatic hormone-resistant prostate cancer: A Southeastern Cancer Study Group trial. Cancer Treat Rep 1987; 71:89-90.

90. Douglass Jr HO, Lefkopoulou M, Davis HL et al. ECOG phase II trials of MGBG, Chlorozotocin, COM multidrug therapy in advanced measurable colorectal cancer. Am J Clin Oncol 1988; 11:646-9.

91. Arteaga CL, Clark GM. Inefficacy of methylglyoxal bis(guanyl-hydrazone) (MGBG) in patients with recurrent head and neck squamous cell carcinoma. Invest New Drugs 1989; 7:281-3.

92. Hoffmann H, Gutsche W, Amlacher R et al. Mitiguazone (Methylglyoxal bis guanylhydrazone): Stand und Perspektiven. Arch Geschwulstforsch 1989; 59:135-48.

93. Simon MS, Eckenrode J, Natale RB. Phase II trial of methylglyoxal bis-guanylhydrazone (MGBG) in refractory small cell lung cancer. Invest New Drugs 1990; 8 Suppl 1: S79-81.

94. Von Hoff DD, Blumenstein BA, Pollock TW et al. Methylglyoxal

bis-guanylhydrazone in advanced bladder cancer. Eur J Cancer 1990; 26:848-9.

95. Winter JN, Ritch PS, Rosen ST et al. Phase II trial of methyl-glyoxal-bis(guanylhyrdazone) (MGBG) in patients with refractory multiple myeloma: An Eastern Cooperative Oncology Group (ECOG) study. Cancer Invest 1990; 8:143-6.

96. Bukowski RM, Fleming TR, Macdonald JS et al. Evaluation of combination chemotherapy and phase II agents in pancreatic adenocarcinoma. A Southwest Oncology Group study. Cancer 1993; 71:322-5.

97. Yagoda A, Petrylak D. Cytotoxic chemotherapy for advanced hormone-resistant prostate cancer. Cancer 1993; 71(3 Suppl):1098-109.

98. von Hoff DD. MGBG: Teaching an old drug new tricks. Ann Oncol 1994; 5: 487-93.

99. Seppänen P, Alhonen-Hongisto L, Jänne J. Polyamine deprivation-induced enhanced uptake of methylglyoxal bis(guanylhydrazone) by tumor cells. Biochim Biopphys Acta 1981; 674:169-77.

100. Siimes M, Seppänen P, Alhonen-Hongisto L et al. Synergistic action of two polyamine antimetabolites leads to a rapid therapeutic response in childhood leukemia. Int J Cancer 1981; 28:567-70.

101. Jänne J, Alhonen-Hongisto L, Seppänen P et al. Use of polyamine antimetabolites in experimental tumors and in human leukemia. Med Biol 1981; 59:448-57.

102. Warrell Jr RP, Coonley CJ, Burchenal JH. Sequential inhibition of polyamine synthesis. A phase I trial of DFMO (α-difluoro-methylornithine) and methyl-GAG [methylglyoxal-bis(guanyl-hydrazone)]. Cancer Chemother Pharmacol 1983; 11:134-36.

103. Dunzendorfer U, Knöner M. Therapie mit Inhibitoren der Polyaminbiosynthese bein refraktären Prostatakarzinom. Onkologie 1985; 8:196-200.

104. Herr HW, Warrel RP, Burchenal JH. Phase I trial of α-difluoromethylornithine DFMO) and methylglyoxal bis(guanyl-hydrazone) (MGBG) in patients with advanced prostatic cancer. Urology 1986; 28:508-11.

105. Splinter TA, Romijin JC. Phase I study of α-difluoromethylornithine and methyl-GAG. Eur J Cancer Clin Oncol 1986; 22:61-7.

106. Gastaut J-A, Tell G, Schechter PJ et al. Treatment of acute myeloid leukemia and blastic phase of chronic myeloid leukemia with combined eflornithine (α-difluoromethylornithine) and methyl-glyoxal bis(guanylhydrazone) (methyl-GAG). Cancer Chemother Pharmacol 1987; 20:344-48.

107. Levin VA, Chamberlain MC, Prados MD et al. Phase I-II study of eflornithine and mitoguazone combined in the treatment of recurrent primary brain tumors. Cancer Treat Rep 1987; 71:459-64.

108. Maddox A-M, Freireich EJ, Keating MJ et al. Alterations in bone marrow and blood mononuclear cell polyamine and methylglyoxal bis(guanylhydrazone) levels: Phase I evaluation of α-difluoromethylornithine and bis(guanylhydrazone) treatment of human hematological malignancies. Cancer Res 1988; 48:1367-73.

109. Maddox A-M, Keating MJ, Freireich EJ et al. Polyamines increase in human peripheral blood and bone marrow mononuclear cells following administration of methylglyoxal bis(guanylhydrazone). Chemotherapy 1988; 34:419-29.

110. Maddox A-M, Keating MJ, Freireich EJ et al. Mononuclear cell polyamine content associated with myeloid maturation in patients with leukemia during administration of polyamine inhibitors. Invest New Drugs 1989; 7:119-29.

111. Redgate ES, Boggs S, Grudziak A et al. Polyamines and brain therapy. J Neuro-Oncol 1995; 25:167-79.

112. Sunkara PS, Prakash NJ, Mayer GD et al. Tumor suppression with a combination of α-difluoromethylornithine and interferon. Science 1983; 219:851-53.

113. Resenblum MG, Gutterman J. Synergistic antiproliferative activity of leukocyte interferon in combination with α-difluoromethylornithine against human cells in culture. Cancer Res 1984; 44:2339-40.

114. Sunkara PS, Prakash NJ, Rosenberger AL et al. Potentiation of antitumor and antimetastatic activities of α-difluoromethylornithine by interferon inducers. Cancer Res 1984; 44:2799-802.

115. Heston WDW, Fleischmann J, Tackett RE et al. Effects of α-difluoromethylornithine and recombinant interferon-α 2 on the growth of a human renal cell adenocarcinoma xenograft in nude mice. Cancer Res 1984; 44:3220-5.

116. Talpaz M, Plager C, Quesada J et al. Difluoromethylornithine and leukocyte interferon: Phase I study in cancer patients. Eur J Cancer Clin Oncol 1986; 22:685-89.

117. Kyriakidis DA, Kortsaris A. Effects of human interferon and α-difluoromethylornithine on T47D cells. J Interferon Res 1986; 6:527-33.

118. Sunkara PS, Bowlin TL, Rosenberger AL. Effects of murine α-, β-, and γ-interferons in combination with α-difluoromethylornithine as inhibitor of B16 melanoma and Lewis lung carcinoma in mice. J Biol Response Mod 1989; 8:170-79.

119. Talpaz M, Nishioka K, Gutterman J. Clinical studies of α-difluoromethylornithine and α-interferon combination in cancer patients. In: Bachrach U, Heimer Y, eds. The Physiology of Polyamines Boca Raton: CRC Press, 1989:293-99.

120. Kubota S. Synergistic antiproliferative activity of human fibroblast

interferon in combination with α-difluoromethylornithine against human gastric cancer cell in vitro. Cancer 1992; 69:2395-99.

121. Ganju V, Edmonson JH, Buchner JC. Phase I study of combined α-interferon, α-difluoromethylornithine, and doxorubicin in advanced malignancy. Invest New Drugs 1994; 12:25-27.

122. Klouche M, Kirchner H, Holzel F. Antiproliferative effects of interferon γ in combination with α-difluoromethylornithine on human carcinoma cell cultures. J Cancer Res Clin Oncol 1994; 120:700-6.

123. Levi JA, Wiernick PH. Combination therapy with 5-azacytidine (NSC-102816) and methyl-GAG (NSC-32946) in previously treated adults with acute nonlymphocytic leukemia. Cancer Chemother Rep 1975; 59:1043-5.

124. Warrell Jr RP, Straus DJ, Young CW. Combination chemotherapy for patients with relapsed malignant lymphoma using methyl-GAG and teniposide (VM-26). Cancer Treat Rep 1982; 66:1121-5.

125. Todd RF III, Garnick MB, Cancellos GP. Phase II trial of combination methyl- GAG and vinblastine in the treatment of metastatic renal adenocarcinoma. Cancer Treat Rep 1982; 66:1585-6.

126. Vogl SE, Camacho F, Berenzweig M et al. Chemotherapy for esophageal cancer with mitoguazone, methotrexate, bleomycin, and cisplatin. Cancer Treat Rep 1985; 69:21-3.

127. Dana BM, Jones SE, Coltman C et al. Salvage treatment of unfavorable non-Hodgkin's lymphoma with cisplatin, amsacrine and mitoguazone: A Southwest Oncology Group pilot study. Cancer Treat Rep 1986; 70:291-2.

128. Kelsen DP, Fein R, Coonley C et al. Cisplatin, vindesine, and mitoguazone in the treatment of esophageal cancer. Cancer Treat Rep 1986; 70:255-9.

129. Takasugi BJ, Perry Dj, Wheeler RH et al. A phase II trial of cisplatin and methylglyoxal bis-guanylhydrazone (MGBG) in recurrent squamous cell carcinoma of the head and neck. Am J Clin Oncol 1986; 9:299-301.

130. Warrell RP, Danieu L, Coonley CL et al. Salvage chemotherapy of advanced lymphoma with investigational drugs: Mitoguazone, gallium nitrate and etoposide. Cancer Treat Rep 1987; 71:47-51.

131. Cabanillas F, Hagemeister FB, McLaughlin P et al. Results of MIME salvage regimen for recurrent or refractory lymphoma. J Clin Oncol 1987; 5:407-12.

132. Hagemeister FB, Tannir N, McLaughlin P et al. MIME chemotherapy (methyl-GAG, ifosfamide, methotrexate, etoposide as treatment for recurrent Hodgkin's disease. J Clin Oncol 1987; 5:556-61.

133. Christian ES, Schreeder M, Salter MM et al. Phase I-II study of cisplatin, VP-16, MGBG, mitomycin, and vinblastine with radia-

tion therapy for non-small-cell lung cancer. Am J Clin Oncol 1988; 11:502-5.

134. Cabanillas F, Velasquez WS, McLaughlin P et al. Results of recent salvage chemotherapy regimens for lymphoma and Hodgkin's disease. Semin Hematol 1988; 25:47-50.

135. Dabich L, Liepman MK. Cisplatin, VP-16-213 and MGBG (methylglyoxal bis guanylhydrazone) combination chemotherapy in refractory lymphoma, a phase II study. Invest New Drugs 1988; 6:231-7.

136. Forastiere AA, Perry DJ, Wolf GT et al. Cisplatin and mitoguazone. An induction chemotherapy regimen in advanced head and neck cancer. Cancer 1988; 62:2304-8.

137. Cabanillas F. Experience with ifosfamide combination in malignant lymphoma. Semin Oncol 1989; 16 (1 Suppl 3): 78-81.

138. Guimaraes JL, Ghosn M, Ostronoff M et al. Phase II trial of methyl-gag and melphalan in metastatic adult renal cell carcinoma. Cancer Invest 1990; 8:623-4.

139. Enblad G, Glimeliua B, Hagberg H et al. Methyl-GAG, ifosfamide, methotrexate and etoposide (MIME) as salvage therapy for Hodgkin's disease and non-Hodgkin's lymphoma. The Swedish Lymphoma Study Group. Acta Oncol 1990; 29:297-301.

140. Hayat M, Ostronoff M, Gilles E et al. Salvage therapy with methyl-gag, high-dose Ara-C, M-Amsa, and ifosfamide (MAMI) for recurrent or refractory lymphoma. Cancer Invest 1990; 8:1-5.

141. Cabanillas F. Experience with salvage regimens at M. D. Anderson Hospital. Ann Oncol 1991:2 Suppl 1:31-2.

142. Mirza MR, Brincker H. MIME combination chemotherapy in recurrent or refractory lymphoproliferative malignancies. A phase II study. Acta Oncol 1991; 30:17-21.

143. Crown JP, Gulati S, Straus DJ et al. Mitoxantrone, etoposide, mitoguazone and vinblastine chemotherapy (MV2) in relapsed and refractory lymphomas. Invest New Drugs 1991; 9:185-6.

144. Dupriez B, Morel P, Fenaux P et al. VIM3-ARA C: An effective salvage regimen in refractory or recurrent aggressive non Hodgkin's lymphoma. A report on 18 cases. Hematol Oncol 1991; 9:259-66.

145. Weick JK, Crowley J, Natale RB et al. A randomized trial of five cisplatin-containing treatments in patients with metastatic non-small-cell lung cancer: A Southwest Oncology Group study. J Clin Oncol 1991; 9:1157-62.

146. Machiels JP, Ferrant A, Martiat P et al. A prospective randomized study of two alternating, non cross-resistant chemotherapies for advanced Hodgkin's disease. Acta Clin Belg 1992; 47:244-50.

147. Urba SG, Forastiere AA, Wolf GT et al. Intensive induction chemotherapy and radiation for organ preservation in patients with

advanced resectable head and neck carcinoma. J Clin Oncol 1994; 12:946-53.

148. Ferme C, Bastion Y, Lepage E et al. The MINE regimen as intensive salvage chemotherapy for relapsed and refractory Hodgkin's disease. Ann Oncol 1995; 6:543-9.

149. Brault P, Gilles E, Ribrag V et al. Salvage treatment of relapsing lymphomas with a non-myelotoxic chemotherapy combining cisplatinum, bleomycin, methyl GAG, and predonisolone. Bulletin du Cancer 1995; 82:1032-7.

150. Kellof GJ, Boon CW, Steele VE et al. Mechanistic considerations in chemopreventive drug development. J Cell Biochem (Suppl) 1994; 20:1-24.

151. Slaughter DP, Southwick HW, Smejkal W. Field cancerization in oral stratified squamous epithelium cancer 1953;Sept: 963-8.

152. Takigawa M, Enomoto M, Nishida Y et al. Tumor angiogenesis and polyamines: 2-Difluoromethylornithine, an irreversible inhibitor of ornithine decarboxylase, inhibits B16 melanoma-induced angiogenesis in ovo and the proliferation of vascular endothelial cells in vitro. Cancer Res 1990; 50:4131- 8.

153. Monte M, Klein S, Jasnis MA et al. Inhibition of lymphocyte and tumor-induced angiogenesis by the administration of difluoromethylornithine. Cancer J 1993; 6:147-50.

154. Jasnis MA, Klein S, Monte M et al. Polyamines prevent DFMO-mediated inhibition of angiogenesis. Cancer Lett 1994; 79:39-43.

155. Nishioka K, Rodriguez Jr T, Liaw H. Methylglyoxal bis(guanylhydrazone) induced apoptosis in a human colon carcinoma cell line and HL-60 cells. Pro Am Assoc Cancer Res 1994; 35:317.

156. McCloskey DE, Casero RA, Woster PM et al. Induction of programmed cell death in human breast cancer cells by an unsymmetrically alkyiated polyamine analogue. Cancer Res 1995; 55:3233-36.

157. Berchtold CM, Kensler TW, Casero Jr RA. The polyamine metabolic pathway as a target for chemoprevention. In: Casero Jr RA, ed. Polyamines: Regulation and Molecular Interaction. Austin: RG Landes, 1995:205-31.

158. Takigawa M, Verma AK, Simsiman RC et al. Polyamine biosynthesis and skin tumor promotion: Inhibition of 12-*O*-tetradecanoylphorbol-13-acetate-promoted mouse skin tumor formation by the irreversible inhibitor of ornithine decarboxylase 2-difluoromethylornithine. Biochem Biophys Res Commun 1982; 105:969-76.

159. Kingsnorth AN, King WWK, Diekema KA et al. Inhibition of ornithine decarboxylase with α-difluoromethylornithine: Reduced incidence of dimethylhydrazine-induced colon tumors in mice. Cancer Res 1983; 43:2545-9.

160. Nigro ND, Bull AW, Boyd ME. Importance of the duration of inhibition on intestinal carcinogenesis by α-difluoromethylornithine in rats. Cancer Lett 1987; 35:153-8.

161. Tempero M, Nishioka K, Knott K et al. Chemoprevention of mouse colon tumors with difluoromethylornithine during and after carcinogen treatment. Cancer Res 1989; 49:5793-7.

162. Reddy BS, Nayini J, Tokumo K et al. Chemoprevention of colon carcinogenesis by concurrent administration of piroxicam, a nonsteroidal antiinflammatory drug with α-difluoromethylornithine, an ornithine decarboxylase inhibitor, in diet. Cancer Res 1990; 50:2563-8.

163. Moon RC, Kelloff GJ, Detrisac CJ. Chemoprevention of OH-induced bladder cancer in mice by oltipraz, alone and in combination with 4-HPR and DFMO. Anticancer Res 1994; 14:5-12.

164. Homma Y, Kakizoe T, Samma S et al. Inhibition of N-butyl-N-(4-hydroxybutyl)nitrosamine-induced rat urinary bladder carcinogenesis by α- difluoromethylornithine. Cancer Res 1987; 47:6176-9.

165. Ratko TA, Detrisac CJ, Rao KVN et al. Interspecies analysis of the chemopreventive efficacy of dietary α-difluoromethylornithine. Anticancer Res 1990; 10:67-72.

166. Tanaka T, Kojima T, Hara A et al. Chemoprevention of oral carcinogenesis by D,L-α-difluoromethylornithine, an ornithine decarboxylase inhibitor: Dose-dependent reduction in 4-nitroquinoline-1-oxide-induced tongue neoplasms in rats. Cancer Res 1993; 53:772-6.

167. Thompson HJ, Herbst EJ, Meeker LD et al. Effect of D,L-α-difluoromethylornithine of murine mammary carcinogenesis. Cancer Res 1985; 45:1170-3.

168. Thompson HJ, Meeker LD, Herbst EJ et al. Effect of concentration of D,L-α-difluoromethylornithine of murine mammary carcinogenesis. Cancer Res 1985; 45:1170-3.

169. Kojima T, Tanaka T, Kawamori T et al. Chemopreventive effects of dietary α-difluoromethylornithine, an ornithine decarboxlase inhibitor, on initiation and postinitiation stages of diethylnitrosamine-induced rat hepatocarcinogenesis. Cancer Res 1993; 53:3903-7.

170. Tutton PJM, Barkla DH. Comparison of the effects of an ornithine decarboxylase inhibitor on the intestinal epithelium and on intestinal tumors. Cancer Res 1986; 46:6091-4.

171. Grossie Jr VB, Ota DM, Ajani JA et al. Effect of intravenous α-difluoromethylornithine on the polyamine levels of normal tissue and a transplantable fibrosarcoma. Cancer Res 1987; 47:1836-40.

172. Nishioka K, Grossie Jr VB, Ajani JA et al. Polyamine-directed preferential nutritional repletion of normal tissues in tumor-bearing hosts. Int J Cancer 1988; 42:744-7.

173. O'Brien TG, Madara T, Pyle JA et al. Ornithine decarboxylase from mouse epidermis and epidermal papillomas: Difference in enzymatic properties and structure. Proc Natl Acad Sci USA 1986; 83:9448-52.

174. Creaven PJ, Pendyala L, Peterili NJ. Evaluation of α-difluoromethylornithine as a potential chemopreventive agent: Tolerance to daily oral administration in humans. Cancer Epidemiol Biomarkers Prev 1993; 2:243-7.

175. Pendyala L, Creaven PJ, Porter CW. Urinary and erythrocyte polyamines during the evaliation of oral α-difluoromethylornithine in a phase I chemoprevention clinical trial. Cancer Epidemiol Biomarkers Prev 1993; 2:235-41.

176. Love RR, Carbone PP, Verma AK et al. Randomized phase I chemoprevention dose-seeking study of α-difluoromethylornithine. J Natl Cancer Inst 1993; 85:732-37.

177. Meyskens Jr FL, Emerson SS, Pelot D et al. Dose de-escalation chemoprevention trial of α-difluoromethylornithine in patients with colon polyps. J Natl Cancer Inst 1994; 86:1122-30.

178. Boyle JO, Meyskens Jr FL, Garewal HS et al. Polyamine contents in rectal and buccal mucosae in humans treated with oral difluoromrthylornithine. Cancer Epidemiol Biomarkers Prev 1992;1:131-35.

179. Mitchell MF, Hittelman WN, Lotan R et al. Chemoprevention trials in the cervix: Design, feasibility, and recruitment. J Cell Biochem (Suppl) 1995; 23:104-112.

180. Mitchell MF, Hittelman WN, Lotan R et al. Chemoprevention trials and surrogate end point biomarkers in the cervix. Cancer 1995; 76:1956-77.

181. Hayase R, Eguchi K, Sekiba K. Polyamine levels in gynecologic malignancies. Acta Medica Okayama 1985; 39:35-45.

182. Becciolini A, Porciani S, Lanini A. Urinary polyamines in patients with advanced cervical cancer or pelvic cancer recurrence during and after radiotherapy. Acta Oncol 1992; 31:327-31.

183. Fernandez C, Sharrard RM, Talbot M et al. Evaluation of the significance of polyamines and their oxidases in the aetiology of human cervical carcinoma. Br J Cancer 1995; 72:1194-99.

184. Nishioka K, Melgarejo AB, Lyon RR et al. Polyamines as biomarkers of cervical intraepithelial neoplasia. J Cell Biochem 1995; Suppl 23:87-95.

185. Meyskens FL, Gerner EW. Development of difluoromethylornithine as a chemoprevention agent for the management of colon cancer. J Cell Biochem 1995; Suppl 22:126- 31.

186. Kadmon D. Chemoprevention in prostate cancer: The role of difluoromethyl-ornithine (DFMO). J Cell Biochem 1992; Suppl 16H:122-27.

187. Bostwick DG. Prostatic intraepithelial neoplasia (PIN): Current concepts. J Cell Biochem; Suppl 16H:10-9.

188. Loprinzi CI, Messing EM. A prospective clinical trial of difluoromethylornithine (DFMO) in patients with resected superficial bladder cancer. J Cell Biochem 1992; Suppl 16I:1530-55.

189. Garewal HS, Sampliner R. Barrett's esophagus: A model premalignant lesion for adenocarcinoma. Prev Med 1989; 18:749-56.

190. Garewal HS, Sampliner RE, Fennerty MB. Chemopreventive studies in Barrett's esophagus: A model premalignant lesion for esophageal adenocarcinoma. Monographs—Natl Cancer Inst 1992; 13:51-4.

191. Gerner EW, Garewal HS, Emerson SS et al. Gastrointestinal tissue polyamine contents of patients with Barrett's esophagus treated with α-difluoromethyl-ornithine. Cancer Epidemiol Biomarkers Prev 1994; 3:325-30.

192. Jänne J, Alhonen L, Leinonnen P. Polyamines: From molecular biology to clinical application. Ann Med 1991; 23:241-59.

193. Marton LJ, Pegg AE. Polyamines as targets for therapeutic intervention. Ann Rev Pharmacol Toxicol 1995; 35:55-91.

194. Takahashi Y, Nishioka K. Survival without tumor shrinkage: Re-evaluation of survival gain by cytostatic effect of chemotherapy. J Natl Cancer Inst 1995; 87:1262-3.

195. Taguchi T. Clinical efficacy of lentinan on patients with stomach cancer: End point results of a four-year follow-up survey. Cancer Detect Prev 1987; Suppl 1:333-49.

196. Grossie B, Ajani J, Ota D et al. Tumor growth recovery after antitumor drug treatment is delayed by difluoromethylornithine. Pro Am Assoc Cancer Res 1992; 33:422.

197. Benvenuto JA, Johnston DA, Nishioka K. The correlation of response with plasma pharmacokinetics and polyamine concentrations in patients with AML receiving amonafide. Cancer Lett 1993; 70:175-9.

INDEX

Numbers in italics indicate figures (f) and tables (t).

A

AbeAdo, 158, 159, 168. *See also* MDL-73811.
Abeloff MD, 253
3-Acetamidopropanal, 29
Acetyl CoA, 2, 164
N-Acetylpropyl aldehyde, 111
Acetylspermidine, 9, 116. *See also* Spermidine.
N^1, 2, 81, 104, 205
Acetylspermine, 9, 116. *See also* Spermine.
N^1, 2, 104, 205
N-Acetyltransferase, 110, 116
Acrolein, 104, 105, 110, 111, 113
Acute lymphoblastic leukemia (ALL), 240-242
Adenocarcinoma, 58, 59, 240, 242, 259, 263. *See also* Cancer.
S-Adenosylmethionine (AdoMet), 2, 8, 9, 13, 159, 160, 166
  decarboxylase (Ado MetDC), 2, 13, 15, 9, 26, 28, 29, 31, 51, 53, 54, 58, 80, 82f, 84, 91, 92f, 151, 153f, 163, 166-168, 176, 255, 256
    gene, 162
    inhibition, 33, 91, 158-162, 168
    mRNA, 28, 162
    regulation, 27f, 173, 174, 178
  decarboxylated, 10, 14, 255, 261
S-Adenosyl-3-thio-1,8-diaminooctane (AdoDATO), 162, 163
AdoDATAD, 163
African trypanosome, 17, 18
Aldehyde dehydrogenase (ALDH), 111, 122t
Alpha-difluoromethylornithine. *See* Difluoro-methylornithine.
Alpha-methylornithine. *See* Methylornithine.
AMA, 158, 161, 162
American Cancer Society, 207
Amine oxidases, 8, 9, 104-106, 108-111, 116, 118, 120, 122t, 123
Aminess, 224, 225t
γ-Aminobutyrate (GABA), 9, 87, 88
1-Aminooxy-3-aminopropane (APA), 155, 157
3-Aminooxy-2-fluoro-1-propanamine (AFPA), 157
Aminopropyl-transferase(s), 2
Angiogenesis, 4, 260
Anthralin, 49
Antioxidant(s), 106, 110, 122t
Antipolyamine antibodies, 235

Antitumor agents/drugs, 60, 157-159, 161, 174, 176, 206, 229, 253-257, 263
Antizyme, 13, 24-26, 33, 201
  mRNA, 25
AP-1, 57
APAHHA, 165
APCHA, 163
Apoptosis, 4, 99-101, 179, 197, 199, 200, 202, 203, 260, 263
  histogenetic, 103
  mechanisms for control by polyamines, 99-124
    direct, 111-117
      intracellular polyamines, 112, 113
      modulation of
        calcium channel activity, 114, 115
        excitatory neurotransmission, 115-117
        transglutamase utilization, 117
      trophic factor withdrawal: mitosis-apoptosis decision, 113, 114
    indirect, 101-111
      in committed progenitors triggered by H_2O_2, 102-108
      induced by intracellular H_2O_2, 108-110
      regulation by acrolein, 110, 111
    in situ localization studies, 117-121
      epidermis, 118, 119
      gastrointestinal mucosa, 119-121
    TNF-induced, 109, 110
  versus necrosis, 100, 101
Arginase, 1
Arginine, 221, 224-230
  decarboxylase, 12
  oxidases, 109
Ask A, 34f
Association pour la Recherche sur le Cancer, 245

B

Bacchi C, 17
Bachrach U, 4, 8, 15, 47f, 251
Baylin SB, 58, 251
BE-373, 166
BE-4444, 175, 194, 195, 206
BEPH-175
Bergeron RJ, 152, 173, 177f
Bey P, 153f, 155
Biosynthetic pathways, 21. *See also* Polyamine(s).